Geology of the country around Taunton and the Quantock Hills

The Quantock Hills rise to over 300 m, an ascent through hill pastures, woodland and forest to open moorland summits; they consist of Devonian sandstones and slates, and within the district similar rocks form the eastern foothills of the Brendon Hills. Taunton lies within the vales of rich farmland, underlain by Permo-Triassic marls, sandstones and conglomerates, which surround the high ground. In the east, Triassic rocks give way to the alluvial flats of the Somerset Levels, interrupted by slight rises of Burtle Beds and the low ridge of the mainly Jurassic Polden Hills. The north-west corner of the district takes in a short stretch of the Bristol Channel coast near the port of Watchet.

The Devonian strata are disposed in a major anticline. Two occurrences of tuff point to volcanicity in Middle Devonian times, and lamprophyre dykes at Hestercombe intrude Upper Devonian slates. One fault-bounded trough between the Brendons and the Quantocks, and another extending northwards from the Quantocks to well beyond the district, contain synclines in younger rocks. An isolated occurrence of Carboniferous Limestone at Cannington Park, some 25 km from the nearest Culm facies of similar age to the south-west, constitutes a guide to the approximate position of a major tectonic discontinuity, the Variscan Front.

Landscape and land use are products of rock type and geological history: upland rough grazing on Devonian rocks, together with commercial forestry and designation as an Area of Outstanding Natural Beauty; lowland arable farming on the sandy soils, and dairy herds on the rich grassland of the marls and the artificially drained pastures of the Levels; widespread quarrying of stone and marl, now virtually ceased; a brief interlude of mining at Dodington, where Devonian limestone was found to be the host rock for copper ores; and a future of agriculture, tourism and light industry.

BRITISH GEOLOGICAL SURVEY

England and Wales

E. A. EDMONDS and
B. J. WILLIAMS

CONTRIBUTORS

Geophysics
J. D. Cornwell

Palaeontology
D. E. Butler
G. Warrington
D. E. White

Geology of the country around Taunton and the Quantock Hills

Memoir for 1:50 000 geological sheet 295, New Series

1835 Geological Survey of Great Britain
150 Years of Service to the Nation
1985 British Geological Survey

Natural Environment Research Council

LONDON: HER MAJESTY'S STATIONERY OFFICE 1985

First published 1985

ISBN 0 11 884281 1

Bibliographical reference

EDMONDS, E. A. and WILLIAMS, B. J. 1985. Geology of the country around Taunton and the Quantock Hills. *Mem. Br. Geol. Surv.*, Sheet 295.

Authors

E. A. EDMONDS, MSc
B. J. WILLIAMS, BSc
British Geological Survey, St Just, 30 Pennsylvania Road, Exeter EX4 6BX

Contributors

D. E. Butler, BSc, PhD, and D. E. White, MSc, PhD
British Geological Survey, London

J. D. Cornwell, MSc, PhD, and G. Warrington, BSc, PhD
British Geological Survey, Keyworth

Other publications of the Survey dealing with this and adjoining districts.

BOOKS

British Regional Geology
South-West England, 4th edition, 1975

Memoirs
Weston-super-Mare (279) 1983
Wells and Cheddar (280) 1965
Bridport and Yeovil (312, 327) 1959
Ilfracombe and Barnstaple (277) 1985

MAPS

1:625 000

Sheet 2 Geological
Sheet 2 Quaternary
Sheet 2 Aeromagnetic

1:250 000

Portland (50N 04W)

1:50 000
Sheet 279 (Weston-super-Mare) 1981
Sheet 280 (Wells) 1985
Sheet 294 (Dulverton) provisional edition 1975
Sheet 295 (Taunton) 1985
Sheet 296 (Glastonbury) provisional edition 1973
Sheet 310 (Tiverton) provisional edition 1975
Sheet 311 (Wellington) 1976
Sheet 312 (Yeovil) 1973

Produced in the UK for HMSO

Dd 737365 C20 5/85

CONTENTS

PLATES

FIGURES

TABLES

PREFACE

The district around Taunton and the Quantock Hills (Sheet 295) was originally surveyed on the one-inch scale by Sir Henry T. De la Beche; the mapping was published on Old Series sheets 20 and 21 in 1834–35, and revised by him in 1839. A resurvey on the same scale, mainly by W. A. E. Ussher with small areas by H. B. Woodward, H. W. Bristow and J. H. Blake, was issued as New Series Sheet 295 in 1907. The provisional edition, compiled by Mr A. J. J. Goode and published in 1975, made use of a six-inch survey of the Devonian rocks by Dr B. D. Webby of Bristol University in 1959–64, and incorporated six-inch mapping of the northern margin of the district by Dr A. Whittaker and Mr J. C. Thackray in 1969–70. Resurvey of the area south of this margin was by Messrs E. A. Edmonds and B. J. Williams in 1977–79, under Mr G. Bisson as District Geologist. This memoir was compiled by Mr Edmonds and edited by Mr Bisson.

Devonian fossils were collected by Dr D. E. Butler, Mr S. P. Tunnicliff and Dr D. E. White; they were identified by Dr Butler and Dr White, who also contributed notes on palaeontology. Dr S. G. Molyneux examined ten samples for acritarchs and made determinations from three. Mr M. Mitchell and Dr A. R. E. Strank identified Carboniferous fossils, and Dr G. Warrington examined samples from the Permo-Triassic and basal Jurassic sequence for palynomorphs. Regional geophysical surveys have been interpreted by Dr J. D. Cornwell, who supplemented them with some local gravity measurements. Photographs listed in an appendix were taken by Mr J. Rhodes and Mr C. Jeffery. Dr J. R. Hawkes provided a petrographical description of the dyke rock from Hestercombe, and Mr C. C. Rundle determined its age.

The 1:50 000 geological map which this memoir describes is in press. Provisional editions of the sheets to west (294) and east (296) were published in 1969. A new edition of the sheet to the north (279), issued in 1980, included a 1.5-km overlap on to Sheet 295.

We gratefully acknowledge the help and co-operation generously afforded by landowners during the survey.

Sir Malcolm Brown, DSc, FRS
Director

Keyworth
Nottinghamshire

1 July 1985

LIST OF SIX-INCH MAPS

The following is a list of National Grid maps included, wholly or in part, in Sheet 295, with dates of survey. The surveyors are Mr E. A. Edmonds, Mr J. C. Thackray, Dr A. Whittaker and Mr B. J. Williams.

Dye-line copies of all complete 1:10 000 sheets may be purchased from the British Geological Survey, Keyworth, and copies are available for public reference in the library of the Geological Museum, London.

ST 02 SE	Edmonds	1978–79
ST 02 NE	Edmonds	1978
ST 03 SE	Edmonds	1978
ST 03 NE	Edmonds	1978
ST 04 SE	Thackray and Whittaker	1970, 1975
ST 12 SW	Edmonds	1978–79
ST 12 SE	Edmonds	1977–79
ST 12 NW	Edmonds	1978
ST 12 NE	Edmonds	1977–79
ST 13 SW	Edmonds	1978
ST 13 SE	Edmonds	1977
SE 13 NW	Edmonds	1977
ST 13 NE	Edmonds	1977
ST 14 SW	Edmonds	1977
ST 14 SW	Whittaker & Edmonds	1969–70, 1975, 1978
ST 14 SE	Whittaker & Edmonds	1970, 1975, 1978
ST 22 SW	Edmonds	1977–79
ST 22 SE	Williams	1978–79
ST 22 NW	Edmonds	1977–79
ST 22 NE	Williams	1978–79
ST 23 SW	Edmonds	1979
St 23 SE	Williams	1978–79
ST 23 NW	Edmonds	1979
ST 23 NE	Williams	1979
ST 24 SW	Whittaker	1970
ST 24 SE	Whittaker	1970
ST 32 SW	Williams	1977
ST 32 SE	Williams	1977
ST 32 NW	Williams	1977
ST 32 NE	Williams	1977
ST 33 SW	Williams	1978
ST 33 SE	Williams	1978
ST 33 NW	Williams	1978
ST 33 NE	Williams	1978
ST 34 SW	Whittaker	1969

GEOLOGICAL SUCCESSION

SUPERFICIAL DEPOSITS (Drift)

Recent and Pleistocene	
Landslip	Collapsed Jurassic strata
Peat	Peat of the Somerset Levels
Alluvium	Silts, sands, clays and gravels
Estuarine alluvium	Silts, sands, clays and gravels
Submerged forest	Tree remains, generally submerged by the River Parrett
River terraces	Silts and gravels
Burtle Beds	Sand and shingle, friable or cemented
Head	Stony and sandy clay and gravel; accumulations in valleys near the coast are shown on the published map; elsewhere, Head is widespread but ill-defined and is not shown on the map

SOLID FORMATIONS

		Generalised thickness m
Jurassic		
Lower Lias (mainly Blue Lias)	Shales with limestones	195
Permo-Triassic		
Lower Lias (Pre-planorbis Beds)	Shales with limestones	7.5
Penarth Group		
Lilstock Formation	Calcareous mudstones, limestones and siltstones	2.5
Westbury Formation	Shales with limestones	12
Mercia Mudstone Group		
Blue Anchor Formation	Marls and siltstones	30
Undifferentiated (red Mercia Mudstones) including the Somerset Halite Formation	Marls, mudstones and siltstones with some thin sandstones and halite	420
Sherwood Sandstone Group		
Otter Sandstone	Sandstones, locally pebbly	50
Budleigh Salterton Pebble Beds	Conglomerates	30
Littleham Mudstone	Marls and mudstones	45
Vexford Breccias	Breccias with some sandstone	30
Wiveliscombe Sandstone	Sandstones with some breccias	75 seen
Carboniferous		
Upper Carboniferous: (Namurian)		
Rodway Siltstones	Siltstones with sandstones	100 seen
Lower Carboniferous: Dinantian		
Cannington Park Limestone	Limestones	25 seen
Carboniferous and Devonian		
Pilton Shales	Mainly shales	60 seen

(*continued*)

Devonian		
Upper Devonian		
Pickwell Down Sandstones	Sandstones	60 seen
Morte Slates	Slates with some sandstones	?500
Upper and Middle Devonian		
Ilfracombe Slates		
Leighland Slates	Slates with sandstones and limestones	225
Cutcombe Slates	Slates with limestones	110
Avill Slates-and-Sandstones	Slates and sandstones	140
Middle Devonian		
Hangman Grits		
Little Hangman Sandstones	Mainly sandstones	150
Rawn's Shales-and-Sandstones	Shales and sandstones	50
Trentishoe Grits	Mainly sandstones	600
Middle and Lower Devonian		
Lynton Slates	Mainly slates	75
Intrusive igneous rock		
Lamprophyre	Permo-Carboniferous lamprophyre intrusions of the Hestercombe area	

NOTES

Throughout this memoir the word 'district' refers to the area represented by the 1:50 000 geological sheet 295 (Taunton and the Quantock Hills).

National Grid references are given in square brackets. All lie within the 100-km square ST.

Many dips are given in the form 10°/195°; the first number is the angle of dip and the second is its full-circle bearing measured clockwise from True North.

The authors of the fossil species are given in the Index of fossils.

Numbers preceded by A refer to photographs in the Survey's collections. Numbers preceded by E refer to the Survey's Sliced Rock Collection.

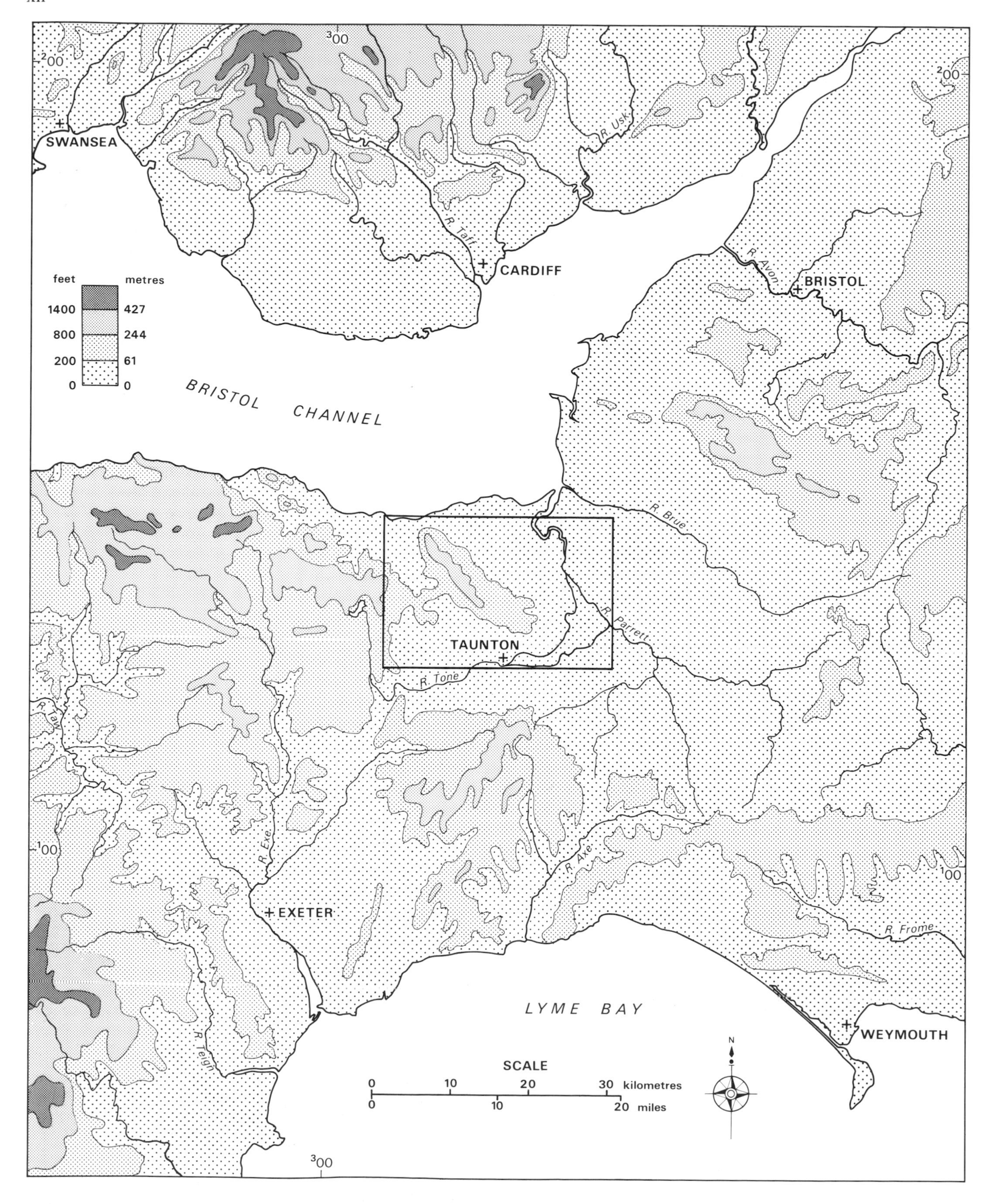

Figure 1 Sketch-map showing the position of the Taunton district

CHAPTER 1

Introduction

POSITION AND PHYSIOGRAPHY

The district of Taunton and the Quantock Hills lies in central Somerset (Figure 1). It extends to the Bristol Channel coast in the neighbourhood of Watchet, takes in the eastern foothills of the Brendon Hills, the whole of the Quantock Hills, the western Polden Hills and the westernmost Somerset Levels. Taunton lies on its southern margin and Bridgwater in its north-eastern quadrant.

A range from broad alluvial flats just above sea level to open moorland at altitudes of 300 m dictates both scenic and climatic contrasts. Rich sheltered farmland, underlain by Permo-Triassic[1] rocks, nestles between the Brendon and Quantock hills and forms the Vale of Taunton Deane and the undulating ground between the Quantocks and Bridgwater. Farther east, the alluvial and peaty flats bordering the River Parrett are cut by an irregular but rectilinear grid of willow-lined rhines; their dead-level expanse serves to emphasise the slight rises marking patches of Burtle Beds and the low ridge of the Polden Hills.

1 The term 'Permo-Triassic' is used in this memoir to cover the combined Permian and Triassic.

The main topographic feature of the district, and an Area of Outstanding Natural Beauty, is the Quantock Hills, of Devonian rocks; these trend north-westwards and are about 18 km long and 5 km wide. The steepest slopes face south-west, but an ascent from any direction is generally along narrow sheltered lanes through hill pasture, natural woodland and cultivated forest to open rolling heather moorland summits with only scattered stunted trees. Trentishoe Grits, the lowest division of the Hangman Grits, form the highest ground; Will's Neck rises to 384 m above OD.

Valleys cut in the Devonian rocks of the Quantock Hills are commonly deep and steep-sided, and most contain streams that appear too small to account for the amount of erosion. The same is true of the eastern end of the Brendon Hills. It is tempting to speculate that some of the upland valleys are re-excavating wadis cut in Permo-Triassic times, and modified by local ice during the Pleistocene. Lowland drainage is mainly to the River Parrett in the east, and via the River Tone to the Parrett from the west. The Tone enters the Parrett at Burrow Bridge, whence flow through Bridgwater to the sea is extremely sluggish, the gradient being less than 0.2 m per kilometre. Tidal waters reach upstream to Langport, east of the present district.

Plate 1 Northern summits of the Quantock Hills: view north-westward to the Bristol Channel. The hills here are of Little Hangman Sandstones (A 13852)

MAN AND INDUSTRY

Neolithic Man walked the ancient ridgeway along the spine of the Quantock Hills, and developed coppicing of the adjoining woodland. However, traces of early settlement, Bronze Age, Iron Age or even Roman occupation, are, except in the east, largely confined to a few hill forts and scattered artefacts and coins. The name Quantock is probably of Celtic origin.

Mixed grass and arable farming flourishes on the soils overlying Permo-Triassic and Jurassic rocks. The Morte Slates and upper Ilfracombe Slates carry mainly pasture, and the lower Ilfracombe Slates and Hangman Grits commercial forests and rough heather and bracken moorland. In the period between wartime felling of the trees and the establishment of extensive Forestry Commission plantations in the 1920s, the Quantock Hills supported about eight sheep per square kilometre. At present the same area of forest supports, directly or indirectly, eight people.

The Somerset Levels were probably covered by a shallow sea in Pliocene times and during periods of high sea-level in the Pleistocene. Forest of pine and birch grew at the close of the Devensian cold period, before rising sea-levels of the Flandrian transgression created widespread salt marshes. Subsequently the lowest peat began to form. Boggy landscapes of the Bronze Age and Iron Age were traversed by causeways founded on branches and brushwood, and spasmodic flooding by the sea led to the construction of lake villages which were periodically abandoned and reoccupied. The earliest records of land reclamation and sea-defences date from Norman times, and such activity has continued sporadically ever since. Cutting of the major King's Sedgemoor Drain was authorised by an Act of 1791. In the countryside so created embankments contain rivers and support roads well above the level of the intervening flats of pasture with their network of ditches. Floods have remained a threat and occurred, for example, in 1607, 1703, 1811, 1917 and 1919. In 1929 the bank of the River Tone gave way at Athelney and 4000 hectares were inundated. In the 18th century many infants slept in cradles specially designed to float. During the 19th century farmers practised 'warping', the deliberate controlled flooding of grassland by muddy river water ('thick water') to distribute a coating of fertile silt.

A number of attempts to locate and work metalliferous ores have been made in Devonian rocks, but only in the neighbourhood of Dodington has mining been carried on—on a limited scale for a small yield of copper. Hangman Grits have been dug for roadstone, and are still so used by the Forestry Commission, as have younger Devonian rocks. Limestones within the Ilfracombe Slates contain many pits now overgrown with vegetation, and old kilns on lower ground commonly mark places where calcareous sandstones of Permo-Triassic age, or contained limestone pebbles, have been burnt for lime. These younger sandstones have also been much used for building, as have Jurassic limestones; the former are easily shaped and the latter, although not very durable, commonly break naturally into regular blocks. Another source of limestone within the district is the inlier of Carboniferous Limestone at Cannington Park. Peat cutting, for horticultural use and fuel, takes place mainly east of the present area.

Communications in the district have followed a common pattern: early tracks and roads, development and decline of canals and railways, modern roads. Canals ran from Taunton to Tiverton, Bridgwater and Chard, the last an ambitious project incorporating four inclined planes and three tunnels, and the River Tone Navigation to the River Parrett Navigation. All that remain of the railways are the main lines from Taunton to Exeter and Bristol and beyond, and to London, and the private West Somerset Railway now plying the old track from Minehead to Bishops Lydeard. The M5 motorway has recently been driven across the district.

Taunton is a market town and succeeded Somerton as the County town of Somerset. Its population is approaching 40 000 and it has grown as a communications centre linking the rich farming vales. Current manufacturing industries are based on the production of clothing and leather goods.

Bridgwater (pop. 26 000) emerged as a seaport and likely growth area after the Norman Conquest. By the end of the 14th century its prosperity was well founded on immigrant Flemish weavers and the cloth industry they created. Seaborne imports have included coal from Swansea and iron and lead from Bristol. In 1850 ships berthed at Bridgwater at the rate of 4000 a year, but now most vessels using the River Parrett tie up at Walpole Wharf. Shipbuilding, never a large industry, ended about 1907. Bridgwater was once one of the major centres of brick and tile manufacture in the west country, and in 1850 there were 23 works in or near the town, but mass production in eastern England killed the local industry. The parish church is built mainly of Otter Sandstone from Wembdon, with a spire of shelly limestone quarried from Ham Hill, south-east of the district. Modern trade centres on the making of clothing, footwear and plastics, some electrical engineering and general marketing activities covering the eastern Quantocks and the Somerset Levels. Soils on the Mercia Mudstone and alluvium provide rich grazing which at one time led to the local production of Bridgwater cheese.

Of the smaller settlements in the west, Wiveliscombe and Milverton have grown, whereas Crowcombe has declined from a small but busy market town. Watchet, possessed of a royal mint 1000 years ago and later noted for fishing, clothmaking and the working of alabaster dug from the cliffs, retains a well-used harbour of four hectares area, taking ships of up to 2400 tonnes and 5 m draught which serve local paper mills. The church font at neighbouring Williton is made from Watchet alabaster. Kilve was the site of experimental production of oil from local oil shale. Farther east Stogursey, created a 'town' in Norman England and characterised by buildings of local Liassic limestone, was outgrown by Cannington, whose long history of settlement is attested by one of the largest Iron Age hill forts in the west of England. Combwich, an old ferry point on the line of the track along the spine of the Polden Hills, was a port in the 19th century. Exports of bricks and tiles, including those produced at the village, ceased as silting up progressed, but the port was reopened in recent years to serve construction work at Hinkley Point nuclear power station. Salt within the Mercia Mudstone was extracted at Puriton by pumping brine from so-called 'treacle mines', but production ceased in the 1920s. Manufacture of explosives at the village was facilitated by digging the Huntspill River to provide a supply of water; early excavation to 7.3 m, with heaping of the spoil upon the banks, resulted in bulging of the river bed, and the channel was therefore cut to a depth of only 3 m. Chedzoy and Westonzoyland owe their development to small 'islands' of Burtle Beds rising just sufficiently above the marshy Levels to permit standard methods of cultivation. Stoke St Gregory and North Curry were centres of the trade in withies, which grew mainly on the Levels in the south-east of the district where peat is patchy and thin.

Groundwater supplies are available within the district from the important aquifer of the combined Budleigh Salterton Pebble Beds and Otter Sandstone. Lesser quantities may be drawn from the breccias and sandstones at the base of the local Permo-Triassic sequence and from the thick alluvial deposits in the east. The Devonian strata yield little, even the sandstones being well cemented and of low permeability. Surface supplies are gathered from the Quantock Hills, and small reservoirs have been constructed on Devonian rocks and on the largely impermeable Mercia Mudstone.

A future based on agriculture and tourism seems certain, with increasing light industry around the main centres of population. Patterns of forestry in the uplands may change, perhaps towards less dense planting and more broadleaf trees, and continuing drainage and flood control of the Somerset Levels may lead to some arable farming in areas now predominantly devoted to grazing. It seems just possible also that the next few decades will see increased working, perhaps working out, of the peat deposits, including those now considered too deep and too waterlogged, and the result may be extensive inland waterways—a Somerset equivalent of the Norfolk Broads.

GEOLOGICAL HISTORY

The oldest rocks in the district (Figure 2) are the Lynton Slates, so called on the basis of lithological and structural correlation with similar rocks in north Devon. They are probably of Lower and Middle Devonian age, and originated as muds in fairly quiescent shallow seas with only minor varia-

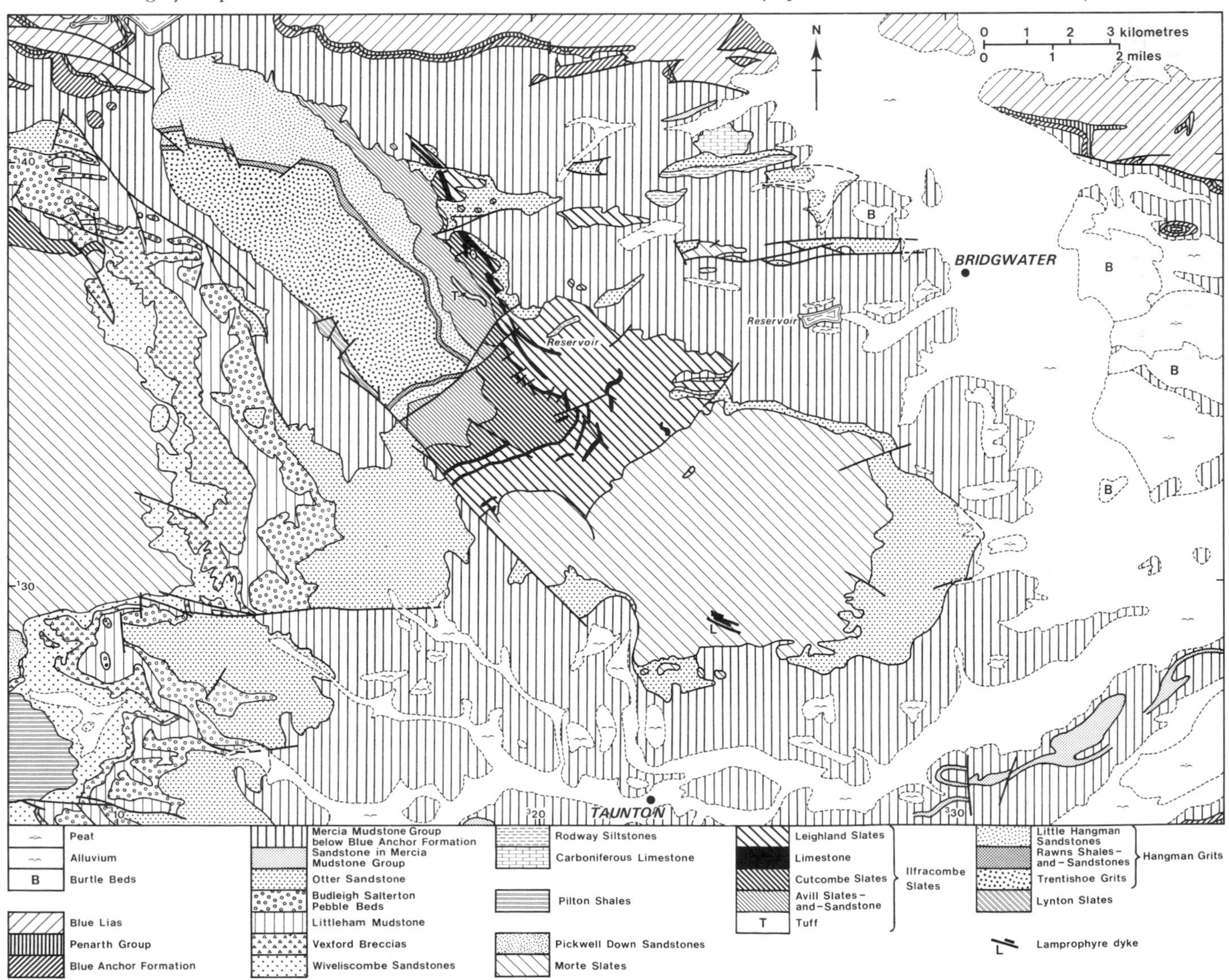

Figure 2 Geology of Taunton and the Quantock Hills

tions in rates of deposition. Southward recession of the shoreline, with a resultant extension from the north of the Old Red Sandstone land mass, created a coastal plain over what is now northernmost Devon and north-west Somerset, and sandy pebbly sediments were laid down by rivers crossing this plain from the north. Possibly the coastal plain was subject to periodic sheet flooding. Thus originated the wholly Middle Devonian Hangman Grits, a predominantly arenaceous succession within which broad lithological correlations can be made between the Quantock Hills and the coastal outcrops to the west.

A return to shallow marine sedimentation in late Middle Devonian times is marked by the slates and sandstones of the lower Ilfracombe Slates, some of which contain shells suggesting a littoral environment. The Cockercombe Tuff lies within these beds. It is unique in the west Somerset area, except for a thin possible correlative at Holford, and its source, probably a submarine eruption, is unknown.

The middle Ilfracombe Slates are predominantly argillaceous but contain the Rodhuish Limestone; the latter is thin and lenticular except at Pepper Hill, where it contains corals, suggesting the possibility of a fairly shallow-water origin. Overlying slates with sandstones and limestones, of the upper Ilfracombe Slates, have a persistent coral limestone, the Roadwater Limestone, at their base, and probably originated by rapid deposition in shallow water.

A return to the quiet waters of a shelf sea is marked by the Morte Slates. Some sandstones are present, commonly in thicker and more sharply defined beds than is usual in north Devon, but they nevertheless represent only short-lived disturbances by sand-carrying currents.

The second major southward migration of the Devonian shoreline ushered in a coastal landscape of shallow lagoons and deltas to which sands and muds, now represented by the Pickwell Down Sandstones, were carried by rivers from the north. No representatives of the overlying Upcott Slates and Baggy Sandstones of north Devon and west Somerset occur in the Taunton district, and the next youngest rocks present, the Pilton Shales, span the Devonian – Carboniferous junction. Their fossiliferous shales and calcareous siltstones point to the re-establishment of a shelf sea which, evidence from the Bideford and Barnstaple districts suggests, was shallow at first and slightly deeper later.

The relevance of the presence of Carboniferous Limestone at Cannington Park, and Upper Carboniferous siltstones, shales and sandstones near by, to a possible major structure between those occurrences and the inliers of Upper Devonian rocks east of the Quantock Hills will be discussed later. However, it is clear that earth movements of the Variscan orogeny preceded the deposition of Permo-Triassic rocks. Devonian strata were folded into a major Quantock Anticline trending east-south-east, and minor folds, some overturned, are common, especially in the more argillaceous form ations. Major faults of Variscan age normal to the generally north – south compressive forces are not common, and the only evidence of igneous intrusion possibly associated with the orogeny is a lamprophyre at Hestercombe. A major fracture bounding the Quantock Hills on their south-western side appears, from the evidence of Upper Devonian boundaries to east and west, to be a large dextral wrench fault. However, it was active in Permo-Triassic times, possibly as a normal fault bounding the basin between the Quantock and Brendon hills.

The Variscan movements left a landscape of uplands and intervening basins, undergoing erosion and deposition in an arid climate. Wet-season torrents carried sandy and stony debris downhill and spread it across an irregular surface of older rocks. Wearing down of the highlands, and possibly greater but less spasmodic rainfall, resulted in the accumulation of clays of the Littleham Mudstone in inland seas or lakes. The succeeding pebble beds are fluviatile deposits; some of the rivers flowed from the Carboniferous Limestone areas of South Wales. They are succeeded by sands, followed by thick marls and mudstones in the Mercia Mudstone Group, formerly the 'Keuper Marl', which originated as calcareous muds and silts laid down in a large lake or inland sea from which the Quantock and Brendon hills stood out as much-denuded islands.

The Mercia Mudstone Group bows up existing upland valleys, although less strikingly than it does around the Mendip Hills, suggesting that drainage channels which originated prior to or during the Permo-Triassic are being exhumed at the present time. These red marls contain sandstones locally, and also sequences characterised by rock salt and gypsum. They are succeeded conformably by the uppermost Triassic rocks, marls and siltstones of the Blue Anchor Formation overlain by Penarth Group shales with limestones, and the basal beds of the Lias, marking a passage from lake and desert flat to shallow sea, part of a widespread marine transgression. The only Jurassic strata of the district, clays and limestones of the Blue Lias above the appearance of *Psiloceras*, mark a continuing spread of the incoming sea. Apart from the major faults bounding the Permo-Triassic basins, and associated parallel faults, the only large fracture affecting post-Carboniferous rocks is an east – west fault through Ash Priors.

No evidence remains of the history of the district throughout the rest of the Mesozoic and all the Tertiary. The oldest Quaternary deposits are those of the second river terrace, of uncertain but possibly Wolstonian age. Sea levels fell as advancing Wolstonian ice probably blocked the Bristol Channel, creating 'Lake Maw', which flooded the lower Severn valley and much of the lower ground of the Taunton district and perhaps overflowed southwards near Chard. Deposits of the first river terrace probably date from the succeeding (Ipswichian) interglacial period and may be correlated with possible beach deposits, the Burtle Beds. During the Devensian stage ice advanced no farther south than south Wales and the adjoining Bristol Channel area, but much Head formed in the tundra-like landscape south of the ice front. Finally warmer climate, retreating ice and rising sea levels ushered in the Flandrian transgression about 10 000 years ago. Alluvial and modern beach deposits belong to this stage. The peats of the Somerset Levels began to form about 6000 to 7000 years ago; they have yielded archaeological evidence ranging from Neolithic to Roman times. Remains of a submerged forest are present in the estuary of the River Parrett.

Earth tremors recorded in the district in 1276, 1682 and 1839 suggest that some of the faults, perhaps mainly those trending north-west and with a long history of activity, are yet capable of slight movement.

PREVIOUS RESEARCH

As for all of south-west England, the foundation of geological research is De la Beche's 'Report on the geology of Cornwall, Devon and west Somerset' (1839). Baker published notes on the geology of Somerset (1851) and the limestone at Cannington Park (1852). The Bridgwater Levels were described by Clark (1854), and an early account of the geology of the Quantock Hills was written by Payne (1854). Dawkins's (1864; 1865) reviews of the Rhaetic (now the Penarth Group) and associated strata of Somerset were preceded by several related shorter papers by other workers. Etheridge wrote a regional structural study (1867) and a local one relating to Watchet (1873). Perceval (1872) returned to the study of the limestone at Cannington; he identified corals collected by Baker, and confirmed earlier tentative suggestions of a Carboniferous age rather than equivalence with Devonian limestones of the Quantocks and elsewhere. Hicks (1896; 1897) studied the Morte Slates.

Ussher published descriptions of the Permo-Triassic rocks and their subdivisions (1875; 1876), the Palaeozoic rocks (1881), and both together (1879; 1889; 1900), and contributed to studies of the structure of the district (Champernowne and Ussher, 1879). He later wrote the Geological Survey memoir for the Wellington district (1906) and the first edition of the present book (1908).

Since the publication of Ussher's memoir, further work on the Cannington Park Limestone has been carried out by Wallis (1924), Whittaker (1975b; 1978), Whittaker and Scrivener (1978; 1982), Lees and Hennebert (1982) and Mitchell and others (1982); also Paul (1937) and Goldring (1955) have established the Devonian – Carboniferous age of the Pilton Shales. Evens and Wallis (1930) located and described the 'diorite' near Hestercombe. A. N. Thomas's (1940) detailed description of the Permo-Triassic rocks of north-west Somerset was preceded by Hallam's (1934) work on the Hangman Grits of the Quantocks and succeeded by Webby's (1966a) covering all the Devonian rocks of those hills.

Research on the Quaternary history of south-west England in general owes much to G. F. Mitchell (1960; 1972) and Stephens (1970), and on the Bristol Channel coast in particular to Kidson (1970; 1971).

Regional summaries of Palaeozoic palaeontology and stratigraphy have been prepared by House and Selwood (1966), and of the geology of south-west England by Edmonds and others (1975). EAE

CHAPTER 2

Devonian

GENERAL ACCOUNT

Lynton Slates

Devonian rocks crop out in the west of the district between Sampford Brett and Wiveliscombe, in the Quantock Hills, and in inliers near East Quantoxhead at Radlet and at Charlinch. From east of Crowcombe through Triscombe to Bagborough Hill, along the western edge of the Quantock Hills, there crops out a sequence of slates and siltstones, with a little sandstone. These rocks are generally pale greenish grey, locally stained red or purple, and some are brown or grey. Subordinate siltstone is common but the succession is distinctly more argillaceous than the arenaceous Hangman Grits immediately to the east. The junction between the two formations is not exposed. Signs of faulting are evident towards the southern end of the crop, and the junction is presumed to be faulted. The argillaceous nature of the rocks, and their position below strong thick sandstones in the crest of a major anticline, have ensured that they have accommodated much of the tectonic movement associated with the folding and are, therefore, extensively fractured. This makes thicknesses difficult to estimate, but probably only about 75 m of the formation are present at outcrop.

Ussher (1908) described these rocks as Ilfracombe Series, and considered them to be downfaulted against the Hangman Grits. Webby (1966a) thought that they underlay the Hangman Grits; he called them Little Quantock Beds, and considered that they were possibly equivalent to the Lynton Slates. Ussher (1908) recorded traces of crinoids, and Webby (1966b) noted *Chonetes* sp. and *Tentaculites* sp. Dr Butler reports that a fauna of the same general type, was collected during the recent survey (BGS specimens DEA 3139–84; 3891–3986). He notes that the chonetaceans, which appear to lack accessory septa in the brachial valve, are severely distorted in outline, but seem distinct from those forms so far recorded from the Lynton Slates of north Devon (see Edmonds and others, 1984). The fauna provides no useful evidence of age. However, the rocks resemble parts of the local Ilfracombe Slates, and also the Lynton Slates of north Devon. It is suggested that a position in the crest of the east-south-eastward-plunging Quantock Anticline is the most likely structural interpretation, and hence that correlation with the Lynton Slates is indicated. The Lynton Slates (of Lynton) are predominantly argillaceous in their upper part (Edmonds and others, 1984), and the slates here described on the west side of the Quantock Hills may represent these uppermost beds. The transition to Hangman Grits evident in the type area has perhaps been cut out by faults in the Quantocks. Simpson (1964) accorded the Lynton Slates in north Devon an Emsian – Eifelian age.

Hangman Grits

The Hangman Grits make up the northern part of the Quantock Hills, including all the high moorland. They consist of sandstones with subordinate shales and quartz-pebble and mud-pellet conglomerates. The sandstones are predominantly fine or fine to medium grained, strong, thickly bedded or massive, and commonly purple or purplish brown. The name Hangman Grits, first used by Etheridge (1867), is retained for historical reasons, although the word 'grit' wrongly described most of the sandstones which dominate the succession.

Ussher (1908) quoted a description by Flett of four specimens of sandstone: E 5726 (Pardlestone Hill), E 5727 (south of Vinny Combe), and E 5728 (Smith's Combe), all from the Little Hangman Sandstones, and E 5729 (Triscombe Combe), from the Trentishoe Grits. Specimen E 5729 was the finest grained; specimens E 5726 and E 5727 were coarse and gritty and contained rock fragments up to 15 mm long. All the rocks consisted mainly of quartz, feldspar, fragments of micaceous shale, greywacke, quartzite and ?felsite, zircon, yellow and blue tourmaline, iron oxides, and a little white mica mostly secondary after feldspar. The quartz was partly granitic, partly sheared. The feldspar was principally orthoclase, with some oligoclase, and was rarely fresh; much was replaced by aggregates of white mica, quartz and kaolin. Some of the quartzite fragments contained chlorite and white mica. A few bits of micropegmatite were present. The finer rocks showed considerable induration, and new quartz had been deposited in optical continuity with the original grains.

Ussher (1908) discounted earlier suggetions that the northernmost rocks of the Quantock Hills could be separately delineated and might be Lynton Beds. He was not able, mapping at the one-inch scale, to subdivide the Hangman Grits, but he did consider the possibility that older (Foreland type) grits on the west side of the hills were overlain unconformably by younger (Hangman type) grits farther east. This followed upon his tentative conclusion (1889) that the Hangman Grits and Foreland Grits of north Devon should not be equated, although he recognised that their correlation would solve many stratigraphical and structural problems. They are now mapped as one (Edmonds and others, 1985).

Evans (1922), working in the Combe Martin area, divided the Hangman Grits into Trentishoe Grits (914 m) at the base, overlain by Rawn's Beds or Rawn's Shales (61 m), and Little Hangman Beds (122 m). Later (*in* Evans and Stubblefield, 1929) he reclassified the strata above his Rawn's Beds into Sherrycombe Beds overlain by *Stringocephalus* Beds, and this fourfold division was adopted by Lane (1965), who suggested thicknesses of 1067 m, 101 m, 82 m and 101 m. More recently Tunbridge (1978) distinguished a fifth division, at the base; his (ascending) succession was Hollowbrook Formation (70 m), Trentishoe Formation (c. 1250 m), Rawn's Formation (148 m), Sherrycombe Formation (90 m) and Little Hangman Formation (?100 m). Thus total thicknesses proposed for the Hangman Grits of north Devon have ranged from 1097 m (Evans, 1922) through 1351 m (Lane, 1965) to 1668 m (Tunbridge, 1978).

In the Quantock Hills, Hallam (1934) divided the Hangman Grits into Triscombe Beds overlain by Hodder's Combe Beds and Sherry Combe Beds. However, Webby (1966a) showed that Hallam's top division rightly belonged in the Ilfracombe Slates. He estimated the thickness of the Triscombe Beds at about 460 m near Triscombe and increasing north-westwards, and of the Hodder's Combe Beds as about 300 m in the area south of Dowsborough but increasing gradually north-westwards from there. Webby's divisions were used on the provisional edition of Sheet 295, published in 1975. He described both the Triscombe Beds and the Hodder's Combe Beds as comprising sandstones with siltstones and conglomerates; the distinguishing feature which guided his mapping was the presence of pale green sandstones in the Triscombe Beds. Webby (1966a) suggested a correlation between his Triscombe Beds and the Trentishoe Grits of north Devon.

The recent survey showed a thick basal division of the Hangman Grits—up to 600 m of sandstones with subordinate shales, siltstones and conglomerates, with no mappable subdivisions either colour-based or lithological. Overlying these rocks are strata which include much arenaceous material but are characterised by the presence of purple and maroon shales and siltstones throughout a thickness typically of about 50 m. The argillaceous content of these beds has rendered them somewhat more readily eroded than the strata below and above, and they have commonly been sought out and followed by streams. Hence mapping of this division is based on lithologies, colour and topography. At the top of the Hangman Grits are beds similar to those of the bottom division but of lesser thickness—possibly up to 200 m in the north, but thinner in the east and south. The similarities of this three-fold division of the Hangman Grits of the Quantock Hills to that suggested for the same rocks in north Devon by Evans (1922), a classification later modified but fundamentally sound, have led to the adoption of names intended to suggest correlation with the north Devon sequence: Trentishoe Grits, Rawn's Shales-and-Sandstones and Little Hangman Sandstones.

There is no good direct palaeontological evidence of the age of the Hangman Grits. Kidston (*in* Ussher, 1908) compared a fragment from the formation with the 'Corduroy plant', which has been recorded from Middle and possibly Lower Devonian localities in Scotland. Ussher's (1908) record of *Natica* and *Myalina* probably refers to Ilfracombe Slates. Only plant fragments were found by Webby (1966a) and during the recent survey. The indirect evidence is the possible Eifelian age of the upper Lynton Slates (Simpson, 1964) and the Givetian age of the lower Ilfracombe Slates, which suggests that the Hangman Grits may be wholly Middle Devonian, perhaps mainly Eifelian but Givetian towards the top.

Ilfracombe Slates

The Ilfracombe Slates crop out in the middle region of the Quantock Hills, from West Bagborough eastwards to Enmore and northwards to Holford, as well as in an inlier near Radlet and in a small area at the western edge of the district north of Rowdon Farm. They consist of slates, siltstones, sandstones and limestones. In the type area the sequence is about 545 m thick (Edmonds and others, 1985), and the corresponding figure for the Taunton district is about 475 m.

Divisions first identified by Webby (1966a) are adopted here, with their names modified only to indicate main rock types. In Table 1 the successions in north Devon and in the Taunton district are compared; the generalised thicknesses of the formations in metres are listed, together with the named limestones contained within the formations. The limestones are shown opposite their probable equivalents, as first worked out by Webby (1966b) and based mainly on his study of coral faunas.

Table 1 Ilfracombe Slates successions in north Devon and in the Taunton district (average thicknesses in metres)

North Devon (Edmonds and others, (1984)		Taunton district	
Kentisbury Slates 300 (slates with sandstones)		Leigh Barton Limestone	Leighland Slates 225 (slates with sandstones and limestones)
Combe Martin Slates 120 (slates with limestones)	David's Stone Limestone	Holwell Limestone	
	Combe Martin Beach Limestone	Aisholt Limestone	
	Jenny Start Limestone	Roadwater Limestone	
Lester Slates-and-Sandstones 75 (slates and sandstones)	Holey Limestone	Rodhuish Limestone	Cutcombe Slates 110 (slates with limestones)
Wild Pear Slates 50 (slates with limestones			Avill Slates-and-Sandstones 140 (slates and sandstones)

Table 2 Corals and stromatoporoids collected from the Ilfracombe Slates of the Taunton District

Fossil	Rodhuish Limestone	Roadwater Limestone	Aisholt Limestone	Holwell Limestone
ANTHOZOA				
Coenites?	1	10		
Thamnopora cronigera	2			20(?), 22, 23(?)
T. cronigera towards *Pachyfavosites polymorphus*	1	5		
Xystriphyllum aff. *quadrigeminum*	2			
Alveolitella? cf. *duponti*		3, 5		21, 22
A. aff. *fecunda*		3		
Alveolites aff. *complanatus*		3		
A. aff. *maillieuxi*		3		
A. spp.		6, 8		16, 17, 19, 20, 21
Argutastrea sp.		4		
Chaetetes cf. *inflatus*		3		17, 18
Coenites escharoides		3		21, 22(cf.), 23
Columnaria sp.		11(?)		
Disphyllum aequiseptatum		3(cf.)		17
D.?		3		16
Endophyllum aff. *abditum*		8	14	
E. sp.		9		23
Pachyfavosites polymorphus	6(aff.), 7		23, 23(aff.)	
P. polymorphus towards *T. cronigera*		7		
Phillipsastrea aff. *hennahi*		3		
Plasmophyllum (P.) sp.		8		
Scoliopora cf. *denticulata*		3, 4, 5(?)		17, 19
Syringaxon sp.		5		23(?)
Temnophyllum sp.		3, 4, 6		
T.?		3, 5		16, 17, 18, 22
Thamnophyllum caespitosum		3		16
Thamnopora boloniensis		3	13(cf.)	21
T. cervicornis		3, 5	13	21(cf.), 22(?)
T. cervicornis towards *T. reticulata*		3		16, 19(cf.), 21(cf.)
T. spp.		9,(?), 10	12(?), 14(?)	17, 18, 19(?)
Alveolites [*Coenites*] *medius*			14(?)	16, 21, 22, 23
Chaetetes sp.			14(?)	21
Emmonsia sp.			15	
Scoliopora sp.			14	23(?)
?Acanthophyllum (*Neostringophyllum*) sp.				21
Alveolitella cf. *fecunda*				16, 17(?), 18, 19
Alveolites (*Tetrilites*) cf. *tenuissimus*				23
Aulopora?				19, 21
Beiliupora?				23
Chaetetes cf. *rotundus*				18, 23
Donia aff. *philomena*				23
Heliophyllum sp.				21, 22
'*Heterophrentis*'*?*				22
Pachyfavosites?				22
Stringophyllum sp.				17, 18(?)
Tabulophyllum?				17
Thamnophyllum				
Thamnopora cf. *polyforata*				22
T. cf. *tumefacta*				19
HYDROZOA				
Actinostroma sp.		6		16, 18(?)
Clathrodictyon sp.		3, 8		
Stachyodes sp.		4, 5		17(?)
Stromatopora sp.		4, 5, 6(?)		
Stromatoporella?		3, 5		17, 18, 20
Stromatoporoids—not determined		7, 11		

Localities 1–23 are listed on pages 15–17

The faunal lists are based on collections of the British Gelogical Survey, supplemented in the case of localities 3, 4, 9 and 17 by material in the Webby Collection, Geology Department, Bristol University

Fossil identifications are by Dr D. E. White

The threefold division of the Ilfracombe Slates of the Taunton district is based primarily on the presence of sandstones within the top and bottom divisions, and their near-absence from the intervening strata; the persistent Roadwater Limestone is taken as a convenient base of the top division.

The Avill Slates-and-Sandstones comprise grey and brown slates with siltstones and well-developed sandstones, and range up to 150 m in thickness. In the area of Cockercombe and Keeper's Combe these strata contain a band of greenish grey tuff up to 18 m thick about two-thirds of the way up the succession (p. 15). Flett (*in* Ussher, 1908) described the rock as either a crushed ash or a crushed vesicular lava. A tuff exposed in Holford Glen (p. 14) is similar except for its purple colour, but is only 1.5 m thick; the two are probably at the same horizon, and the purple colour is most likely mainly secondary staining.

Webby (1966a) recovered from the Cockercombe Tuff fossils which indicated that the volcanic debris had accumulated under the sea. He also noted marine fossils elsewhere in the Avill Slates-and-Sandstones, including occurrences above the tuff near Adscombe and in beds near the top of the formation north of Friarn. Webby and Thomas (1965) reported brachiopod, bivalve, bryozoan and crinoid remains in strata just above the tuff in Holford Glen.

EAE, BJW

The Cutcombe Slates comprise up to 130 m of brown and grey slates with siltstones and traces of thin sandstones. Discontinuous limestones up to 5 m thick, the Rodhuish Limestone, occur about mid-way up the succession in some places. The limestone is characteristically thick bedded or massive, with some interbedded slates, and has locally yielded a sparse coral fauna (Table 2) including *Thamnopora cronigera* and *Xystriphyllum* aff. *quadrigeminum* at Pepper Hill. Sampling for conodonts has proved unproductive. It seems possible, judging mainly from width of outcrop, that the Cutcombe Slates are slightly thinner in the north than in the south.

The Leighland Slates are made up of grey and brown slates, siltstones and sandstones and include limestones mainly at four horizons. A generalised thickness of 225 m is suggested, but the succession appears to thicken from Cothelstone Hill eastwards to Broomfield Hill and thence north-eastwards to Wind Down where 325 m of strata may be present. At the base lies the Roadwater Limestone, persistent throughout the Devonian outcrop, about 10 m thick, grey or pinkish grey, massive and locally recrystallised, and commonly containing a varied fauna of corals and stromatoporoids (Table 2).

Webby (1966a) pointed out that, numerically, tabulate corals and stromatoporoids predominate over rugose forms. Tabulate corals present include species of *Alveolitella*, *Chaetetes*, *Coenites*, *Pachyfavosites*, *Scoliopora* and *Thamnopora*, and there is also a wide variety of rugose corals including species of *Argutastrea*, *Endophyllum*, *Disphyllum*, *Phillipsastrea*, *Plasmophyllum*, *Syringaxon*, *Temnophyllum* and *Thamnophyllum*. Stromatoporoids present include species of *Actinostroma*, *Stachyodes* and *Stromatopora*. Samples of the limestone from various localities have proved virtually barren of conodonts.

Above the Roadwater Limestone lie 20 to 70 m of slates, locally calcareous, with siltstones and sandstones. They are succeeded by the Aisholt Limestone, a discontinuous grey massive crinoidal limestone up to 15 m thick at Lower Aisholt. This rock trends east-north-eastwards across the north-western slopes of Cothelstone Hill, where it is only 2 m thick, and thickens to 10 m in the neighbourhood of the axis of the Quantock Anticline. The Aisholt Limestone is not particularly fossiliferous (Table 2); tabulate corals recorded include species of *Emmonsia*, *Scoliopora* and *Thamnopora*, but only one rugose form, *Endophyllum* aff. *abditum*, has been found.

Some 40 to 90 m of strata overlying the Aisholt Limestone are generally similar to the rocks immediately below it, and are succeeded by the coral-rich Holwell Limestone, another discontinuous limestone up to 10 m thick, poorly developed on the north-western slopes of Broomfield Hill but thicker and well exposed in Holwell Combe and on Hawkridge Common. The Holwell Limestone ranges from thin crinoidal bands to grey massive limestone, locally sandy. As observed by Webby (1966a, p. 331), many of the corals occurring in the Roadwater Limestone are also represented in the Holwell Limestone (Table 2). Tabulate corals, which numerically predominate, include species of *Alveolitella*, *Alveolites*, *Chaetetes*, *Coenites*, *Pachyfavosites*, *Scoliopora* and *Thamnopora*; rugose corals include species of *Columnaria*, *Donia*, *Endophyllum*, *Heliophyllum*, *Tabulophyllum?*, *Thamnophyllum* and *Stringophyllum*. Stromatoporoids are also present.

The Leighland Slates become slightly more sandy upwards, and 100 m or more of slates with sandstones and scattered limy bands lie between the Holwell Limestone and the Leigh Barton Limestone, which is mappable only south of Cothelstone Hill, south-east of Wind Down and south-west of Enmore. At these places up to 2 m of grey and pinkish grey crinoidal limestones occur with calcareous siltstones and slates. Perhaps 20 to 30 m of locally calcareous slates with sandstones lie at the top of the Leighland Slates, between the Leigh Barton Limestone and the base of the Morte Slates. Similar rocks north-west of Stogumber between the Morte Slates outcrop and the overlying Permo-Triassic rocks to the north appear to be about 60 m thick and they contain no mappable limestones.

Taxonomic and biostratigraphic studies of the coral and stromatoporoid faunas of south-west England are necessary before their full potential for correlation can be utilised, a point stressed by Scrutton (1975). However, Webby (1964) reported that corals from the Rodhuish and Roadwater limestones of the Brendon Hills included typical Middle Devonian species, such as *Heliophyllum halli* and '*Cystiphyllum*' (= *Plasmophyllum*) *secundum*, together with genera which are restricted to the Middle Devonian elsewhere in Europe and North America. He concluded that the overall evidence, based on the coral faunas of these beds in the Brendon Hills, indicated that the age of the Rodhuish Limestone was mid- to late Givetian and that the Roadwater Limestone was of late Givetian age. On similar evidence Webby (1966a) concluded that the corals of the Roadwater Limestone of the Quantock Hills confirmed a Givetian age (possibly mid- or late) and that the Holwell Limestone, which has a fauna comparable with that of the Roadwater Limestone, was also of late Givetian age. Although it has not been possible to confirm the occurrence of all the taxa used by Webby in assessing the age of the limestones, nevertheless it is agreed that the overall aspect of the coral faunas indicates a Middle Devonian, Givetian, age for the limestones of the Ilfracombe Slates up to and including the Holwell Limestone.

Ussher's (1908) record of *Tentaculites ?annulatus* on Broomfield Hill was regarded as setting an upper limit of mid-Frasnian on the upper Leighland Slates, and Webby consequently placed the Givetian–Frasnian boundary within the strata between the Holwell Limestone and the Leigh Barton Limestone, a position roughly in accord with that suggested by Orchard (1979) for the north Devon sequence, assuming the limestone correlations in Table 1 to be correct. It is also the approximate position of the stage boundary used in the Ilfracombe district Memoir (Edmonds and others, 1984).

EAE, BJW, DEW

Morte Slates

The western crop of the Morte Slates is in continuity of outcrop with the Devonian rocks of the Brendon Hills. Although predominantly argillaceous, typically lustrous silvery grey slates, the Morte Slates of north-west Somerset nevertheless contain more sandstone, in more sharply defined beds, than do the corresponding rocks in north Devon. Webby (1965a) mapped three divisions, on the basis of the middle one containing most sandstones. In the area of outcrop that falls within the Taunton district no such division is readily discernible, although sandstones are fairly common north of Brompton Ralph and rare to the south. Silvery grey, greenish grey and purple-stained slates and silty slates with subordinate siltstones contain scattered sandstones, generally in thin ill-defined bands but in places in distinct beds.

The only known fossiliferous localities in this area are the Oakhampton and Combe quarries, north of Wiveliscombe, from which Hicks (1897) recorded brachiopods, bivalves, trilobites and crinoid remains. He regarded the fossils as indicative of a Lower Devonian age. Ussher (1908) included the formation in the Middle Devonian, though he recorded from Oakhampton Quarry the occurrence of the commonly Upper Devonian *Cyrtospirifer verneuili* (Murchison). The specimen upon which this determination was undoubtedly based (BGS Us 1344) is not, in fact, identifiable at specific or even generic level. Nevertheless, the strata are placed as Upper Devonian by analogy with the north Devon sequence.

To the east, Morte Slates crop out at the south-eastern end of the Quantock Hills. They comprise grey and brown slates and silty slates with siltstones and some sandstones. Webby (1966a) was unable to delineate there the three divisions he proposed for the Morte Slates of the Brendon Hills, but thought that all were represented. He also recorded traces of a few brachiopods, bivalves and crinoids near the base of the generally unfossiliferous succession. Thicknesses are impossible to calculate and difficult to estimate. Webby (1966a) thought that quarries just west-south-west of North Petherton showed several hundred feet of strata, and that the Morte Slates of the Quantock Hills were 4000 to 5000 ft thick (about 1200 to 1500 m). However, as with the Variscan folding elsewhere in north Devon and Somerset, much of the movement was accommodated by the more argillaceous rocks and the extent of overfolding and repetition is unknown. Perhaps as little as 500 m of strata are present.

Pickwell Down Sandstones

North-west of Wiveliscombe the Morte Slates are succeeded by Pickwell Down Sandstones, reddish brown, purple and grey sandstones, shales and slates, about 60 m of which are present in the small outcrop included within the Taunton district. The top of the succession is hidden by Permo-Triassic rocks, but the beds must be faulted against Pilton Shales, which crop out only 200 m away to the south.

Pilton Shales

Brown and lilac-brown shales with subordinate locally calcareous sandstones and traces of silty limestone are exposed south of Wiveliscombe. The base of the succession must be faulted and the 60 m or so of beds present probably lie mainly in the lower half of the formation. Calcareous fossil-rich bands typical of the Pilton Shales occur.

EAE, BJW

Fossils collected during Ussher's and the present survey include forms typical of the Pilton Shales of Barnstaple, the type area. Some of the assemblages include elements diagnostic of Goldring's (1955) Pilton A, which he correlated with the late Famennian *Wocklumeria* Stufe. Though it is possible that part of the succession is of Carboniferous age, no fossil evidence to that effect has been obtained.

As in the Barnstaple area, productacean brachiopods are important constituents of the Pilton A macrofauna and include *Hamlingella goergesi*, *Mesoplica praelonga*, *Whidbornella caperata* and forms comparable with *Hamlingella piltonensis* and *Steinhagella steinhagei*. Among other brachiopods are *Cyrtospirifer verneuili*, cf. *Centrorhynchus letiensis* and cf. *Chonetes sauntonensis*. Bivalves, which include *Ptychopteria damnoniensis* and species of *Leptodesma* and *Palaeoneilo*, are subsidiary. The remaining noteworthy macrofaunal elements are the bryozoan *Fenestella*, the gastropod *Straparollus* (*Philoxene*) *vermis* and the trilobite *Phacops* (*Omegops*) *accipitrinus*; crinoid columnals are fairly common.

One locality, with a Pilton A macrofauna, also yielded a small number of mainly broken conodonts, including *Pseudopolygnathus* cf. *striatus* and *Polygnathus* spp.

DEB

Conditions of deposition

The earliest depositional environment recorded by the rocks of the Taunton district was the shallow tranquil sea in which were deposited the muds, silts and sands that gave rise to the Lynton Slates. Marine sedimentation ceased following a southward retreat of the shoreline, leaving an Old Red Sandstone land surface. The Hangman Grits appear to thicken northwards, as do some of their component beds. Mud-pellet conglomerates and quartz-pebble conglomerates are commoner in the north than in the south. Thick bedding, channel fill and local cross-bedding all indicate strong currents. Very few fossils have been found apart from scattered plant fragments. Thus the evidence suggests that high land lay to the north, over what is now south Wales, and that rivers from there spread sediment across the coastal plain. Holwill and others (1969) envisaged spasmodic flash floods and deposition of top-set beds in a southward-growing delta. The Rawn's Shales-and-Sandstones, of fairly uniform thickness, may indicate the presence for a time of shallow lakes in which some muds accumulated but which were also subject to spasmodic incursions of floodwater carrying much coarse sediment. Hallam's (1934) view that sedimentation took place separated by a barrier from the main land mass to the north was based on the presence of garnet near Cardiff and its absence from the Quantocks. However, he seems to have been comparing Lower and Upper Old Red Sandstone near Cardiff with probable Middle Old Red Sandstone of Somerset.

Northward advance of the shoreline in Givetian times created the marine environment in which originated the slates, limestones and sandstones of the Ilfracombe Slates. The Avill Slates-and-Sandstones were laid down in a shallow sea, probably not far from the shore. Webby and Thomas (1965) considered that at Holford the lower strata of the succession showed evidence of a littoral origin; their opinion was based on a fauna of bivalves and gastropods, the presence of shells of the bivalve *Myalina* up to 13 mm thick in the umbonal region, and the occurrence in those shells of borings possibly attributable to intertidal worms. Their evidence suggests the approximate position of a northward-migrating shoreline. Tuff within the Ilfracombe Slates is known only in the Quantock Hills, where it is much thinner at Holford than in Keeper's Combe; if its submarine accumulation is presumed to have followed upon submarine eruption, then that eruption may have been located to the south-east or east (see Webby, 1966b, fig. 2E).

The Cutcombe Slates may mark the establishment, by continued northward marine transgression, of the slightly deeper water of a tranquil shelf sea. However, Webby (1966b) equated their representatives in the Brendon Hills with prodelta muds, and suggested that a pause in the influx of mud, or perhaps current action, created local conditions favourable to coral growth. He recognised a Brendon biotope in the Rodhuish Limestone in the Brendon Hills, characterised by the predominance of compound and solitary rugose corals over tabulate corals and stromatoporoids, and he tentatively suggested that the Brendon biotope accumulated in comparatively shallow sub-turbulent water. However, at exposures of the local equivalent of the Rodhuish Limestone in the Quantock Hills, corals are rare or absent.

Renewed southerly growth of deltas resulted in shallower, slightly more turbulent water in which both muds and sands were deposited and corals grew. The rocks subsequently formed are the Leighland Slates, and they contain the Givetian – Frasnian (Middle – Upper Devonian) junction. The Roadwater Limestone of the Quantock Hills contains a varied coral fauna which Webby (1966a) called the Quantock biotope, characterised by tabulate corals and stromatoporoids which predominate over rugose forms. This suggested to Webby (1966a) even shallower and more turbulent water than existed at the time farther west, where the Brendon biotope occurs in the Roadwater Limestone of the Brendon Hills. The presence of sandstone beds in the north of the outcrop points to a near-shore position and possible rapid deposition. The Aisholt Limestone is poorly fossiliferous and may have formed in water deeper than the turbulent sea of the Roadwater Limestone. The Holwell Limestone has a coral fauna typical of the Quantock biotope, suggesting an origin similar to that of the Roadwater Limestone of the Quantock Hills. The Leigh Barton Limestone, present at only a few localities and generally only as sporadic thin lenses of crinoidal limestone, contains no corals, and it may be that the waters were too shallow and too turbulent for such growth. Throughout the upper part of the Leighland Slates the progressively younger beds appear to contain progressively more sandy sediment, and Webby (1966b) interpreted this change as a transition from a prodelta to a delta-platform environment. It seems possible that the Devonian coral limestones grew on slight rises of the sea floor, just clear of the accumulating muds, and that they may have undergone some subsequent reworking locally.

Another transgression re-established the quiescent shelf sea in Frasnian times, and muds deposited then and during the Famennian stage are now represented by the thick sequence of Morte Slates. In the Taunton district these rocks include more and thicker sandstones than the corresponding rocks of north Devon (Edmonds and others, 1984), and may reflect slight fluctuations in depth as well as in the amount and nature of sediment. Webby (1966b) pursued this analysis to the suggestion of alternating prodelta and delta-platform deposits.

The Pickwell Down Sandstones represent the re-establishment over north Devon and Somerset of an Old Red Sandstone landscape. Marine sedimentation gave way to fluviatile, lacustrine and deltaic deposition, with only scattered fossil plant fragments being preserved.

From Morte Slates to Pilton Shales the rocks of north Devon tell a story of slowly migrating shorelines and of onshore, near-shore and shallow sea sedimentation (Edmonds and others, 1985). However, the Upcott Slates and Baggy Sandstones, which conformably succeed the Pickwell Down Sandstones, are not exposed in the Taunton district. The Pilton Shales comprise shales and siltstones with limy and sandy bands and lenses, and were formed in a shallow sea during the transition from Devonian to Carboniferous times.

EAE, BJW, DEW

DETAILS

Lynton Slates (Figure 3)

The northernmost evidence of Lynton Slates comprises rubbly outcrops of green and brown slates north and south-east of Little Quantock Farm [148 365]. Poor exposures of similar slates, locally silty, occur alongside the road from there to Triscombe, and one of them [1518 3599] shows subordinate fine-grained thinly bedded sandstone. Indifferently preserved chonetacean brachiopods were collected from this place during the present survey, along with tentaculitoideans and crinoid debris. Webby (1966a) recorded *Chonetes* sp., *Tentaculites* sp. and crinoid columnals from this roadside.

A small valley [152 360] to [153 362] north of the road contains much rubbly pale green slate and silty slate, typical of the formation, with some sandstone. In a small old quarry [1554 3543] just south-west of the Blue Ball Inn, purple-stained grey lustrous silty slates are exposed. A laneside quarry [1621 3452] north-east of Rock Farm has grey, green and red slates and siltstones in its western part, but more fine-grained sandstone, some showing lens bedding, on strike to the east; the rock is blocky and much fractured, and cut by north–south faults.

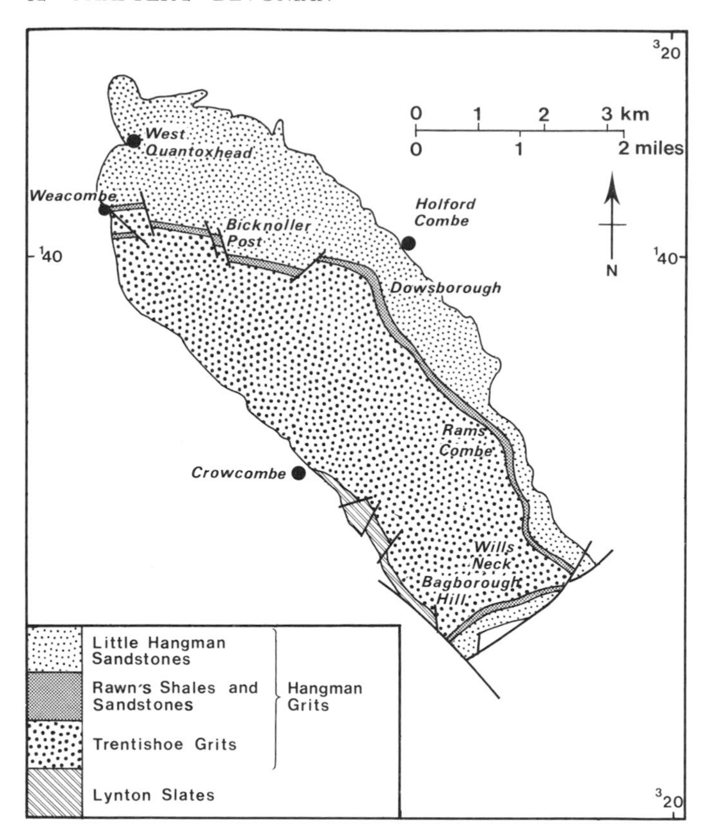

Figure 3 Outcrops of the Lynton Slates and the Hangman Grits

Hangman Grits (Figure 3)

TRENTISHOE GRITS

Weacombe to Crowcombe

Weacombe Hill [120 402] is littered with sandstone debris, mainly fine to medium grained, with some conglomeratic sandstone. To the south, in Bicknoller Combe, a disused quarry [1153 3992] shows 35 m of fine-grained quartzitic sandstone and silty sandstone with subordinate quartz-pebble conglomerate, mainly towards the base. Argillaceous bands and lenses occur up to 0.2 m thick. The sandstones are typically thickly bedded, but locally thin. Much of the rock, especially the argillaceous material, is extensively sheared, but all the beds dip westwards at 20° to 40°. Fracture surfaces show purple and black traces of iron and manganese oxides, a few green specks, possibly indicative of copper, and dark grey films of metallic or crystalline appearance. Purple and brown sandstone debris abounds within the combe and on the slopes.

A small quarry [1197 3924] near Quantock Moor, now difficult of access, exposes fine-grained sandstones with thin shales dipping at 10° to 20° to west or west-north-west. Similar sandstones crop out sporadically in Paradise Combe [124 388] to [128 391]. Debris on the high moorland of Thorncombe Hill [131 390] attests to the presence within the sandstones of sandy conglomeratic beds, some with quartz pebbles up to 20 mm across and others with silty pellets.

Sandstones have in the past been quarried from several places in Halsway Combe. At the lowest and most westerly quarry [1326 3800] fine-grained sandstones with interbedded purple silty shales dip at 20°/235°. Some 200 m to the east [1345 3800], in Halsway Quarry, fine-grained sandstone 3 m thick is overlain by rubbly siltstone and shale 0.5 m, massive sandstone 4 m, sandstone and shale 1.5 m, fine-grained sandstone 3 m, sandstone, siltstone and shale 3 m, and thickly bedded fine-grained sandstone with shaly partings 5.5 m (Figure 4). The beds dip at 15°/240°. In the north bay [1351 3808] of Halsway Quarry fine-grained purple, grey and pale green feldspathic quartzitic sandstones occur with interbedded purple-stained shales and siltstones and quartz-pebble and mudstone-pellet conglomerates.

Exposures [1400 3732], [1403 3723] in Crowcombe Park of beds probably near the base of the Hangman Grits show variegated grey and purple siltstones and shales among the sandstones. In a quarry [1444 3680] in Crowcombe Combe similar rocks are sheared and extensively fractured into blocks; they lie near the conjectured fault separating Lynton Slates from Hangman Grits, but the lithologies suggest a pre-faulting transition from one to the other such as probably occurs on the north Devon coast (Edmonds and others, 1985). Sandstones and siltstones dipping at 20°/020° [1488 3658] just north of Little Quantock Farm are similarly indicative of somewhat argillaceous basal Hangman Grits. A quarry [1505 3661] to the east contains thickly bedded grey fine-grained quartzite with some greyish green cleaved shale.

Rams Combe to Wills Neck

A small quarry [1680 3764] on the south side of Rams Combe has been opened by the Forestry Commission in rocks at the top of the Trentishoe Grits, dipping at 25°/055° beneath the adjacent Rawn's Shales-and-Sandstones. The strata are purple sandstones with greyish green mudstones and sandy conglomerates containing either pebbles or mud pellets. Thinly bedded fine-grained sandtones with subordinate silty shales and siltstones are exposed [1591 3696] in the trackside at Quantock Farm, and in a small quarry [1699 3708] in Quantock Combe fine-grained quartzites and sandstones with slaty partings show signs of faulting.

On the north side of Triscombe Combe about 20 m of fine-grained purple-grey and brown thickly bedded and massive quartzitic sandstones, with argillaceous partings and quartz veins, dip at 10° to just north of east in a quarry [157 359]. The large Triscombe Quarry [161 356] lies 0.5 km to the south-east. It shows grey, green and purple massive and thickly bedded fine-grained sandstone and quartzite, with some shaly bands and a little conglomeratic sandstone containing pellets of mudstone and siltstone. Traces of thicker argillaceous strata, commonly rubbly and giving rise to degraded faces, occur in a few places. The sandstones contain scattered plant fragments and exhibit large-scale wedge bedding and some micaceous bedding planes. About 80 m of strata are exposed in the south-east end of the quarry.

Faulted sandstones and slates crop out [1618 3474] on the slopes of Bagborough Hill just above the Lynton Slates. An apparently artificial gully [170 351] on the high ground east of Wills Neck cuts through purple-stained flaggy fine-grained sandstones and gritty sandstones.

RAWN'S SHALES-AND-SANDSTONES

Weacombe to Bicknoller Post

Fault-displaced outcrops of notably purple and silty successions appear to underlie valleys near Weacombe, although the outcrops are narrow and carry much sandstone debris. In the lower reaches of Weacombe Combe siltstones dip at 60°/330° [1118 4088], and old quarries show rubble of silty sandstones [1150 4092] and purple siltstones inclined at 60°/080° [1168 4089]. Ussher (1908) noted grits and mudstones hereabouts. A smaller valley to the south contains a quarry in fine-grained sandstones and locally slaty siltstones [1130 4048], and a track cutting through purple and grey siltstones and mudstones, locally micaceous, with a little sandstone, dip 45°/040° [1153 4045 to 1149 4051]. The upper reaches of Weacombe Combe contain some fine-grained sandstones cropping out sporadically in the stream gully, and small pits or crags showing purple siltstones with silty sandstones and cleaved shales [1195 4060; 1196 4058; 1197 4053].

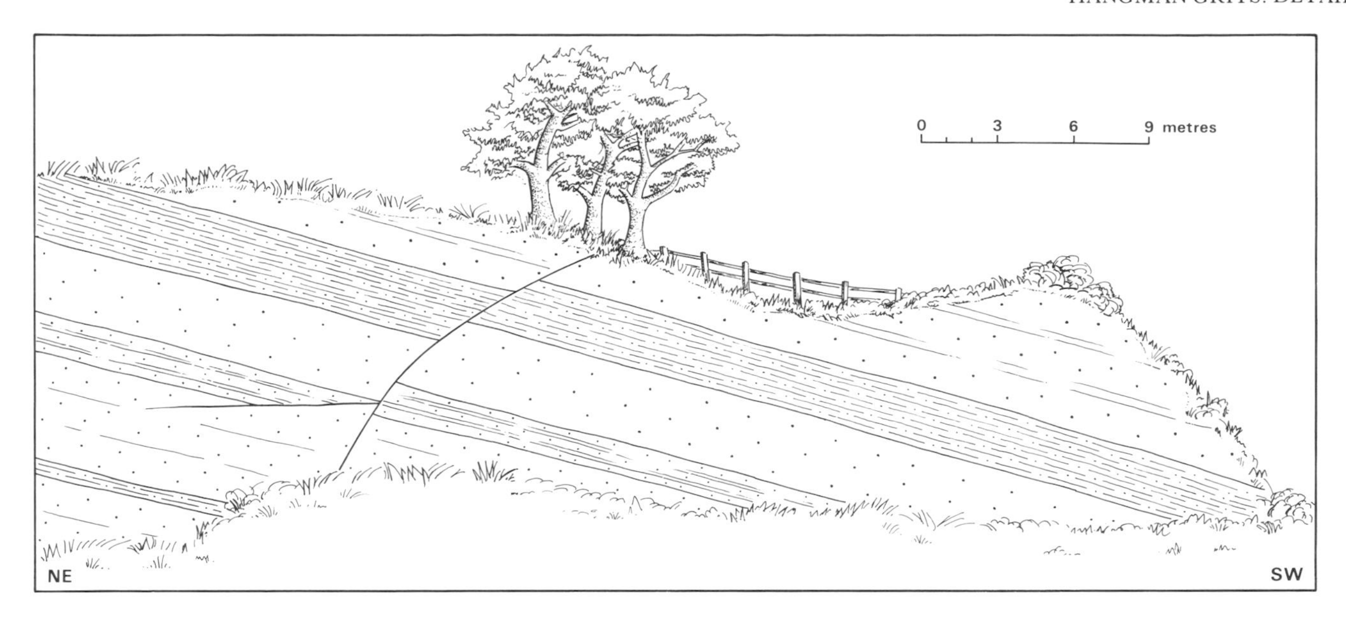

Figure 4 Trentishoe Grits in the south bay of Halsway Quarry

Plate 2 Triscombe Quarry.

The Trentishoe Grits comprise massive and thickly bedded sandstones and quartzites with interbedded shales and some conglomerate, and exhibit large-scale wedge bedding (A 13827)

Rubble dug at Bicknoller Post [1287 4035] comprises purple fine-grained sandstone and siltstone. Rubble extending along Sheppard's Combe to the south-east is predominantly of sandstone but includes purple micaceous siltstone.

Holford Combe to Bagborough Hill

The upper reaches of Holford Combe contain scattered outcrops of siltstone and fine-grained sandstone. Trackside exposures [1652 3783 to 1703 3754] in Rams Combe show purple siltstones and shales with some fine-grained sandstone. Debris of sandstone, some medium grained, gritty and feldspathic, and of quartz-pebble and mud-pellet conglomerate may be of the same formation or downwash from adjoining formations. Purple siltstones west of the stream [1698 3755] dip at 10° east-north-east.

Just east of the junction of Rams Combe and Quantock Combe purple lustrous slaty shales, possibly at the base of the Rawn's Shales-and-Sandstones, overlie sandstone, grit and conglomerate [1738 3732]; the beds dip gently eastward. A short distance downstream, silty sandstones on the north bank dip at 20°/060° [1746 3728], and purple and grey slaty shales, silty shales and fine-grained sandstones on the south bank dip at 20°/070° [1746 3722].

Purple and reddish brown siltstones and slaty silty shales in Cockercombe [1772 3618; 1779 3619] dip at 30°/140° locally [1771 3615]. Farther south a track cuts across purple siltstones and shales with subordinate sandstone [1776 3578 to 1781 3586], and a small combe [181 355] on Aisholt Common contains much debris of purple siltstone and shale together with sandstone.

Traces of shale occur sporadically in the valley [1826 3499 to 1796 3492] separating Middle Hill from Lydeard Hill. Rubbly exposures on the main Quantocks watershed to the west, just south-east of Wills Neck, show fine-grained sandstone [1719 3473] and red and cream-coloured slaty shales striking east-north-east [1697 3463 to 1689 3456].

Little Hangman Sandstones

West Quantoxhead to Holford Combe

West Quantoxhead Quarries [113 416] are cut in purple, brown and greenish grey massive and bedded fine-grained quartzitic sandstones, rarely calcareous, with some siltstones. In places the sandstones show wedge bedding and channel-fill structures and small-scale cross bedding. Debris in the western quarry [112 415] suggests the presence of subordinate mudstone-pellet and quartz-pebble conglomerates. Scattered plant fragments occur, as do a few thin quartz veins. The rocks are much broken by joints, of which the main sets trend north – south dipping steeply or vertically, and north-west – south-east, dipping mainly south-westerly. Dips are between north and north-west at 15° to 30°. In the central quarry [113 415] 50 m of strata exhibit slight fold flexures. In the eastern quarry [114 416], which was described by Webby and Thomas (1965), the sandstones and siltstones show cross bedding and convoluted bedding, and cross-bedded sandstones form a large channel filling.

Old quarries [1192 4256; 1217 4254] near Perry contain purple, grey and brown medium-grained sandstones, locally flaggy, dipping at 25°/030°. To the south, on Stowborrow Hill, another quarry [1200 4183], opened for walling stone, shows 5 m of similar sandstones, with silty and shaly partings and cut by irregular joints; the bedding dips at 17°/100°. A small pit [1194 4134] on the west side of Vinny Combe Plantation showed lilac and buff micaceous grit with plant fragments when seen by Ussher (1908). Exposures in and near Smith's Combe include the following: about 2 m of purple and grey sandstone, possibly flexed into a gentle anticline, in an old quarry [1315 4226]; pavements [1335 4230; 1339 4222] and a small scarp [1389 4220] of similar rock; thinly bedded fine-grained sandstones and silty sandstones dipping at up to 30° east-north-east in the stream course [1297 4161 to 1300 4178]; sandstones dipping gently between north-north-east and north-east and cut by joints dipping steeply south-south-west in Gay's House Combe [1309 4107 to 1311 4161].

The Willoughby Cleeve stretch of Hodder's Combe [1435 4015 to 1505 4090] cuts through massive and thickly bedded fine-grained and silty sandstones with subordinate quartz-pebble conglomerates. An old quarry [1504 4085] near the top of the Hangman Grits shows massive purple sandstones with sandy conglomerates containing quartz pebbles or mudstone pellets, dip 15° eastward. In a slightly larger quarry [152 405], near Combe House Hotel in Holford Combe, broken sandstones are disposed in a tight anticline/syncline pair plunging at 15° to just south of east.

Dowsborough to West Bagborough

The hill upon which stands Dowsborough Camp [160 391]bears several small outcrops of rubbly purple and grey fine- to medium-grained sandstone, and much debris of sandstone with lesser amounts of conglomerate. The outcrop of Little Hangman Sandstones narrows southwards to about 200 m in Quantock Combe [176 373], where occur rubbly sandstone, grit and conglomerate. Similar rocks are present in Cockercombe [178 362 to 181 363], together with some siltstone. A laneside exposure [1807 3641] north of the stream, shows massive and thickly bedded purple fine-grained quartzitic sandstones, locally containing flakes of mudstone and siltstone, overlain by variegated purple, grey and green silty shales and siltstones, all the beds dipping at about 30°/050°; this locality is taken as the junction between the Hangman Grits and the Ilfracombe Slates.

The easternmost exposure of Little Hangman Sandstones, in a small pit [1858 3522], shows the sandstones to contain some interbedded cleaved shales. On the southern limb of the Quantock Anticline, from Higher Durborough Plantation [182 349] to the southern end [168 340] of Bagborough Hill, evidence from small outcrops and surface brash suggests the presence of sandstones with subordinate shales or slates and a little grit.

Ilfracombe Slates (Figure 5)

Avill Slates-and-Sandstones

At the confluence [1551 4119] of Hodder's Combe and Holford Combe reddish brown fine-grained sandstones and slates are overlain by 1.5 m of purplish maroon tuff beneath bedded fine-grained sandstones. Just downstream, the same tuff and overlying grey fine-grained sandstones, are faulted against Permo-Triassic conglomerates and breccio-conglomerates (Figure 6) by a fracture running north-west – south-east. Webby and Thomas (1965) recorded the following fossils from immediately above the tuff: *Cyrtospirifer* sp., *Atrypa?*, *Nuculoidea* sp., Bryozoa and crinoid columnals. An old quarry [1540 4103] on the west side of Holford Combe shows thickly bedded sandstones overlain by slates; Ussher (1908) recorded gastropods and *Petraia* at this locality. Sandstones and slates alongside a road [1558 4093] have yielded *Myalina?* sp. nov., *Edmondia?*, *Spathella* sp., *Pedasiola* cf. *rhenana*, *Bellerophon?*, *Euryzone?*, *Spinocyrtia?* and *Thamnopora* sp. (Evans and others, 1914; Webby and Thomas, 1965). Webby and Thomas (1965) noted the *Myalina?* shells to be thick and to contain worm borings. To the south-east, disturbed mottled grey, green and purple siltstones with silty slates and thin sandstones dip at 25°/070° in an old quarry [1572 4074], probably the one from which Ussher (1908) recorded fossils identified by R. Etheridge as *Favosites cervicornis*, *Petraia celtica?*, *Atrypa desquamata?*, *Tentaculites*, *Fenestella plebeia*, *Actinocrinus* and plant? fragments, and 4 m of mainly fine-grained sandstones with argillaceous partings dip at 35°/050° by the roadside [1634 4029].

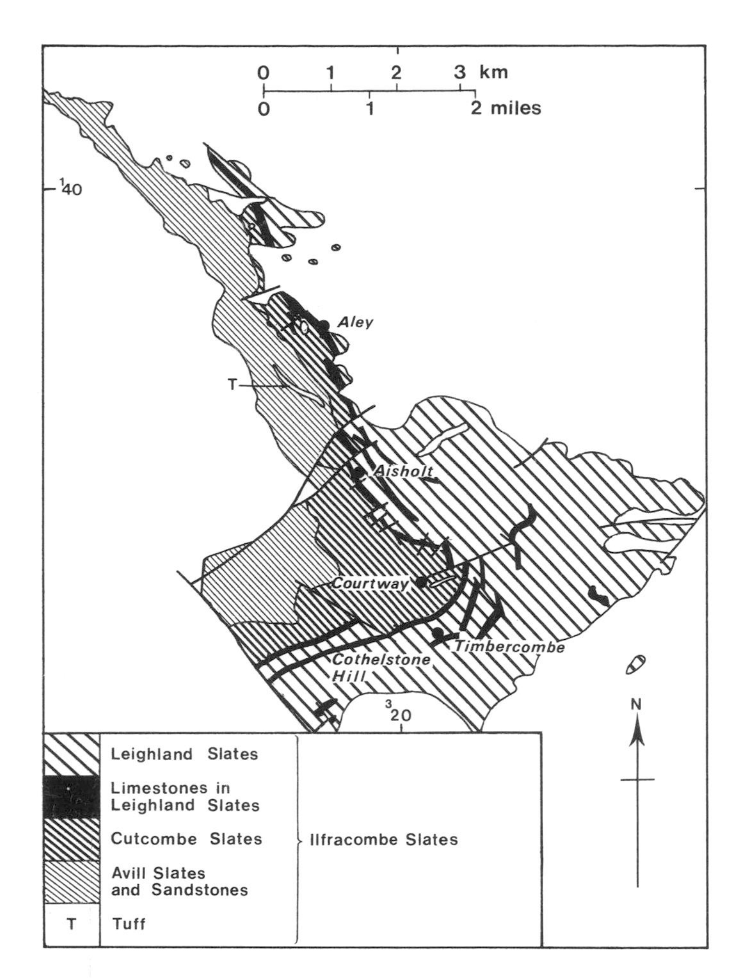

Figure 5 Outcrop of the Ilfracombe Slates

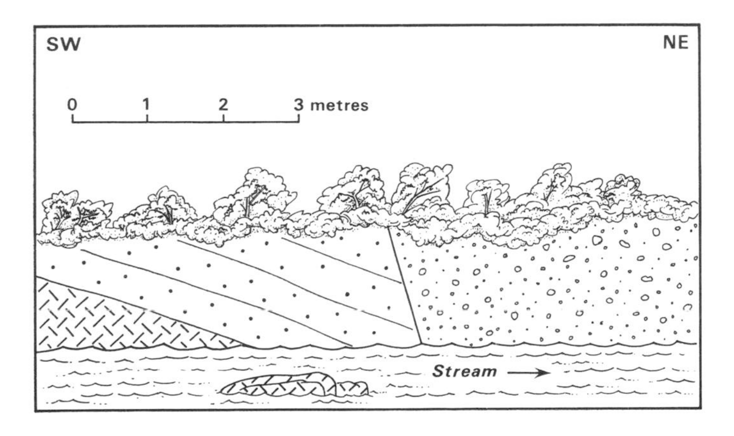

Figure 6 Faulted Devonian and Permo-Triassic rocks in Holford Glen

Exposures on the southern edge of Duke's Plantation show grey, green and red slates, silty slates and thin-bedded fine-grained sandstones dipping at 10° to 25°/070° to 085° [1684 3938; 1692 3936]. To the east, near Walford's Gibbet, old quarries [1750 3945; 1755 3941] contain thinly bedded purple and grey fine-grained quartzitic sandstones with green and red silty mudstones dipping at 55° to 60°/070°.

At the roadside [1742 3848] on the eastern slopes of Great Bear, the top beds of the Avill Slates-and-Sandstones comprise thin-bedded fine-grained quartzitic sandstones and mottled purple and grey slates. Quarries [1770 3873; 1782 3864] north of Friarn are in thickly and thinly bedded fine-grained sandstones, locally calcareous, with subordinate siltstones and slates, dipping at 70°/070°. Webby (1966a) noted a gastropod and Bryozoa at this locality.

The lane west of Adscombe cuts through slate, siltstones and locally calcareous sandstones dipping at 20°/020° [1804 3782]; Webby (1966a) obtained a spiriferoid brachiopod and crinoid columnals from the beds, and they yielded the bivalves *Guerichia* aff. *simorini* and *Palaeoneilo?* during the survey. To the south-west, in Quantock Combe, variegated purple and greyish green slates typical of the Avill Slates-and-Sandstones crop out [1770 3745; 1782 3744] just above the underlying Hangman Grits. Similar rocks with siltstones and thin sandstones are exposed sporadically in the forest tracks of Keeper's Combe and Cockercombe. A poorly preserved fauna collected during the survey from a laneside exposure [1812 3644] comprised *Hemitrypa* sp., *Polypora* sp., a bifoliate cryptostome and other bryozoans, rhynchonellacean and spiriferacean brachiopods including *Athyris* cf. *concentrica*, a bellerophontacean gastropod and a crinoid columnal. An old quarry [1825 3710], now fairly overgrown, shows 18 m of massive greyish green oxide-spotted lithic tuff cut by cleavage planes dipping at 28° to east or east-south-east; some slates are present. The tuff is delineated mainly on the evidence of debris, but small exposures [about 1865 3665] occur on the wooded slopes of Cockercombe and it may be from here that Webby (1966a) obtained the Bryozoa, crinoid columnals and indeterminate brachiopods which led him to the conclusion that the tuff accumulated under water. The base of the formation is exposed to the west, farther up the combe.

Interbedded thin sandstones and grey or purplish grey slates near the base of the formation are extensively exposed on the north-west side of Lydeard Hill [around 174 344]. Strata midway up the succession have been quarried [1714 3356] and comprise fine-grained quartzitic sandstones with limestones and thin slaty bands. A nearby old quarry [1743 3348] is completely obscured by tip and scrub, but traces of what appears to have been a limekiln suggest that enough limestone was present to warrant extraction. Strata at the top of the formation on the southern side of Lydeard Hill include thin sandstones and slates in a lane [1762 3337] and massive and thickly bedded fine- to medium-grained sandstones in quarries [1783 3331; 1790 3343]. Corresponding strata on the eastern side of the hill [around 187 346] contain fewer thick sandstones. EAE

Cutcombe Slates

The northernmost occurrence of Rodhuish Limestone is seen in a quarry [1773 3942] on the northern side of Bin Combe to comprise finely crystalline limestone, with some interbedded slates, dipping at 50°/080°. Poorly preserved tabulate coral fragments occur in thin limestones in the floor of a track close by [1773 3945] including *Coenites?* and possible examples of *Thamnopora cronigera* varying towards *Pachyfavosites polymorphus* (Table 2, loc. 1). A grassed old pit [1815 3822] north of Adscombe shows only scattered fragments of slate and sandstone but is on strike with a quarry [1833 3794] in Rodhuish Limestone at Adscombe, where massive and thickly bedded grey limestones with interbedded slates dip at 40°/065°. Slates below the limestone crop out [1876 3720] alongside the track at the mouth of Keeper's Combe. The main development of Rodhuish Limestone is near Pepper Hill, where a quarry [1898 3722] contains an overturned syncline (p. 58) in massive and thickly bedded pinkish grey and purple crinoidal limestone; slates and calcareous slates underlie and overlie the limestone. Probably about 3 m of limestone are present, containing the tabulate coral *T. cronigera* and the compound rugose coral *Xystriphyllum* aff. *quadrigeminum* (Table 2, loc. 2). Smaller limestone quarries occur nearby [1905 3719; 1911 3717], and corresponding strata on the southern side of Cockercombe comprise purple silty slates with thin limestones and sandstones [1915 3678].

Hunt's Lane [1890 3530 to 1889 3478], east of Durborough Farm, and an adjoining lane [1891 3478 to 1901 3490] cut through slates and silty slates with a few thin sandstones and traces of limestone. Similar rocks crop out extensively in the area around Bishpool Farm and Courtway, mainly in lanesides and tracks and nowhere as large exposures. The Rodhuish Limestone has been quarried [2056 3390] south-east of Courtway; the pit was almost filled when seen, but showed 2 m of dark grey massive limestone overlain by calcareous silty slates, dipping at about 30°/150°. A second pit [2082 3409], on strike to the east-north-east, is now grassed over but was probably opened for limestone; slates are exposed in the adjoining hedge. Traces of an old pit [1922 3347] south-east of Kenley Bottom show much slaty rubble and scattered blocks of grey fine-grained limestone, possibly the Rodhuish Limestone.

Leighland Slates: Roadwater Limestone

The northernmost occurrence of the Roadwater Limestone is that carrying the copper ores of Dodington (p. 63). A quarry [1723 4042] just south of Dodington Hall shows 5 m of grey massive limestone, traversed by scattered calcite veins, in purple silty and calcareous slates. An extensive fauna of tabulate and rugose corals and stromatoporoids is present (Table 2, loc. 3). Apart from coelenterates Webby (1966a) also recorded *Spirorbis* sp. and ?algal structures from this locality.

Old quarries [1784 3972; 1782 3964] south of the A39 road show calcite-veined limestone with subordinate slates and sandstones. Webby (1966a) identified *Alveolites* aff. *densatus*, *Chaetetes inflatus*, *Disphyllum aequiseptatum* (including forms gradational into *Temnophyllum inflatum*) and *Thamnopora* aff. *cervicornis*, together with stromatoporoids including *Stachyodes* sp. He recorded a similar fauna from the quarry [1793 3940] on the northern side of Bin Combe, which is in limestones, calcareous slates and calcareous sandstones.

In a quarry [1833 3827] south-west of Over Stowey massive and thickly bedded grey limestone with calcite veins is exposed, containing the rugose corals *Argutastrea* sp. and *Temnophyllum* sp., together with the tabulate coral *Scoliopora* cf. *denticulata* and stromatoporoids including *Stachyodes* sp. (Table 2, loc. 4). Webby (1966a, p. 327), in addition to coelenterates, recorded shell fragments and crinoid columnals from this locality. A smaller quarry [1846 3820] to the south-east contains reddish brown limestone and calcareous sandstone.

Adscombe Quarry [186 381] is a large disused pit showing 8 m of massive and thickly bedded grey and reddish brown limestone with calcareous sandstones and calcareous slates, yielding corals and stromatoporoids (Table 2, loc. 5). Massive and thickly bedded limestone in a quarry [1885 3773] adjoining the drive south of Aley appears to be fairly flat-lying. Just north-west of Plainsfield massive grey limestone with calcareous sandstone and variegated red and green slates have been dug from a quarry [1933 3698] almost surrounded by Otter Sandstone.

About 0.5 km south-west of Plainsfield, quarries [1916 3618; 1919 3614; 1919 3610] adjoining Parsons' Lane show thickly bedded red, purple and grey fine-grained limestone with red and green variegated slates contining calcareous lenses. Limestone from one quarry [1916 3618] yielded corals and stromatoporoids (Table 2, loc. 6) and, in addition, an incomplete conodont, identified by Dr D. E. Butler as *Icriodus* sp., close to *I. arkonensis*. A smaller quarry [1928 3602] to the south-south-east contains similar limestone.

Traces only of the Roadwater Limestone occur at Aisholt, and the crop is mapped mainly from the presence of calcareous slates. About 350 m south-south-east of the village, an old quarry [1949 3528] at the roadside shows grey fine-grained limestone with slates, and it may be this locality at which Webby (1966a) noted oolitic limestone. Grey fine-grained limestone is exposed alongside the road to the south-east [1974 3514].

Several old quarries [1964 3492; 1967 3491; 1975 3487; 1981 3477; 1998 3470] east of Luxborough Farm show thinly and thickly bedded and massive grey fine-grained crystalline limestones up to 7 m thick, with calcareous slates containing calcareous lenses, which have yielded *P. polymorphus* with some colonies approaching the form of *Thamnopora cronigera* (Table 2, loc. 7). *Acanthophyllum* (*Neostringophyllum*) *concavum*, *Thamnopora cervicornis* and a ?stromatoporoid have been recorded from these quarries by Webby (1966a). Similar quarries farther east show 8 m of massive grey limestone with associated slates [2033 3457; 2043 3457] and at a laneside section [2058 3451] have yielded a small coral fauna including *Endophyllum* aff. *abditum* and *Plasmophyllum* (*P.*) sp. and the stromatoporoid *Clathrodictyon* sp. (Table 2, loc. 8). From quarries near Merridge Webby (1966a) has recorded numerous corals, including *Alveolites* spp., *E. abditum* and *Thamnopora* spp., as well as Bryozoa [2077 3450].

The entrance to Holwell Cave [2105 3400] lies in a quarry cut in massive grey sandy crinoidal limestone with some argillaceous limestone and calcareous slates. The main cave trends roughly east – west and is some 30 to 40 m long, from 1 m to possibly 5 m wide and from 1.5 m to possibly 5 m high. Small north – south cracks are present but the main fissure trends down dip. The limestone is largely obscured by wet slime and the whole cavern is wet, with most water at the western end. Traces of stalactites and stalagmites remain. Ussher (1908) quoted Crosse's (1851) record of aragonite crystals on the walls and roof at the western end.

Old quarries [2083 3365] 300 m north-north-west of the Traveller's Rest public house expose massive dark grey limestone overlain by greyish brown cleaved siltstones and silty slates capped by brown sandstones and siltstones. Webby (1966a) recorded *Chondrites* at this locality. The beds dip at about 12° to the south-east. Quarries [2015 3320] west of Timbercombe show 5 m of grey limestone weathering to brown, whence Webby (1966a) obtained *Thamnophyllum caespitosum*, *Thamnopora* sp., Bryozoa, indeterminate spiriferoid and terebratuloid brachiopods and crinoid columnals.

A line of overgrown old pits [1956 3331 to 1870 3300] extends across the north-western side of Merridge Hill and Cothelstone Hill, marking the working of grey and purple cleaved crinoidal limestone with calcite veins and associated calcareous slates. Webby and Thomas (1965) noted the presence of *Acanthophyllum* sp., *Alveolites medius*, *Alveolites* sp., *Chaetetes* sp., *Disphyllum?* sp., *T. caespitosum*, *Thamnopora. cervicornis* and the finding by Dr F. J. W. Holwill of a scutellid trilobite. A small quarry [1801 3267] east of East Bagborough, showing grey fine-grained limestone with calcite veinlets and some calcareous slates, lies 200 m north-east of the Cothelstone Fault.

Leighland Slates: Strata above the Roadwater Limestone

The rocks underlying the main western crop of Morte Slates north of Rowdon Farm and Escott show no exposed limestone. Sporadic roadside exposures are largely of silty slates. Slates, locally silty or sandy, with interbedded sandstones dip at about 10° southwards [0912 3812] just north of Escott.

An old quarry [1807 3988] alongside the A39 road 1 km west of Nether Stowey shows fine-grained sandstones and siltstones dipping at 35° to 40° east-north-east; it was probably from this locality that Ussher collected material which included *Oligoptycherhynchus?* and *Eoschizodus* aff. *holzapfeli*. Similar sandstones to the south-east are associated with coarser gritty sandstone containing mudstone flakes in one quarry [1826 3960] and are sheared and fractured in another [1840 3931].

In an inlier 2 km east-south-east of Nether Stowey, an old quarry

[2066 3882] 250 m north-east of Halseycross Farm was mostly filled when examined, but showed disturbed limestone, possibly Leigh Barton Limestone, and sandstone. Webby (1966a), however, saw massive sandy limestones overlain by thinner calcareous sandstones and siltstones, and recorded *Spathella?*, *Bellerophon?* and crinoid columnals; he suggested a littoral or shallow-water origin.

Between Aisholt and Timbercombe, strata between the Roadwater Limestone and the Aisholt Limestone are visible as sporadic outcrops of slates and silty slates with some siltstones, but form no large exposures.

The Aisholt Limestone quarried [1940 3605] in the valley north of Aisholt contains possible examples of the tabulate coral *Thamnopora* sp. (Table 2, loc. 12). It trends south-eastward along the edge of Aisholt Wood as thin limestones in calcareous slates. Farmyard exposures [2016 3508] at Lower Aisholt show grey limestone with interbedded calcareous siltstones and silty slates, and a nearby quarry [2021 3494] shows 15 m of cleaved massive grey crinoidal limestone containing *Thamnopora* cf. *boloniensis* and *T. cervicornis* (Table 2, loc. 13). Calcareous sandstones [2076 3473] north-east of Good's Farm may represent the same horizon. Massive cleaved grey limestone of the Aisholt Limestone has been quarried [2134 3410] south-south-east of Great Holwell, slates with cleaved limestones crop out [2123 3383] farther south, and quarries [2118 3360] 300 m north-east of the Traveller's Rest public house are in 10 m of massive grey cleaved crinoidal limestone. *Endophyllum* aff. *abditum* and tabulate corals including *Scoliopora* sp. are present at this locality, where, in an exposure immediately above the quarry, several examples of the squamulate tabulate coral *Emmonsia* were obtained (Table 2, locs. 14, 15). A small pit [2082 3307] 350 m south-south-west of the Traveller's Rest shows only calcareous slates and sandy slates, and a larger quarry [2065 3301] to the west-south-west, now filled, contains some limestone blocks. Its was probably this last quarry that yielded '*Atrypa*, *Orthis*, *Spirifer*, *Fenestella* and crinoids' (Ussher, 1908, recording Payne, 1854). The Aisholt Limestone, from a small pit [1966 3305] on Merridge Hill to another [1811 3253] in Cothelstone Park, is represented by calcareous slates with thin crinoidal limestones.

Slates and silty slates with siltstones and scattered thin sandstones between the Aisholt Limestone and the Holwell Limestone are exposed only sporadically, mainly in roadsides and lanesides as, for example, north of Lower Aisholt [2011 3532 to 2008 3542].

The Holwell Limestone was probably that worked [1951 3620] 400 m south of Plainsfield; calcareous sandstones are exposed at the side of the small pit. Larger faces may be seen in a line of quarries across Hawkridge Common [1994 3569; 2013 3560; 2027 3558; 2049 3551; 2061 3548] (Table 2, locs. 16–20), in which fairly massive grey limestones up to 2 m thick are interbedded with calcareous slates and siltstones. The thickest succession exposed is 10 m. The limestones contain a varied fauna of corals and stromatoporoids, including *Alveolitella* cf. *fecunda*, *Alveolites medius*, *Chaetetes* cf. *inflatus*, *C.* cf. *rotundus*, *Disphyllum aequiseptatum*, *Scoliopora* cf. *denticulata*, *Stringophyllum* sp., *Thamnophyllum caespitosum* and *Thamnopora* spp.. Apart from the coelenterates, Webby (1966a) also recorded shell fragments and Bryozoa.

A small quarry [2143 3466] 700 m east of Good's Farm contains cleaved massive grey limestone, with a varied coral fauna (Table 2, loc. 21). The fossiliferous nature of the rock suggests that it is the Holwell Limestone rather than the Aisholt Limestone. Webby (1966a) recorded a rich coral fauna but thought that it was a separate lens stratigraphically between the two. However, the rock is here taken to be Holwell Limestone repeated by folding.

Massive grey cleaved coral-bearing limestones of the Holwell Limestone have also been worked in another line of quarries along the eastern side of Holwell Combe [2207 3509; 2208 3497; 2199 3479; 2180 3471; 2184 3433; 2181 3428]. Massive and cleaved grey limestones with sandy limestones and calcareous slates are exposed up to 9 m thick. The varied coral fauna from one of these quarries [2180 3471] (Table 2, loc. 22) includes *Heliophyllum* sp.; the collection from another [2184 3433] (Table 2, loc. 23) includes *Alveolites* spp., *C.* cf. *rotundus*, *Coenites escharoides*, *Donia* aff. *philomena*, *Endophyllum* sp. and *Pachyfavosites polymorphus*, and a specimen of *Columnaria* sp. from this vicinity is in the Webby Collection at Bristol University.

Traces of thin crinoidal limestone across the north-western slopes of Broomfield Hill [215 337 to 211 330] may represent the Holwell Limestone; Webby (1966a) recorded *Thamnopora* sp., and it may have been from an old pit [2155 3349] hereabouts that Ussher (1908) obtained *Tentaculites ?annulatus*, *Chonetes?* and crinoid columnals. Slates with thin sandstones above the Aisholt Limestone include calcareous traces [1823 3238] on the south-western slopes of Cothelstone Hill, possibly at the horizon of the Holwell Limestones.

EAE, DEW

A road [211 353 to 214 360] up Merridge Hill shows sporadic exposure of slates and fine-grained sandstones above the Holwell Limestone, beds which contained *Chondrites* in boreholes at the dam site [211 364] of Hawkridge Reservoir and which were also exposed during construction of a small dam [2170 3566] farther south-east.

The lane running south from Enmore to Broomfield Hall cuts through cleaved pink and grey crinoidal limestone in slates [2374 3470], the Leigh Barton Limestone. Folded slates and sandstones (p.59) above this limestone have been quarried [2468 3515] east of Enmore; Ussher (1908) recorded 10 m of strata.

A quarry [2275 3456] west of Heathcombe Farm, now showing only rubble of slate and sandstone, yielded crinoids to Ussher (1908). Webby (1965b) described *Quantoxocrinus ussheri* found in siltstones at Wind Down [221 339], and several small quarries in silty slates and sandstones between the Holwell and Leigh Barton limestones, some showing gentle folding, occur in the wood. The Leigh Barton Limestone has been quarried [2301 3379; 2301 3375; 2320 3362] just north-east and east of Ruborough Camp; it comprises cleaved grey crinoidal limestone with calcareous silty slates and lies not far below the Morte Slates. Slates and sandstones just below the Morte Slates in the road [2211 3312 to 2205 3281] north of Ducks' Pool contain crinoids (Ussher, 1908).

In Badger Copse, quarries [1870 3191; 1884 3197; 1903 3213; 1896 3184] in the Leigh Barton Limestone show up to 3 m of massive and thickly bedded cleaved grey crinoidal limetone and calcareous slate; Webby (1966a) recorded *Chonetes* sp., shell fragments and crinoid columnals.

Morte Slates (Figure 7)

Combe Cross to Oakhampton

Grey slates with thin sandstones are exposed on the steep valley slopes north of Combecross Farm [0855 3696] and in the road [092 375 to 094 374] north-west of Stogumber. A small pit [0861 3707] near Combecross Farm is now filled with rubble, but Ussher (1908) noted an anticline in slates and grits in a quarry thereabouts. Roadside faces up to 5 m high [0761 3640; 0775 3610; 0784 3605; 0830 3540] south of Combe Sydenham show slates with silty beds and lenses following gentle flexures.

A roadside quarry [0776 3404] south-west of Elworthy contains slates and slaty sandstones (p. 59). Another [1062 3366] at Willett, shows easterly-dipping joints. Small exposures abound on Willett Hill [096 335], in and north and west of Brompton Ralph [086 323], and in the valleys of Combe Bottom [083 306] and from Tolland [102 321] to Moor Mill Farm [109 301].

Oakhampton Quarries [085 301] have been dug in well-cleaved grey and purple slates with traces of silty streaks (p. 59). Whidborne (*in* Hicks, 1897) identified fossils collected from here as: *Dalmanites* (*Cryphaeus*) *laciniatus* ?var. *occidentalis*, *Aviculopecten mundus*,

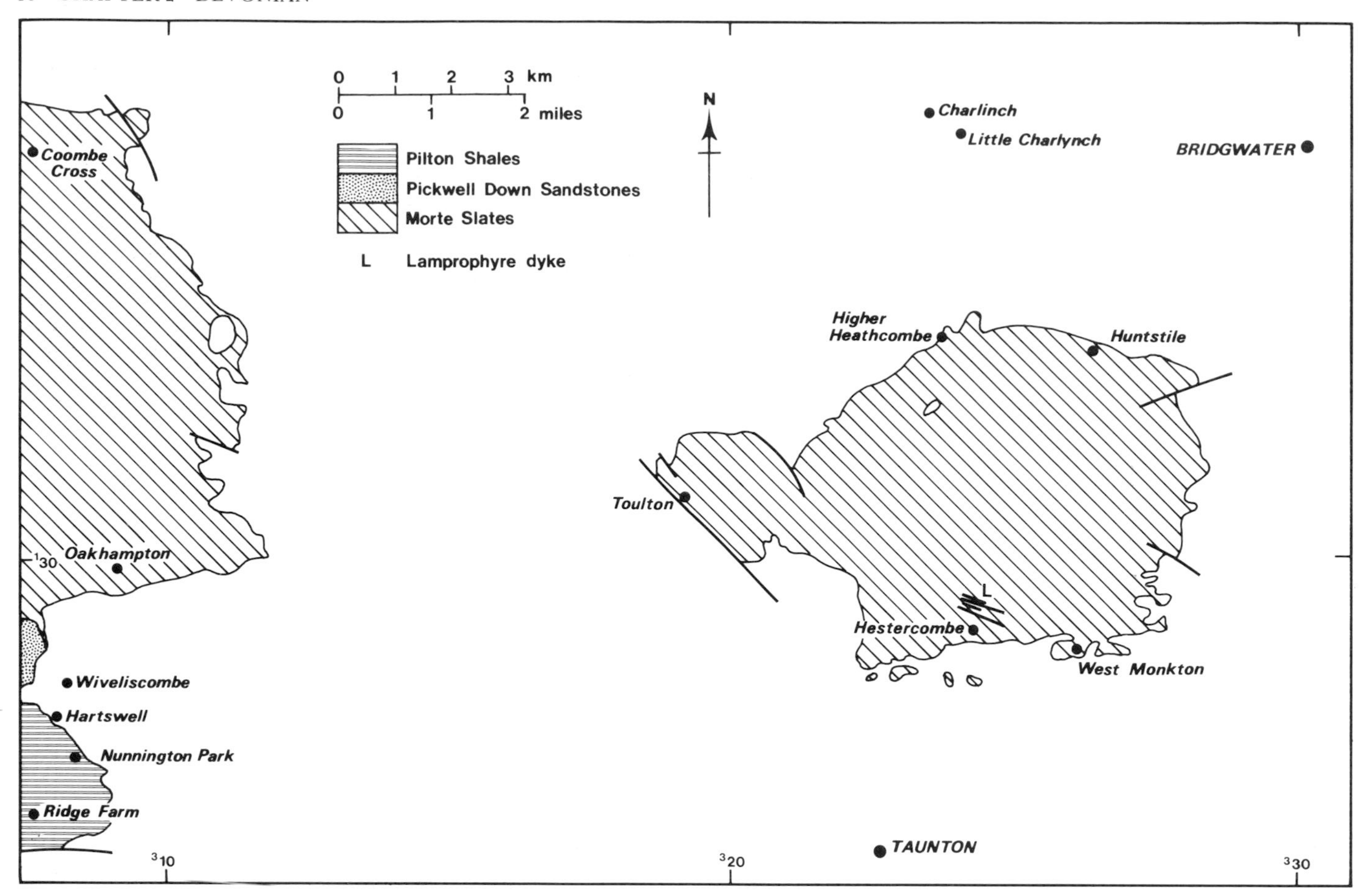

Figure 7 Outcrops of the Morte Slates, Pickwell Down Sandstones and Pilton Shales

Limoptera semiradiata, *Spirifera* sp., *Rhynchonella hercynica?*, *R. nympha?*, *Stropheodonta taeniolata* and crinoid remains. Ussher (1908) recorded the collection of *Spirifer verneuili*, *?Pterinopecten mundus* and *Bactrites?*. Dr D. E. Butler has examined Ussher's material and reports that the record of '*Spirifer verneuili*' is based upon an indeterminable spiriferacean mould; the remaining specimens are too poor for identification. Dr S. G. Molyneux has reported that a rock sample from the quarries yielded an impoverished microflora which included *Veryhachium downiei* (range Ordovician to Devonian) and indeterminate acanthomorphitic and sphaeromorphitic acritarchs.

Charlinch and Little Charlynch inliers

West of Charlinch church [2385 3780] purple slate and sandstone were noted in a hedge bank, and on the fields to the east there are abundant fragments of sandstone, siltstone, quartz and a little slate. On a rise west of Little Charlynch there are fragments of sandstone and slaty sandstone and Webby (1966a) saw a small outcrop of brown thinly bedded fine-grained sandstones, laminated cleaved siltstones, and silty slates. These rocks are classified as Morte Slates, following Webby.

Toulton – Higher Heathcombe – Hestercombe

Grey slates and silty slates are sporadically exposed just east of Toulton and in the lane [1969 3061 to 1982 3144] running north from Cushuish (p. 59). Outcrops in Ball Covert [201 321], of slates, silty slates and siltstones, have yielded nuculid bivalves and crinoid ossicles (Webby, 1966a). An old quarry [2035 3014] in Tetton Park shows disturbed purple and grey slates.

North of Tanyard three large disused quarries lie to the east of Beech Copse. The most northerly [2152 3095] is in 10 m of purple fine-grained sandstones and silty slates (p. 59). A second quarry [2164 3081] shows mainly silty slates and the third [2197 3085] is in cleaved purple and grey sandstone with slates.

The grounds of Fyne Court, Broomfield, contain a quarry [2210 3237] in grey lustrous slates and silty slates whose cleavage dips at 45°/180°, and exposures of silty slates [2258 3231; 2274 3235] (see p.59).

Old pits [2383 3379] near Higher Heathcombe Farm show silty slates whose cleavage planes dip at 25°/180°, but widespread debris attests the presence of thin sandstones. An old quarry [2482 3333] at Patcombe Farm has provided brown, grey and purple silty slates and siltstones for use as building and walling stone; ?rhynchonellids and crinoid columnals have been recorded (Webby, 1966a). In an old quarry [2471 3239] 0.6 km east-north-east of Stream Farm slates and silty slates show traces of kink bands and silty and sandy boudins. Slates around and north of Yalway [242 304] have cleavage planes inclined at moderate to steep angles both northerly and southerly.

Slates with thin sandstones are exposed in a small pit [2263 2928] south-east of Kingston St Mary (p.59). Gadd's Bottom, north of Upper Cheddon, is a narrow valley containing numerous small exposures and two small quarries [2318 2920; 2331 2911]; both quarries are in slates with sandstone beds up to 0.3 m thick and in the western quarry the face is cut by two small faults (Figure 8; p. 60).

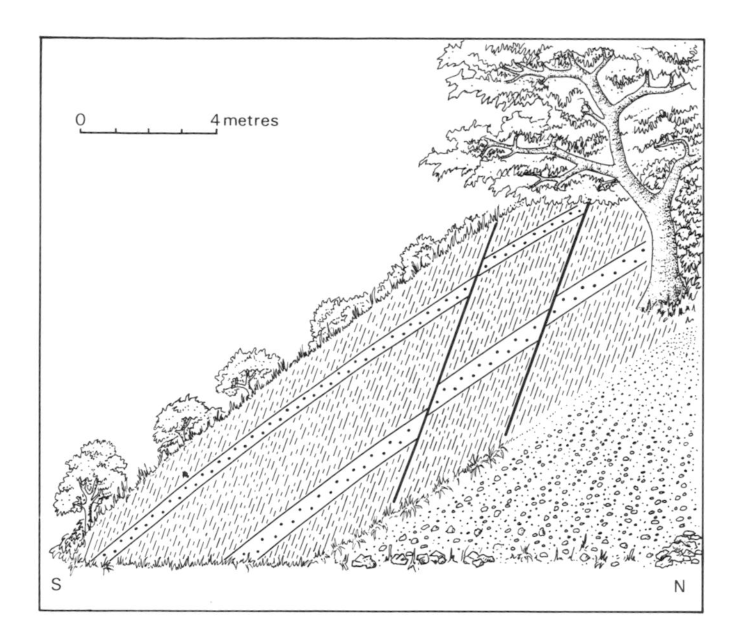

Figure 8 Quarry in Morte Slates, north of Upper Cheddon

Hestercombe [243 289 to 244 294] contains much exposed slate, silty slate and generally cleaved sandstone. Webby (1966a) recorded laminated, cross-laminated and convolute-laminated siltstones thereabouts, and Ussher (1908) noted that one quarry [2422 2915], in slates with sandstones, was worked for whetstones. A larger quarry [2468 2915] to the east, in slates with quartzites, provided building stone for Gotton. EAE

Huntstile to West Monkton

The parkland around Halswell House bears a dense brash of brownish grey to greenish grey silty slate, in places deeply reddened. In a wood [2545 3329] 3 m of brownish grey cleaved siltstones contain a rusty-weathered sandstone bed 90 mm thick. An old quarry [2610 3293] 750 m to the south-east shows 3 m of brown siltstone with thin beds of ferruginous fine-grained sandstone. A stream runs northward from here in Huntstile Bottom, and reveals an intermittent section in reddish brown to maroon-brown and greenish grey siltstone and silty slate, with thin reddish brown sandstone bands. At Huntstile Farm [2667 3371] 2 m of pinkish brown lustrous slates have a cleavage dip of 30°/170°, and in a roadside section 200 m to the south-east 2 m of brownish grey silty slate and siltstone dip at 25°/172°. At Hill Barn [2660 3280] 2 m of pinkish grey silty slate interbedded with pinkish brown siltstone dip at 70°/185°; greenish and pinkish grey silty slates are intermittently exposed in the banks of the road leading from here eastwards to Dancing Hill.

King's Cliff Quarry [277 326] is a large old working containing extensive exposures of brownish grey cleaved siltstones and silty slates interbedded with brown fine-grained sandstones. Near Ashfield House reddish brown and maroon-brown laminated and cleaved siltstone with subordinate fine-grained sandstone bands dips at 10°/090° [2782 3226].

A large old quarry [253 323] in Rooks Castle Wood reveals about 20 m of brownish grey cleaved siltstones and silty slates, with thin fine-grained sandstones; cleavage dips are all to the south and vary from 38° to 48°. At the southern end of the wood grey slate and silty slate exposed in a track [2537 3206] contains thin bands of finely laminated sandstone.

At Clavelshay [2535 3119] 3 m of pinkish to purplish grey silty shale and siltstone with thin sandstone bands dip at 10°/135°, and at Clavelshay Farm [2532 3100] pinkish grey cleaved siltstone has a cleavage dip of 20°/180°. At Hunting House [2648 3125] pinkish grey silty slate with much vein quartz is highly contorted and shattered; 300 m to the south-east a trackside exposure [2668 3109] reveals 3 m of brownish grey cleaved siltstone and silty slate with thin fine-grained sandstones which are often finely laminated, and 250 m south of King's Farm 3.5 m of maroon-brown and pale brown siltstone with brownish grey silty slate are seen in a roadside exposure [2753 3083]. At Farringdon the road cutting [2776 3125] is in brownish grey silty slate with pale brown siltstone and pale brown slate, the cleavage dipping at 40°/180°. Maroon to reddish brown cleaved siltstone has a cleavage dip of 70°/176° at Shearston [2804 3082] and the slate debris hereabouts is extensively red-stained.

A borehole [2566 2988] at Quantock Farm proved 36.58 m of red, brown and grey slate with a 0.6 m hard quartzitic band 2.06 m from the surface. At Woodball Cottage [2541 2931] grey silty quartz-veined slate has a cleavage dip of 55°/185°, and similar rocks have a cleavage dip of 80°/180° near Hill Farm Cottages [2526 2910]. At New Cross [2540 2852] pale brown siltstones and silty slates with thin fine-grained sandstones are cut by irregular quartz veins. To the east of Woodball Plantation, 700 m south of Quantock Farm, 5.2 m of pinkish brown laminated and cleaved siltstones are exposed in an old quarry [2581 2919], and an infilled quarry near West Monkton [261 289] still contains a few outcrops of pale pinkish green siltstone with a cleavage dipping at 45°/168°.

Three old quarries in Burlinch Plantation, 0.8 km east-south-east of Quantock Farm, yield important exposures: in one [2630 2954] brownish grey silty slate, grey siltstone and fine-grained sandstone were seen; in a second [2632 2938] brownish grey silty slates with thin fine-grained sandstones; and in the third [2645 2940] pale brown and brownish grey cleaved siltstones. In Coombe Bottom, the steep-sided valley leading south-south-east towards Coombe, highly contorted pinkish brown fine-grained sandstone and siltstone with quartz veins are exposed [2676 2975], and 100 m to the east pink and purplish brown siltstone and thinly bedded fine-grained sandstone have a cleavage dip of 45°/112°. In a large old quarry [270 291] west of the road at Coombe pinkish brown fine-grained sandstones and cleaved finely laminated siltstones with some silty slates are now largely obscured by infilling. The large old quarry [272 291] east of the road is also mostly obscured but similar rocks are exposed. No definite traces of the quartz-diorite sills described from these Coombe localities by Webby (1966a, p. 341) were discovered during the recent survey. Pinkish grey silty slates and siltstones are exposed in the road cutting [2748 2902] south of Thurloxton, and 6.2 m of brownish grey silty slate and siltstone are exposed in roadside exposures [277 288] in Adsborough, with cleavage dips up to 80° to slightly east of south; 200 m east of here a small inlier about 80 m across is revealed as Morte Slates by the surface brash. A little to the south a rather large inlier of Morte Slates is cut through by the M5 motorway at Merricott Barn [279 284]. One of the boreholes drilled during the preparatory work for the motorway was some 30 m to the north-east of the boundary of the inlier [2804 2833] and revealed the following section:

	Thickness m	*Depth* m
TOP SOIL AND HEAD		
Clay, soft, reddish brown, sandy and silty, with gravelly traces	4.55	4.55
OTTER SANDSTONE		
Sandstone, reddish brown to grey, fine-grained; some slate fragments	1.50	6.05

Breccia, angular slate fragments with some quartz in silty argillaceous fine-grained sandstone matrix	4.95	11.00
Sand (driller's log, no core recovered)	2.50	13.50
MORTE SLATES		
Siltstone, pale grey, cleaved, interbedded with fine-grained sandstone	0.30	13.80

Another borehole [2806 2827], 55 m to the south-south-east, was sited within the inlier and proved:

	Thickness m	*Depth* m
TOP SOIL AND HEAD	2.70	2.70
MORTE SLATES		
Siltstone, greenish grey, sandy, strongly cleaved and highly weathered; cleavage inclined at 60° to 70° to the core	1.80	4.50
Siltstone, pale grey, sandy, highly cleaved, with fine-grained silty sandstone and dark grey argillaceous siltstone; becoming very finely laminated below 9.0 m; occasional quartz veins; 0.1 m laminated pink and pale grey siltstone at 11.1 m; cleavage inclined at 60° to 70° to the core	9.25	13.75

BJW

Pickwell Down Sandstones (Figure 7)

Around the north of Greenway Farm [077 284] there is much surface debris of reddish brown and purple sandstone. Roadside exposures [074 282] to [076 280] west of Wiveliscombe show purple sandstones with subordinate slates. An old quarry [0772 2790] on the edge of the town is in thickly bedded grey and purple fine-grained sandstone, with subordinate slates, dipping at 55°/340°.

EAE

Pilton Shales (Figure 7)

A quarry [0782 2733] west of Hartswell is in shales and siltstones with decalcified earthy bands and lenses. A rock sample from an outcrop [0815 2651] west of Nunnington Park was examined for acritarchs by Dr S. G. Molyneux and yielded a form resembling *Micrhystridium campoae;* macrofossils collected from this exposure were as follows: *Streptorhynchus?*, *Schizophoria?*, *Murchisonia?*, *Goniophora* aff. *chemungensis*, *Modiomorpha?*, *Palaeoneilo tensa?* and cf. *Sanguinolites? contractus*; this assemblage is not typical of the Pilton Shales, serving only to suggest a late Devonian or early Carboniferous age. Acritarchs from a roadside pit [0830 2637] were identified as the long-ranging *Veryhachium downiei* by Dr Molyneux; macrofossils from this locality were cf. *Hamlingella piltonensis*, *Cyrtospirifer?*, *Eoschizodus?*, *Palaeoneilo?*, *Ptychopteria damnoniensis* and crinoid columnals, an assemblage suggestive of Pilton A, the late Famennian subdivision of the formation. At Nunnington Park a degraded roadside pit [0884 2639] shows lilac-purple shales and siltstones, from which Ussher (1908) recorded '*Spirifer verneuili*'; what is almost certainly the material referred to by Ussher has been re-examined, and consists only of indeterminable rhynchonellaceans and spiriferoids including *Athyris?*.

An old quarry [0758 2586] 240 m north-west of Ridge Farm yielded the following macrofossils preserved in reddish brown siltstones and in dark grey limestones; *Fenestella* sp., *Rhombopora?*, cf. *Chonetes sauntonensis*, cf. *Steinhagella steinhagei*, *?Cyrtospirifer verneuili*, an indeterminable rhynchonellacean, *Straparollus* (*Philoxene*) *vermis*, *Phacops* (*Omegops*) *accipitrinus* and crinoid columnals; a few conodonts were obtained from a limestone sample, the majority being *Pseudopolygnathus* similar to both *P. striatus* and *P. expansus*; *Polygnathus* cf. *inornatus inornatus* is also present; the macrofauna is indicative of Pilton A. Another old pit [0729 2594], 300 m to the west-north-west, exposes lilac and purple shales, siltstones and fine-grained sandstones with silty limestone bands and lenses, dipping at 80°/165°; a Pilton A fauna collected by Ussher from this locality comprises *Fenestella* sp., cf. *Centrorhynchus letiensis*, *Cyrtospirifer?*, *Hamlingella goergesi*, *Whidbornella caperata*, *Leptodesma* sp., *Palaeoneilo* sp. and crinoid columnals. Similar rocks crop out at Ridge Farm [0776 2568] and in a ploughed-over pit [0786 2534] to the south, where Ussher collected a Pilton A fauna of *Fenestella* cf. *plebeia*, *C. verneuili*, *Mesoplica praelonga*, an indeterminable chonetacean, *Phacops* sp. and crinoid columnals. Goldring (1957) recorded *H. goergesi* from Sminhay [082 254]. Strata such as are seen at Ridge Farm, occur alongside the disused railway track [0743 2517] at Woodlands Farm and dip at 65°/165°. There is no clear evidence of the faulted junction between these rocks and Permo-Triassic sandstones, noted by Ussher (1908, p. 31) in the railway cutting immediately west of the present district.

EAE, DEB

CHAPTER 3
Carboniferous

GENERAL ACCOUNT

The exposed Carboniferous rocks of the district comprise (Viséan) Carboniferous Limestone and (Namurian) Rodway Siltstones. The former crops out in the vicinity of Cannington Park. The latter form an inlier extending east – west through Rodway, and similar rocks occur in another inlier at Swang Farm. The nearest exposed rocks of Culm facies lie 25 km away to the south-west.

Lower Carboniferous rocks, including grey limestones, locally of oolitic aspect[1], in places fine-grained and porcellanous, with cherty bands, were proved to a depth of 966.35 m in the Knap Farm Borehole (p. 22), where they rested on 139.56 m of Lower Carboniferous shales and mudstones with subordinate limestones. Reef limestones and dolomites of Waulsortian type were present, and traces of baryte, galena, pyrite, hematite and pyrolusite were found in the core. Such a thick accumulation of limestone probably extends both west-north-west and east-south-east beneath the Permo-Triassic rocks. Although the lowest Carboniferous rocks in the borehole were argillaceous and incompetent, and were considerably disturbed, there was no sign of a major fault.

Wallis (1924) assigned an S_1 Subzone (*Seminula* Zone) age to the limestones of Cannington Park. George and others (1976, p. 16) referred the rocks at this locality to the upper part of the Arundian, but the faunas collected during this survey indicate Arundian and Holkerian ages for the strata at outcrop. In the thick succession of Dinantian limestones proved in the Knap Farm Borehole, the Viséan–Tournaisian boundary was taken at the depth of 485 m and the Carboniferous – Devonian boundary at 1104 m.

The Rodway Siltstones comprise siltstones, sandstones and shales. Webby (1966a) noted brown sandstones on the summit of the hill formed by the Swang Farm inlier, and flaggy micaceous purplish maroon siltstones and sandstones east of Rodway. The only evidence of the age of these rocks is that from the Withiel Farm No. 1 Borehole (p. 23), which passed through beds of late Namurian age containing *Gastrioceras cancellatum* (Whittaker, 1975b).

No junction between the Carboniferous Limestone and the Rodway Siltstone is exposed. In both the Withiel Farm No. 1 and No. 2 boreholes (p. 23) the contact was a normal fault, and in the former the fault lay only 5.66 m below strata of the *G. cancellatum* Zone.

Probably the shales and mudstones at the base of the Carboniferous succession originated in moderately deep water, but the overlying limestones are carbonate sediments of a shelf sea whose waters may only rarely have exceeded a few metres in depth. The presence of reef limestones at Cannington Park suggests the possibility that there was a barrier reef at the southern edge of a shallow sea covering the Mendip Hills and Bristol area, beyond which, to the south and south-west, lay deeper water characterised by different conditions of sedimentation (see also Chapter 8). The succeeding Namurian Rodway Siltstones accumulated in slightly deeper, but nevertheless shallow, sea water. In contrast, the nearest Culm-facies rocks of comparable ages are deeper water deposits; their Lower Carboniferous limestones include turbidites, unlike most of the 'Lower Culm' sequences elsewhere, interbedded with dark grey shales and cherts, and their Namurian strata are largely shales and turbiditic sandstones of a marine basin.

1 Lees and Hennebert (1982) noted that in the limestones in the Knap Farm Borehole diagenetic micritisation had been operative and that micritised crinoids might have been mistakenly identified as ooids in earlier works. In this Memoir the term 'oolitic' has been retained in macroscopic descriptions of hand specimens.

DETAILS

Lower Carboniferous: Carboniferous Limestone (Figure 9)

A small inlier at Edbrook has been quarried [2372 4028] and now shows about 2 m of limestone. Subsidence hollows between there and the main outcrop 300 m to the east suggest the presence of Carboniferous Limestone at shallow depth.

Small exposures [2409 4032] north-east of Horn Hill are of limestone dipping at 12° to 15° to just west of north. The rock is cut by vertical north – south joints whose faces carry horizontal slickensides. An old quarry [2418 4030] to the west shows 6 to 7 m of massive grey apparently coarsely oolitic limestone with crinoids and a few corals. Some joints trend north – south but most of the jointing is irregular.

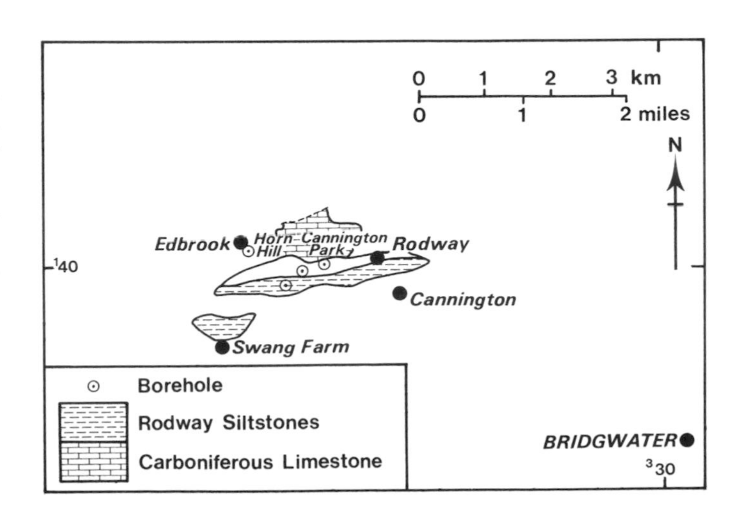

Figure 9 Outcrop of the Carboniferous strata

A quarry [2465 4075] at Coy Farm, on the northern edge of the outcrop, exposes 18 to 25 m of massive limestone. The joints are mostly irregular but include a set of vertical fissures trending north-south, the faces of which carry horizontal slickensides. Red staining is common, especially near the vertical joints. In the quarry face, dark grey poorly oolitic recrystallised limestone is overlain by paler grey coarsely oolitic limestone with crinoid ossicles. A fossiliferous band is present at both the eastern and the western sides of the quarry and contains rugose corals and large crinoid ossicles; if this is a single band, which can be correlated across the quarry, it suggests a uniform sequence and a gentle northerly dip. Baryte occurs as veins in the eastern side of the quarry and as fragments elsewhere. Some debris contains *Lithostrotion*.

A roadway [2477 4077] into the quarry at Coy Farm cuts through 6 m of massive limestone. The lower part of the section comprises dark grey medium-grained crystalline limestone with scattered ooliths and crinoid fragments. The upper part is paler grey coarsely oolitic limestone with crinoid ossicles, and contains a fossil band with rugose corals and finely ribbed brachiopods. This fossiliferous bed appears to dip at about 10° to 15° northwards. Irregular joints cutting the limestone carry traces of red staining. Crevices in the top of the rock face are in some cases filled with reddish brown stony sandy loam containing fragments of iron-stained baryte and pebbles of ?Devonian sandstone; at the edges of the cracks the limestone is commonly brecciated. Joints cutting the limestone show slickensides on their faces, mainly horizontal but some inclined. At the northern end of the cutting a fossil band occurs at about 1.5 to 2.4 m up the eastern face and 2.4 to 3 m up the western face.

Mr M. Mitchell has identified the following fossils from the Coy Farm quarry: from the bottom of the face in the north-west corner of the quarry [2460 4076], *Axophyllum* aff. *mendipense* and *Lithostrotion martini*; from the bottom of the face in the south-west corner of the quarry [2461 4071], *Axophyllum?*, *Lithostrotion aranea*, *L. martini*, *Syringopora* cf. *geniculata* and a smooth spiriferoid; from the base of a ridge projecting from the south face of the quarry [2466 4071], *Axophyllum* sp. and *L. martini*; from low in the face at the east side of the quarry [2471 4077], *Axophyllum* aff. *mendipense*, *A. vaughani* and a *Lithostrotion* fragment; from low in the face behind and east of the office [2475 4077], *A.* aff. *mendipense*, *L. aranea*, *L. martini*, *Euomphalus?*, and a turreted gastropod; from both sides of the north end of the road cutting [2478 4077], *Axophyllum* sp., *Megachonetes papilionaceus*, a productoid cf. *Gigantoproductus* Θ, and a smooth spiriferoid; from the southern end of the road cutting, 2 to 3 m up the face [2481 4070], a productoid cf. *Gigantoproductus* Θ. Also from this quarry, Dr A. Strank has identified the algae and foraminifera *Endothyra* sp., *Omphalotis* sp., *Koninckopora inflata* and *Nodosarchaediscus* sp. Mr Mitchell notes that *L. aranea* and *A. vaughani* are indicative of Holkerian age and Dr Strank that *Nodosarchaediscus* is common in the Holkerian but rare in the Arundian.

On the southern side of the hill in Cannington Park old baryte workings [2442 4043; 2457 4035] trend between north and north-north-east, in the same direction as distinct vertical joints.

Cannington Park Quarry [251 404] shows 15 m of limestone, some of it dark grey fine-grained non-oolitic and micritic, some pale grey non-oolitic and locally a mosaic of recrystallised calcite, and some pale grey and coarsely oolitic with crinoid ossicles. Oolites are overlain by non-oolites high in the southern face and low in the northern face, suggesting a northerly dip; in general, however, indications of dip are not reliable. The limestone is cut by numerous joints, mainly randomly orientated but with a vertical north – south set in the northern face with which are associated baryte veins. Tabular baryte occurs as large fan-shaped masses. Small veins of the mineral trend in all directions and at all angles; larger ones, up to 0.15 m wide, are generally vertical with a red-stained (?hematitic) core. Ussher (1908) mentioned a record of a vein of red baryte up to 0.91 m wide. Baryte veins in the neighbourhood of the quarry weather at surface to form depressions containing reddish brown sandy loam with baryte fragments. Cracks and depressions at the top of the limestone faces are commonly filled with red sandy clay, in places reminiscent of laminated Triassic Mercia Mudstone.

Ussher (1908) quoted records of a dome-shaped anticlinal structure in Cannington Park Quarry, and noted dips of 55° westerly and 50°/100° in the southern face. His lists of fossils included the corals *Lithostrotion martini*, *L. irregulare*, *L. araenea*, *Clisiophyllum turbinatum* and *Syringopora ramulosa* from the collection in Taunton Museum. Mr Mitchell has identified the following fossils from this quarry: from the west face [2506 4036], *Palaeosmilia murchisoni*; from the bottom of the face [2507 4040], *A.* aff. *mendipense*, *L. martini* and *P. murchisoni*; from the bottom of the face, in the north-west corner of the quarry [2509 4044], *Axophyllum* sp., *Caninophyllum bristoliense*, *Lithostrotion portlocki* and *M. papilionaceus?*. Dr Strank has identified the following algae and foraminifera from the west face: *Pseudolituotuba* sp., *K. inflata*, *Nibelia* sp., *Earlandia vulgaris*, *Palaeotextularia* ex gr. *consobrina*, *Eostaffella* aff. *parastruvei*, *Lituotubellinae*, *Nodosarchaediscus* sp., *Archaediscus* [at *concavus* stage], *Tetrataxis* sp., *Forschia subangulata* and Tournayellidae. *P. murchisoni* is characteristic of the Arundian, and *C. bristoliense* and *L. portlocki* indicate the Holkerian, and the foraminifera *Nodosarchaediscus* sp. and small *P.* ex gr. *consobrina* would accord with a Holkerian age.

The faunas of the quarries at Coy Farm and Cannington Park show Arundian fossils from the two southernmost localities and Holkerian fossils to the north, suggesting a northerly dip, which would confirm the tentative field relationship noted above.

Two Institute of Geological Sciences boreholes at Withiel Farm, No. 1 [2435 3981] at 58 m above O.D. and No. 2 [2452 3993] at 55 m above O.D., both ended in Carboniferous Limestone, which they proved from 138.20 m to 157.68 m and from 40.80 m to 50.85 m respectively (Whittaker, 1975b). The upper part of the limestone was medium to pale grey, oolitic and massive, with traces of green shale near the top, and the No. 1 borehole contained some pink-stained limestone conglomerate or breccia; Mr Mitchell identified *Palaeosmilia?* and (in a pebble) *Lithostrotion martini*. The lower part of the limestone was pale grey and recrystallised, locally porcellanous or marble-like, but with traces of ooliths.

The IGS Knap Farm Borehole [2479 4011] was sunk to examine the Carboniferous Limestone and what lay beneath it (Whittaker and Scrivener, 1978; 1982; Mitchell and others, 1982; Lees and Hennebert, 1982); a summarised log is as follows:

	Thickness m	*Depth* m
Carboniferous (Dinantian)		
Cannington Park Limestone: Limestones, mainly pale grey with a coarse-grained oolite-like texture; bedding dips at about 40°; fissure filled with Triassic sediment; probably equivalent to the Goblin Combe Oolite, Arundian	93.20	93.20
Knap Limestone: Limestones, pale grey, porcellanous near the top but coarser-grained below; some oolite-like bands, dolomitic bands, and patches of crinoidal limestone are present; bedding dips increase downwards from 35° to 45°; in places fissures are filled with Triassic sediment, others are lined with calcite and a little baryte and pyrolusite. Arundian	156.35	249.55

	Thickness m	Depth m
Cynwir Castle Limestone: Limestones, dark grey, fine-grained, with abundant fissures; dips vary from 30° to 41°; veins of calcite carry hematite and a little baryte; stylolites are common. Arundian	101.66	351.21
Cynwir Cherty Limestones: Limestones, dark grey, mostly fine-grained; scattered grey or black chert bands and nodules are present down to 410 m and below this depth the limestone is locally stained pink or red, with more abundant chert horizons; a few thin bands of calcareous sandstone and silty shale are present below 453 m; in the lowest part of the sequence wisps of hematised mudstone are inclined at 25°. Arundian to 449.05 m; Chadian to 485.0 m; Ivorian below	206.47	557.68
Cannington Reef Limestones: Limestones, reefs, grey, fine-grained or porcellanous in places, with many layers of dolomitised limestone; the beds of dolomite are locally coarse grained and fissured, with abundant crinoidal debris at some levels; stylolites are common; the base is sharply defined. Ivorian	220.73	778.41
Black Rock Limestone: Limestones, medium to dark grey, and medium- to fine-grained; chert-rich zones occur down to 886 m, and dark grey limestones below, with argillaceous wisps and partings and scattered cherty patches; specks of galena were found in calcite veins at 957 m. Ivorian to 944.0 m; Hastarian below	187.94	966.35
Lower Limestone Shale: Shale and mudstone, dark grey, with subordinate bands of crinoidal limestone; the mudstones are locally silty, especially towards the base of the succession; thin shelly bands occur in the mudstones; the strata are overfolded and cleaved in places; a 0.31-m limestone at the base contains rounded sandstone pebbles and has a sharp bottom contact inclined at 40°. Hastarian to 1104.0 m; Devonian below	139.56	1105.91
Devonian		
Coy Sandstone: Sandstones, dark greenish grey, fine- to medium-grained, with interbedded argillaceous strata and scattered limestones which are locally pebbly; marcasite nodules and disseminated pyrite are present throughout; the general dip is about 30°	47.09	1153.00

Upper Carboniferous: Rodway Siltstones

The soil on the inlier north of Swang Farm [231 389] bears much rubble of red and greyish brown siltstone, sandstone and shale. Immediately north of the farm red and purple sandstones and siltstones up to 0.2 m thick, with interbedded shales, dip at 10°/180°; about 2 m of beds are exposed, much cleaved and disturbed. In a laneside section [2351 3910] just north of Ashford Farm interbedded red sandstones and greyish green and red siltstones and shales dip at 20°/220° but have been disturbed by creep.

The IGS Swang Farm No. 1 [2295 3891] and No. 2 [2296 3891] boreholes proved Palaeozoic rocks from 17.17 m to 44.78 m and from 18.44 m to 28.98 m respectively. The rocks were mainly grey and purple siltstones with thin fine-grained sandstones, pale grey or purple-stained and locally bioturbated, and one 1.55-m bed of purple medium-grained sandstone. *Chondrites* and crinoid ossicles were noted. A Devonian age has been suggested for these beds (Whittaker, 1978), but they are possibly Namurian.

Traces of maroon siltstone and shale occur in a lane [2317 3969] south-west of Oatley Farms and fine-grained sandstone at Knoll Green [2374 3977]. Farther east purple shales crop out in a lane [2407 3988] and maroon siltstones and thinly bedded sandstones in a small pit [2432 3981]. Webby (1966a) saw a 2.44-m-deep temporary trench in the lane at Chad's Hill, north-west of Cannington, which exposed grey and brown even-textured micaceous fine-grained sandstones and siltstones with pale green speckling and faint lamination, and on the east side of the lane [253 399] chocolate-brown fine-grained sandstones are intermittently exposed and dip at 35°/005°; 350 m to the east a roadside exposure [2565 3998] reveals brown flaggy micaceous fine-grained sandstone and siltstone. Alongside the track east of Rodway occur purple and greenish purple fine-grained sandstones [2583 4004] and reddish purple siltstones, sandstones and silty mudstones [2587 4004]. An old pit [2623 4005] near the eastern end of the Rodway inlier shows purple fine-grained micaceous sandstone.

The Withiel Farm No. 1 Borehole proved Rodway Siltstones to 138.20 m; the No. 2 Borehole proved them, beneath Otter Sandstone, from 3.45 m to 40.80 m. The beds were dark grey micaceous siltstones with thin grey sandstones, stained purple and green in the top 18.57 m (No. 1) and 11.12 m (No. 2). They were much disturbed, and locally extensively fractured by fairly steeply inclined faults marked by slickensides. Recumbent folds were noted at several levels. Near the junction with the underlying limestone, the Rodway Siltstones were stained red and showed small-scale cycles of sandstone, siltstone and shale. Goniatites from red-stained ferruginous silty sandstone at 132.45 m in the No. 1 Borehole were identified by Dr W. H. C. Ramsbottom as *Gastrioceras crencellatum*, characteristic of the late Namurian *G. cancellatum* Marine Band.

EAE, BJW

Descriptions of the Permo-Triassic rocks in the extreme north of the district are based largely on Whittaker and Green (1983).

Wiveliscombe Sandstones

In the north-west of the Taunton district the lowest Permo-Triassic strata are buff and red sandstones, generally thickly bedded, friable and readily eroded. Locally the rocks are harder and more competent, owing to the presence of calcareous cement, and have been worked for building stone. Although generally well graded, in some places the sandstones contain scattered small pebbles; a few breccia bands occur, mainly near the Devonian – Permian unconformity and towards the overlying Vexford Breccias.

Soft-weathering sandstone, or sandrock, is common just north of the Ash Priors Fault, and also westward towards Wiveliscombe. West of the latter town fragments of local Devonian rock are common in sandstones near the unconformity. In the south-western extremity of the district the lowest Permo-Triassic rocks include much sandy breccia; they are distinguished from the overlying Vexford Breccias largely by their friable nature and ease of weathering.

Thicknesses of the Wiveliscombe Sandstones at outcrop range from 25 to 75 m, but considerably more is likely to be present in the central part of the western Permo-Triassic basin (Chapter 8). The Puriton Borehole [319 409] (McMurtrie, 1911) ended after penetrating 177.18 m of 'Lower Sandstone'.

Vexford Breccias

The Vexford Breccias range from 20 m to 40 m in thickness. They comprise angular and subangular fragments of sandstone, slate and quartz in a sandy matrix whose grains are mostly angular but locally rounded; rounded fragments are plentiful, if less common, and locally include a few of Carboniferous Limestone. The breccias are generally well cemented and form a distinct scarp. Interbedded sandstones are present; some are thin and impersistent, but others are up to 1 m thick, sharply defined and extensive. These thicker sandstones occur mainly towards the top and bottom of the succession.

North of Stogumber the rocks are locally conglomeratic; Carboniferous Limestone pebbles are present, similar to but smaller than those in the younger Budleigh Salterton Pebble Beds (see below). In places in this northern area the top strata are poorly consolidated and gravelly, and alternation of strong and soft-weathering beds is attested by degraded banks and hard outcrops in cuttings near Stogumber Station. Farther south, towards Vexford, the succession includes beds of sandrock and also calcareous sandy breccia, and an old limekiln adjoins a filled quarry at Dean's Cross.

Breccias around Lydeard St Lawrence contain beds of variably pebbly sandstone up to 0.5 m thick. Disconnected outcrops along the north side of the Ash Priors Fault show the presence of some interbedded sandstone in a formation which makes topographic features that are conspicuous in some places and indistinct in others.

In the neighbourhood of Wiveliscombe the breccias make a marked feature and are seen to overlie friable sandrock. Contained pebbles include both Lower Carboniferous chert of the Culm facies and Carboniferous Limestone possibly from the Mendip Hills or South Wales. Some of the interbedded sandstone is calcareous, and similar rock occurs within the breccias between Wiveliscombe and Milverton. The breccias in the south-west of the district form Bathealton Lands Covert, a wooded scarp rising steeply eastwards from the underlying stony sands.

Littleham Mudstone

Few good exposures occur of the soft Littleham Mudstone between the more competent Vexford Breccias below and Budleigh Salterton Pebble Beds above. The formation comprises cuboidally-fractured red calcareous mudstones, generally weathered to calcareous clay or marl, locally spotted or mottled greenish grey and with subordinate amounts of greenish grey mudstone and a little buff or greenish grey sandstone. The sandstones are generally thin and without topographic expression, although small features occur locally, as near Pyleigh. Silty and sandy beds are common towards the base of the Littleham Mudstone in the area west of Milverton.

The formation is generally evident only as a reddish brown clay or silty clay soil, indistinguishable in nature and in calcicole vegetation from that of the red Mercia Mudstone Group rocks. Old marlpits, now commonly degraded, flooded and overgrown, are common. Larger pits at and near Milland's Farm [100 280] are probably the remains of the old brickworks referred to by Ussher (1908) as near Davey's Farm.

The Littleham Mudstone, although its outcrop runs irregularly north–south, appears to be slightly thinner (30 to 35 m) in the westernmost outcrops than farther east (40 to 55 m). Sporadic exposures along the lane from Slape Moor to Quaking House, west of Milverton, span about 45 m of strata in a total thickness of about 55 m and constitute the only sizeable section through the formation.

Samples collected during the recent survey from near Bicknoller [1064 3890] and Milverton [1050 2680; 1060 2650], and examined by Dr G. Warrington, yielded no palynological evidence of age. One [1050 2680] contained a few simple trilete miospores and a possible fragment of a densospore cingulum, which may all have been reworked from Carboniferous rocks.

Budleigh Salterton Pebble Beds

The Budleigh Salterton Pebble Beds, commonly and conveniently, if arbitrarily, taken as the basal formation of the Triassic, consist mainly of conglomerates. Pebbles within the conglomerates range in size up to 0.5 m across. Breccio-conglomerates occur locally, as do interbedded sandstones and pebbly sandstones, and the rocks, although commonly with a strong calcareous or ferruginous cement, are in places soft-weathering and gravelly. The sandy matrix consists of mainly sub-rounded grains and resembles the coarser parts of the overlying sandstone. The topographic feature associated with the pebble beds is the strongest and most persistent within the Permo-Triassic rocks of the district.

Contained pebbles are mainly of Devonian rocks of local

type and presumed local origin: sandstone, siltstone, slate and limestone. They range from rounded to subangular. Pebbles of Carboniferous Limestone (Martin, 1909), many of them large, are commonest in the north of the district; they are very well rounded, pale grey, massive and locally oolitic, in contrast to the purple and grey, commonly sheared and less regular fragments of Devonian limestone.

Ussher (1908) noted broad distinctions between the pebble beds of three areas. Quarries in the Sampford Brett area show massive conglomerates accompanied by pebbly sandstones. From Bicknoller to Combe Florey the conglomerates are commonly poorly cemented, perhaps decalcified, and locally weathered to gravel, although they nevertheless form a marked and mappable feature. Farther south, adjacent to the Ash Priors Fault and in the south-western extremity of the district, massive and thickly bedded calcareous conglomerates contain interbedded calcareous sandstones and pebbly sandstones, generally subordinate but in places characteristic of the top part of the formation. Pebbles are typically larger towards the base of the conglomerates than towards the top.

The pebble beds are exposed in many quarries; much of their pebble content has in the past been worked for roadstone, but in many places the presence of old limekilns recalls the practice of hand-picking the limestone pebbles, and digging out the more calcareous beds, to be burnt for lime. Steep joints are common, and local records of caves usually refer to cavities which owe their origin primarily to slight collapses along joints and only secondarily to effects of solution. The formation is generally 30 to 35 m thick. EAE

Otter Sandstone

The Otter Sandstone comprises red, yellow, buff and mottled, fine-grained or fine- to-medium-grained sandstones, locally hard and calcareous but in places soft friable sandrock. Scattered evidence from current-bedding suggests flow from the west, with some flow from the south in the south of the district. Sand grains are generally subangular, although in the coarser calcareous facies they are more rounded. Pebbly sandstones and beds of sandy conglomerate or breccia occur at some localities, usually towards the bottom of the formation or the margin of the basin, and subordinate marls and sandy marls at others, usually but not invariably towards the top. Where extensively cemented, as commonly within the large outcrop at and north of Bishop's Lydeard, the rocks may be considered to be sandy limestones and have been burnt for lime. Ussher (1908) noted the presence of fragments of slate within the sandstones where they rest directly on Devonian rocks, for example around the south-eastern end of the Quantocks foothills.

The passage upwards from conglomerates to sandstones renders the base of the formation somewhat arbitrary. Ussher (1908) noted local traces of marl between the mainly-sandstone upper beds of his conglomerates and the sandstones-with-conglomerate beds of his Upper Sandstones, and took them to mark the junction. The line is now drawn between predominantly conglomeratic and predominantly sandstone successions. Similarly the top of the formation is taken between a predominantly sandstone sequence below and a predominantly marl or mudstone sequence above. The Otter Sandstone ranges from 30 to 60 m in thickness at outcrop; the Puriton Borehole proved 61.57 m. BJW, EAE

Mercia Mudstone Group

Below The Blue Anchor Formation

The beds referred to in this Memoir as the 'red Mercia Mudstone' form the major part of the Mercia Mudstone Group and mainly comprise red cuboidally-splitting mudstones and silty mudstones. These rocks commonly effervesce with hydrochloric acid, and weather at outcrop to calcareous clay or marl. Subordinate greenish grey mudstones are common, as are greenish grey spotting and mottling. Siltstones occur locally. Sandstones are less common but, although thin, are fairly persistent between North Curry and Stoke St Gregory and in the valley of the River Tone 3 km west of Taunton. Some interbedded sandstones occur low in the succession and towards the margins of the Permo-Triassic basins. The top of the succession is taken at a colour change from mainly red silty mudstones to the greenish grey silty mudstones and siltstones of the Blue Anchor Formation.

No reliable estimate of the thickness of this part of the group, based on its outcrop between the Otter Sandstone below and the Blue Anchor Formation above, is possible. Faults cannot be traced with certainty across the red marl countryside, but are presumed to be present. West of the Quantock Hills the Permo-Triassic basin contains north-west-trending faults, and its north-eastern boundary is fault-controlled at least in part. These fractures run within the Mercia Mudstone south of the outcrops of the Blue Anchor Formation. East of the Quantock Hills inliers of Devonian and Carboniferous rocks between Nether Stowey and Bridgwater attest the irregular nature of the Palaeozoic floor. Leighland Slates crop out 300 m from presumed Namurian strata, and it seems likely that a major fault trends roughly west-north-west between the inliers. This and other fractures probably pass between the Otter Sandstone of Nether Stowey and the Blue Anchor Formation to the north. The Puriton Borehole, sited on the red Mercia Mudstone, proved rock salt (the Somerset Halite Formation) within the Group between 183 m and 219.15 m depth, and entered Otter Sandstone at 388.62 m. BJW, EAE

Blue Anchor Formation

At St Audrie's Bay the Blue Anchor Formation comprises 5.19 m of green and dark greenish grey silty mudstones and siltstones (Tea Green Marl) overlain by 24 m of dark grey mudstones and shaly mudstones, and greenish grey and buff-fish grey silty mudstones and siltstones, dolomitic in part (Grey Marl), with two horizons rich in nodular gypsum and some finely laminated mudstones containing worm burrows (Whittaker and Green, 1983). At about 8.2 to 9.7 m above the base of the formation occur persistent siltstones or silty sandstones, with cavities which probably once contained evaporites, overlain by up to 0.05 m of red marl.

The top strata of the formation are ripple-marked siltstones showing sun cracks and erosion surfaces and with conglomeratic beds. Rhaetian fossils have been obtained from the top few metres, but the mapped boundary is drawn at the lithological junction with overlying shales and limestones. Warrington (1971; 1980) presented palynological evidence that these beds and the highest part of the underlying red mudstone sequence are of Rhaetian age.

Mayall (1979; 1981) has divided the Blue Anchor Formation of north Somerset into the Rydon Member below and the Williton Member above, with type sections at Blue Anchor (about 5 km to the west of the district) and in St Audrie's Bay. He considered that the Rydon Member was laid down in an evaporitic lacustrine environment but that the disconformably overlying Williton Member was shallow-water marine. This concept advances the onset of the late-Triassic marine transgression locally to a date earlier than that of the base of the Penarth Group.

Penarth Group

The Westbury Formation at the base of the Penarth Group comprises a little over 12 m of grey or black paper-shales and shaly mudstones with bands and lenticles of dark grey earthy limestone, commonly associated with fibrous calcite ('beef'), and a few thin rippled sandstones. The argillaceous rocks yield bivalves, including *Rhaetavicula contorta*. Vertebrate remains are common locally in the sandstones, and also occur concentrated in several bone-beds.

Overlying the shales at St Audrie's Bay and Puriton is a 1.5-m sequence of pale grey or greenish grey calcareous mudstones, limestones, siltstones and sandstones which make up the Cotham Member of the Lilstock Formation. In the lower part of this member occur contorted slumped calcareous siltstones, ripple marking and polygonal shrinkage cracks.

The succeeding Langport Member, which includes Richardson's (1911) White Lias, comprises a little over 1 m of bands, lenticles and nodules of pale grey limestone interbedded with grey mudstones. Some limestones towards the base are fine grained, porcellanous and laminated; higher ones commonly weather to a distinctive creamy white colour, and at the top is the 'Sun Bed', hard compact fine grained and bluish grey. Above the Sun Bed is about 0.34 m of hard grey calcareous mudstone or marl containing limestone lenticles up to 0.08 m thick; these beds are the lowest part of Richardson's (1911) Watchet Beds.

Pre-planorbis Beds

The Penarth Group is succeeded by mudstones, shales and limestone at the base of the Lower Lias; of these beds, some 5.5 m are below the first occurrence of *Psiloceras* and are consequently classified as Triassic.

Conditions of deposition

The post-Variscan landscape was an arid one of reddened surface rocks in which debris from the high ground was carried down and spread over an irregular surface. Small depressions were filled and barriers of Palaeozoic rock were eroded. Sediments accumulating in adjacent basins coalesced, and successively younger layers overlapped and spread beyond the debris already deposited. Desert weathering and sporadic torrential rains resulted in coarse debris being swept from barren uplands to form screes and ill-sorted poorly bedded breccias. Denudation and more moderate rainfall resulted in finer-grained sediments. Probably occasional differential movement, perhaps sinking of fault-bounded Permo-Triassic basins, and climatic changes, disturbed the general progression from sands and rudaceous deposits to muds. The bowing of Triassic sediments up stream valleys at the margins of the Quantock Hills suggests that drainage courses are commonly in much the same position as in Permo-Triassic times.

The Wiveliscombe Sandstones are generally fairly well graded and show rounded grains. Perhaps they originated in a semi-desert landscape subject to wind erosion and with low rainfall; but they were deposited by rivers, with local spasmodic heavy rain resulting in intercalations of stony detritus. Gradation from sandstones with subordinate breccias to breccias with subordinate sandstones (the Vexford Breccias) points to a passage to seasonal torrential rains with rapid accumulation of angular debris, mainly of local origin, in fans and screes. The few pebbles of Carboniferous Limestone point to some river flow from north of the district.

Rapid denudation, possibly accompanied by rainfall less seasonal and less heavy, led to a preponderance of fine-grained sediment being derived from a landscape of much reduced relief. There seems little doubt that the muds, silts and subordinate sands of the Littleham Mudstone were laid down in water, possibly in part in the lower reaches of river flood plains but probably mostly in warm shallow inland seas or lakes which may have occasionally dried up. Smith (1970), working in northern England, has considered possible widespread inundations in late Permian times and related glacioeustatic movement.

The pebbles of the Budleigh Salterton Pebble Beds, although mainly of local rock, include some of Carboniferous Limestone from farther afield, possibly from South Wales or the Mendip Hills. Laming (1968) suggested that the source might have been a lost Carboniferous Limestone outlier to the west of the district, in the Exmoor region, but there is no other evidence for its existence. The conglomerates are of fluviatile origin and the basin of deposition was extensive; it is defined to some extent by indications of southerly sources in south Devon, westerly sources near Uffculme and northerly sources in north-west Somerset. Within the present district, smaller streams probably flowed from the Brendon and Quantock hills, bringing some more angular fragments. The rounding of relatively soft, far-travelled, pieces of Carboniferous Limestone is readily understood, as is the greater irregularity of locally-derived fragments. Rounded pebbles of, say, hard Devonian sandstone or quartz, which can be matched near by, may nevertheless have been carried from a distance, or been present in Devonian rocks as pebbles, or been moved a short way in a highly abrasive suspension or sludge.

The general upward succession from mudstones (in the Littleham Mudstone) to conglomerates (in the Budleigh Salterton Pebble Beds) implies a change to larger higher-energy rivers with more distant headwaters, and this in turn suggests some differential uplift and resultant higher relief. The explanation is unknown, but could relate to movement on faults bounding the Permo-Triassic basins. Whatever the cause, a new major cycle of erosion was begun, of which the succeeding phase is represented by the fluviatile Otter Sandstone. A. N. Thomas (1940) concluded that most of the sandstones were originally sandy limestones, with original calcite completely isolating the sand grains one from another. Some detrital calcite is present, and some secondary growth of calcite has occurred. However, Thomas believed that most of the calcite was chemically derived from the waters of deposition, and that zones of iron oxide within calcite pointed to intermittent deposition. He also noted small grains of oolitic limestone, possibly Carboniferous Limestone.

The red sediments in the Mercia Mudstone Group commonly possess a groundmass of crystalline calcite or dolomite, and again Thomas (1940) concluded that carbonates and detrital minerals had been deposited simultaneously. Presumably sedimentation took place in confined shallow waters in a hot desert or semi-desert environment in which concentration and deposition of evaporite minerals resulted from evaporation.

Sediments of the Blue Anchor Formation show burrows, lamination and marine fossils. Whittaker and Green (1983) noted that the presence in the upper beds ('Grey Marl') of porphyroblastic sulphate nodules associated with carbonaceous (?algal-mat) mudstones suggested supratidal deposition in a sabkha environment, and that interbedded laminated dolomitised siltstones pointed to low-energy intertidal deposition. Perhaps a sequence of incursions and retreats by the sea preceded the truly marine environment represented by the Penarth Group.

Slightly pebbly sandstones and associated bone-beds near the base of the Westbury Formation in some places suggest deposition in a transgressive littoral zone (Whittaker and Green, 1983). Basal sandstones elsewhere show polygonal cracks filled with sediment from overlying beds, indicating emergence and drying. Ripple marks attest current action, and there is some indication of concentration of shell debris by currents. However, most of the Westbury Formation comprises shales with concretionary, possibly diagenetic, limestones, and probably originated in tranquil deeper water.

Markedly calcareous beds above the shales show fining-upwards, ripple marks, sandy lenticles, structures attributable to slumping or dewatering, and polygonal cracks produced by emergence and drying, all suggesting the increased activity of a shallow-water high-energy environment. The topmost limestones and mudstones possibly formed in warm shelf seas or lagoons in which the water was deeper at some times than at others; the top of the Sun Bed shows borings and sun-cracks. The general upward passage within the Penarth Group from shales to mudstones and limestones is mirrored in a number of similar minor shallowing-upward cycles. EAE, BJW

DETAILS

Wiveliscombe Sandstones (Figure 10)

Stogumber to Lydeard St Lawrence

An old quarry [0995 3778] near Wayshill lies at the top of the Wiveliscombe Sandstones. At its northern end 1.5 m of sandstones dip at 15°/020° beneath 2 m of breccias, and at its southern end 3 m of massive red, brown and yellow calcareous sandstone contain scattered pebbles. The sandstones have been burnt for lime. East of Stogumber 3.5 to 4 m of thickly bedded calcareous sandrock dip at 12°/010° [1002 3740]. Immediately south of the village, at the site of an old brewery, buildings have been constructed of thickly bedded calcareous slightly pebbly sandstone quarried on site; 4 m of strata remain exposed [0965 3681]. A quarry [104 369] between the village and its railway station shows 4.5 m of buff and red thickly bedded calcareous sandstone with subordinate bands of sandy breccia; sandstone has been burnt for lime at the quarry. H. H. Thomas (*in* Ussher, 1908) described red calcareous coarse-grained sand from Stogumber, containing grains of chert and other siliceous sediment.

Lanes [1010 3638 to 1030 3614] south-east of Wood Farm cut through sand and sandrock with pebbly bands and patches and with calcareous films. Ussher (1908) noted interbedded friable pebbly and sandy strata in lanesides near Wood Farm, and sandstone, sandy marl and breccia, the last named composed of small fragments of the nearby Morte Slates, to the south. A depression [1010 3607] north of Preston Farm is often flooded and shows silty marl in its base, indicating the presence of some argillaceous bands in the sandstone of that area. Pebbly sand and sandrock are common around Higher Vexford, and are exposed in a lane [1080 3514].

The only traces now visible of a sandy outlier at Elworthy Cross [0868 3475] are buff and brown sands in the roadsides. Ussher (1908) recorded H. H. Thomas's note of deep red non-calcareous sand, with fairly well rounded grains, from this locality. A. N. Thomas (1940) mentioned breccia bands in the sandstones at Elworthy.

The Permo-Triassic outlier west of Coleford Water is mainly of sandrock that is locally pebbly. A quarry [114 339] shows bedded calcareous sandstone with scattered pebbles overlying breccia with subordinate sandy bands in a 4-m face; the dip is 10° towards the east and an old limekiln stands near the entrance to the quarry. The northern and north-eastern margin of the outlier consists of breccias within the Wiveliscombe Sandstones. The breccias rest on Morte Slates. They crop out in Coleford Water [1158 3404], where 0.7 m of breccia is overlain by 0.9 m of sandstone, and in nearby quarries [1153 3398; 1138 3360]. Just east of the hamlet, calcareous wedge-bedded sandstones in the laneside [1176 3402] lie at the top of the formation and dip eastward beneath breccias.

Sand and sandrock with a few pebbles crop out [1144 3355] at Coleford Farm, and extensive exposures [1170 3296 to 1169 3286] at Embelle Farm show mottled sand and sandrock with thin pebbly streaks. Similar sandrock and mottled sandstone with subordinate breccia bands dip eastward at 5° in the laneside [1203 3214] near Will.

East Town to Bathealton Court

A roadside exposure [1079 3206] in East Town shows 2 m of red sand and sandrock with pale buff streaks and breccia lenses. H. H. Thomas's notes (*in* Ussher, 1908) described dull-red, iron-stained, non-calcareous sandstone of uniform grain at East Town, containing grains of chert and one grain of unaltered cordierite. Red sandrock is much in evidence at Grove Farm [1115 3190 to 1108 3179]. A nearby degraded sandpit, in which has been dumped rubble of Devonian slate and limestone, is probably that in which Ussher (1908) saw brownish red sand containing rubbly calcareous concretions.

Goulden Manor (formerly Golden Farm) stands on the junction between Morte Slates and Wiveliscombe Sandstones, and horizontal calcareous sandrock with traces of breccia exposed nearby [1107 3144] lies very near the local base of the formation. Sand and sandrock, locally with scattered pebbles, are common in roadsides

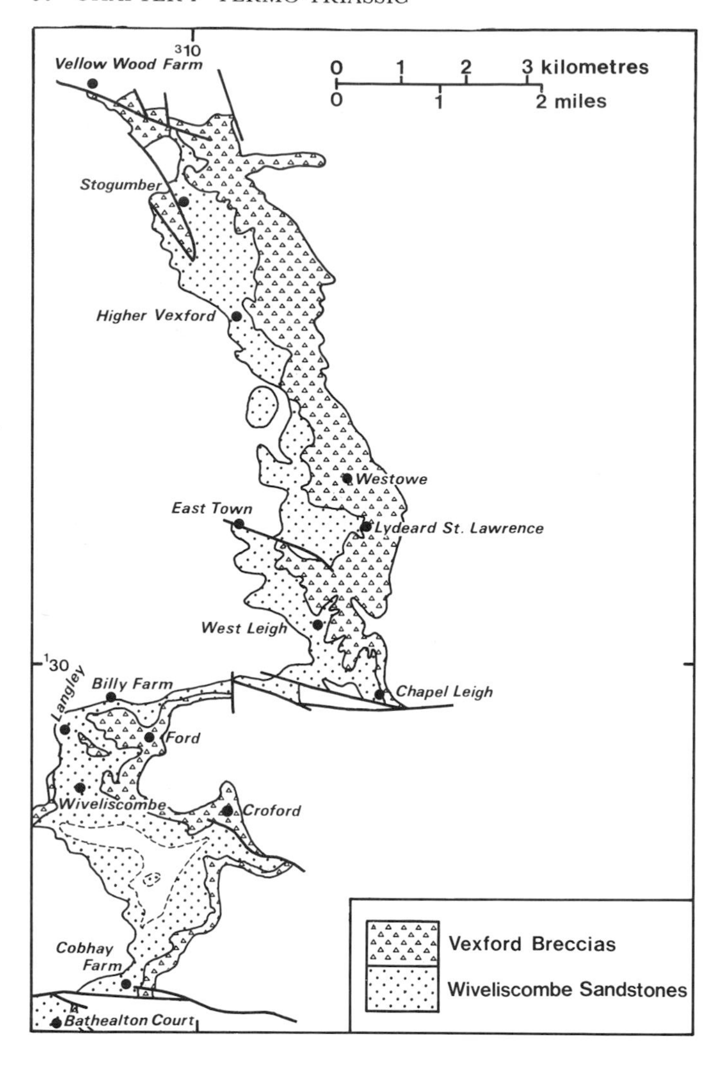

Figure 10 Outcrops of the Wiveliscombe Sandstones and the Vexford Breccias

hereabouts. Such exposures south-east of West Leigh are near the top of the formation and show horizontal sandrock with thin breccia lenses [1224 3027], and red current-bedded sandrock with subordinate breccia [1233 3009].

The road running eastward from Hoccombe traverses current-bedded sand and sandrock with breccia bands up to 0.5 m thick [1159 2981; 1165 2983; 1171 2983; 1185 2977].

Red sandrock [1020 2970] at Goulds Farm rests on silty clay which may be weathered Devonian material or may indicate the presence of marl bands within the Wiveliscombe Sandstones. Traces of red marl occur in sandy head overlying the sandstones farther west [0934 2943].

A lane west-south-west of Billy Farm traverses red sand and sandrock dipping gently eastward and containing thin breccia lenses [0844 2942 to 0826 2929]. It leads into Sandy Lane, running south-west to Langley, which is deeply cut through massive and thickly bedded red and brown sandstones dipping at 10° to 15°/090° to 110°: sections include 10 m of friable, locally calcareous, sandstone [0815 2912]; 5 m of friable sandstone with thin stony lenses and with bands of concretionary iron oxide [0811 2907]; and 5 m of sandstone with a breccia lens up to 0.4 m thick [0807 2902]. Just east of Langley the top of the formation is exposed [0830 3889] (p. 31).

Reddish brown sand and sandrock, locally stony, is common in Wiveliscombe. Tracks and lanes climbing westward from the town, and some steeply sloping gardens between them, show [0774 2798; 0778 2796; 0884 2782; 0744 2768] a narrow outcrop of breccias between the Wiveliscombe Sandstones and the Pickwell Down Sandstones to the west. As might be expected, the breccias contain much Devonian sandstone. They have been mapped as Vexford Breccias, but lie slightly higher than that formation east of the town and could be a marginal facies of the sandstones. The disused Taunton to Barnstaple railway track cuts through 3 m of sandrock overlain by Head [0846 2705] south of Wiveliscombe, red sand and sandrock with scattered pebbles [0954 2763 to 0996 2753] east of the town. H. H. Thomas (*in* Ussher, 1908) described red calcareous marly sandstone from near the latter cutting.

A minor road at Croford shows cuttings in hard pebbly sandrock near the top of the Wiveliscombe Sandstones [1023 2754; 1028 2755; 1034 2752]. A nearby borehole [110 270], sited about 10 m below the top of the formation, proved 78 m of fine- to coarse-grained sandstone, locally pebbly (mainly towards the top), with thin beds of friable sand and scattered marly bands up to 0.75 m thick. Farther south, just below the breccia scarp, red sandrock crops out near the top of the formation [1032 2622; 1025 2609]. Slightly pebbly sandrock is exposed [0926 2550] at Screedy.

Ussher (1908) recorded that a well at Cobhay Farm [0905 2495] proved hard white sand at 10 ft (3.05 m) depth. The farm lies near the top of the Wiveliscombe Sandstones, and a short length of core retained from a well immediately adjoining the buildings was of breccia. The sands and sandrock around Bathealton Court contain many pebbles and also beds and lenses of breccia.

Vexford Breccias (Figure 10)

Yellow Wood Farm to Lydeard St Lawrence

Vexford Breccias are faulted against Budleigh Salterton Pebble Beds in the neighbourhood of Yellow Wood Farm. Exposures [0911 3880] at the farm show roughly bedded purple and red breccias dipping at 15°/010°. The West Somerset Railway between Newton and Yard Farm cuts through purple and brown breccias containing some sub-rounded fragments. A lane south-east of Culverhays traverses purple and brown breccias with a little sandstone overlain by red marls [116 379]. The base of the breccias is exposed at the northern end of a quarry [0995 3778] just north of Stogumber. A narrow outcrop of Vexford Breccias, fault-bounded on its north-eastern side, extends from the southern part of Stogumber to Wood Farm; exposures are scattered and small, and show breccias with pebbly sand and sandrock.

Cuttings of the West Somerset Railway on either side of Stogumber Station [1105 3720] show up to 4.5 m of thickly bedded breccias dipping gently eastward. The rocks contain many small fragments of sandstone, slate and quartz, some angular, others sub-rounded. They are well cemented in places, but locally have weathered to gravelly rubble, and the base of the formation as mapped to the west is an arbitrary line between breccias and sandstones to the east and sands, sandrock, calcareous sandstone and breccia to the west. Sporadic exposures for about 1 km south-eastward along the railway show slightly coarser breccias, and some interbedded sandstone occurs near the top of the formation [1200 3624] at Leigh Wood. A quarry [1115 3670] to the west of Water Farm shows 10 m of breccias with subordinate sandstones. The lane from Water Farm to Heddon Oak cuts through reddish brown breccias, with sandstone beds up to 0.2 m thick towards the top, overlain by red silty marls [1167 3676].

The road from Carslake Farm [1120 3656] to Houndhill [1103 3549] runs very close to the base of the breccias, and sporadic exposures alongside the road and on the adjacent slopes show degraded gravelly breccia and interbedded sandstone. Carslake

Quarry [1153 3595] is now much overgrown but was once a large pit opened for building stone in breccias and slightly pebbly locally friable sandstones. Roadside exposures near Houndhill are of soft sandy breccio-conglomerate with bands of breccia and calcareous sandstone. The lane running south-eastward from Lower Vexford exposes breccias overlain by red marl [1213 3504].

The road leading northward from Rexton Farm [119 345] traverses weathered rubbly breccias and stony pebbly sands. West of the farm, at the base of the formation, breccias overlie calcareous sandstones [1151 3465]. Corresponding strata in a roadside [1179 3402] south of the farm comprise breccias dipping at 15° to the east above locally calcareous wedge-bedded sandstone.

A reputedly deep pit [1202 3334] south-south-east of Dean's Farm is now largely filled but is shown by nearby roadside exposures to lie near the base of the Vexford Breccias. The ruins of an old limekiln stand alongside the road just below the quarry. Ussher (1908) recorded a quarry near Dean's Farm in which current-bedded sands with a few pebbles rested on hard evenly bedded brown calcareous sandstone with scattered stones and bands of breccia, the beds dipping at 7°/055°; it seems likely that this pit passed through thin breccias into calcareous beds at the top of the underlying Wiveliscombe Sandstones, which were burnt for lime.

Breccias at Westowe [1235 3292] overlie sandrock, and an old quarry [1231 3265] to the south shows 2 m of breccia with a 0.2-m band of fine- to medium-grained sandstone. An old pit [1293 3265] and adjacent roadside exposures on the northern outskirts of Lydeard St Lawrence show reddish brown breccias, with some interbedded sandstone at their base, overlying red sandrock. It seems that the small valley running east-south-east from Westowe to Lydeard St Lawrence has been cut through the breccias into the Wiveliscombe Sandstones. Small exposures of breccias with subordinate sandstone occur in Lydeard St Lawrence, and a small quarry [1313 3247] east of the village shows 0.5 m of pebbly sandstone overlain by 1.5 m of breccia.

Chapel Leigh to Bathealton Court

Strongly cemented breccias form a pronounced scarp in the West Leigh – Pyleigh area, where they overlie soft-weathering sandrock. At the foot of the slope north-east of Chapel Leigh 1 m of breccia overlies 2 m of sandrock [1290 2971].

An outlier of Vexford breccias to the west of Chapel Leigh is bounded on its southern side by an offshoot of the Ash Priors Fault. Farther west the formation forms a north – south scarp stretching from this fracture to the main Ash Priors Fault. The slope rising southwards from Goulds Farm [103 297] carries traces of soft-weathered breccia between the sandrock exposed at the farm and silty marls on the higher slopes, and a narrow outcrop of relatively soft sandy breccias and sandstones runs west and south-west to Ford [094 289]. Rising ground west of Ford is crossed by a lane running north-north-west towards Billy Farm, and this lane cuts through coarsely interbedded breccia, sandstone and sandrock [089 288 to 087 293]. The base of the formation is exposed in a road cutting [0830 2889] through an outlier east of Langley, where 1.5 m of sandrock overlain by 3.5 m of breccia dip at 15° north-eastward. Fragments in the breccia include sandstone, quartz, dark grey 'Culm' chert and grey limestone, some of it oolitic, of Carboniferous Limestone type. H. H. Thomas (*in* Ussher, 1908) described the breccia at Langley as highly calcareous with fragments of quartz, grit and chert up to 13 mm across; the larger grains of the matrix were well rounded, almost 'millet seed', the small ones sub-rounded, and the cement partly calcite and partly baryte replacing calcite.

An old quarry [0900 2857] on the northern side of Ridge Hill shows 3.5 m of breccias with subordinate current-bedded sandstone near the base of the formation. In another [094 278], alongside the road to Castle Hill, 3 m of breccia are overlain by 1.3 m of slightly stony locally calcareous sandstone capped by 2.5 m of breccia; the breccias contain fragments of sandstone, quartz and limestone.

Plate 3 Scarp formed by Vexford Breccias, West Leigh.

On the low ground alluvium overlies Wiveliscombe Sandstones; the rising rougher wooded ground consists of Vexford Breccias (A 13861)

Roadside exposures [1031 2761] at Croford show 3.5 m of massive breccia at the base of the formation overlying 1.5 m of slightly pebbly sandrock. The small outlier on which stands Hillacre Farm [1041 2748] consists of breccias with subordinate interbedded sandrock.

The Vexford Breccias occupy a narrow outcrop skirting the rising ground to the south of the valley at Croford. They are locally well cemented and hard, but more typically soft and readily weathered. Farther south, at the foot of the feature north-west and west of Quaking House, breccias are interbedded with calcareous sandstones in a 3.5-m section [1029 2633] and 2 m of breccia overlie 4 m of calcareous sandstone [1029 2608]; the breccias contain fragments of sandstone, quartz and limestone.

The road from Screedy to Farthing's Farm cuts through the base of the formation, showing breccias on calcareous sandstone [0973 2571]. A quarry [0937 2521] south of Screedy is in 6 m of breccias, with fragments of sandstone, quartz and chert, overlain by 2 m of calcareous sandstone, dipping at 10° south-eastward. Another pit [0928 2495], east of Cobhay Farm, shows 4 m of similar breccias apparently inclined at 5°/150°. It may have been at this pit that Ussher (1908) noted hard nodular calcareous sandstone overlying the breccia.

The pronounced scarp to the east of Bathealton Court is formed of hard well-cemented breccias with interbedded sandstone. Exposures show 1 m of thickly bedded pebbly sandstone overlain by 2 m of massive breccia [0824 2449], and sandy stony rock, in part sandy breccia and in part pebbly sandstone 1.5 m, overlain by breccia 0.4 m, separated by a parting of thinly bedded sandstone from overlying massive medium-grained sandstone with scattered pebbles 1 m, capped by breccia 0.6 m [0831 2437].

Littleham Mudstone (Figure 11)

Red marls overlying breccias south of Capton [080 394] are exposed only poorly and sporadically in soil and a few degraded marlpits. Purple and grey shales and siltstones [1064 3889] crop out in a lane north of Newton, and red marls near the base of the formation in a lane [1149 3801] to the south-east.

Stony Head overlies 1 m of red marl in the roadside [1241 3587] at Leigh Farm, and red marls crop out sporadically in lanesides [1216 3503 to 1270 3472] and roadsides [1247 3392 to 1270 3413] north-east and south-east of Rexton Farm and in adjoining old marlpits. Several lanes and roads to the south, which also cross the clayey slopes below the pebble beds scarp, show similar small outcrops. The road from the Friendship Inn [1308 3129] to Combe Down Lodge passes an old pit [1333 3122] in which is exposed greyish green and red silty marl. Just south of the road two small knolls probably represent sandy beds within the marls; a lane crossing one of them cuts through thinly bedded slightly pebbly sandstone [1331 3093].

A largely fault-bounded area of Littleham Mudstone west-south-west of Chapel Leigh contains small exposures of red marl and silty marl, mainly in scattered old marlpits. The lane climbing to an outlier of pebble beds north-east of Ford cuts through red marls [0970 2918], and similar rocks are poorly exposed on the slopes around the outlier of Castle Hill to the south.

Milland's Farm [100 280] contains a pit showing traces of red marl, and two larger pits [0994 2787; 0998 2783], now overgrown and much obscured by tip, lie alongside a lane to the west; together these probably constitute the brickworks identified by Ussher (1908) as near Davey's Farm. Even when seen by Ussher, only 0.6 m of red marly clay were exposed.

Red marls occur at a few localities alongside the old railway track north-west of Milverton. In places [e.g. 1175 2694] marls are associated with pebbles, but it seems likely that the marls are weathered and the pebbles have come from the pebble beds scarp immediately to the north.

Alongside the lane from Slape Moor to Quaking House, horizontal red marls in the lower part of the formation contain beds of red silty sandstone up to 0.3 m thick [1050 2688]. Exposures farther south along the lane, and stratigraphically higher, are mainly of red marl with some mottled and pale greyish green marl. A shallow trench [1000 2563] to the west of Farthing's Farm showed that the 10-m succession up to about 5 m below the base of the pebble beds consisted wholly of red marls. The road from Screedy to Spring Grove House shows a few exposures of red marl [e.g. 0958 2518; 0961 2512].

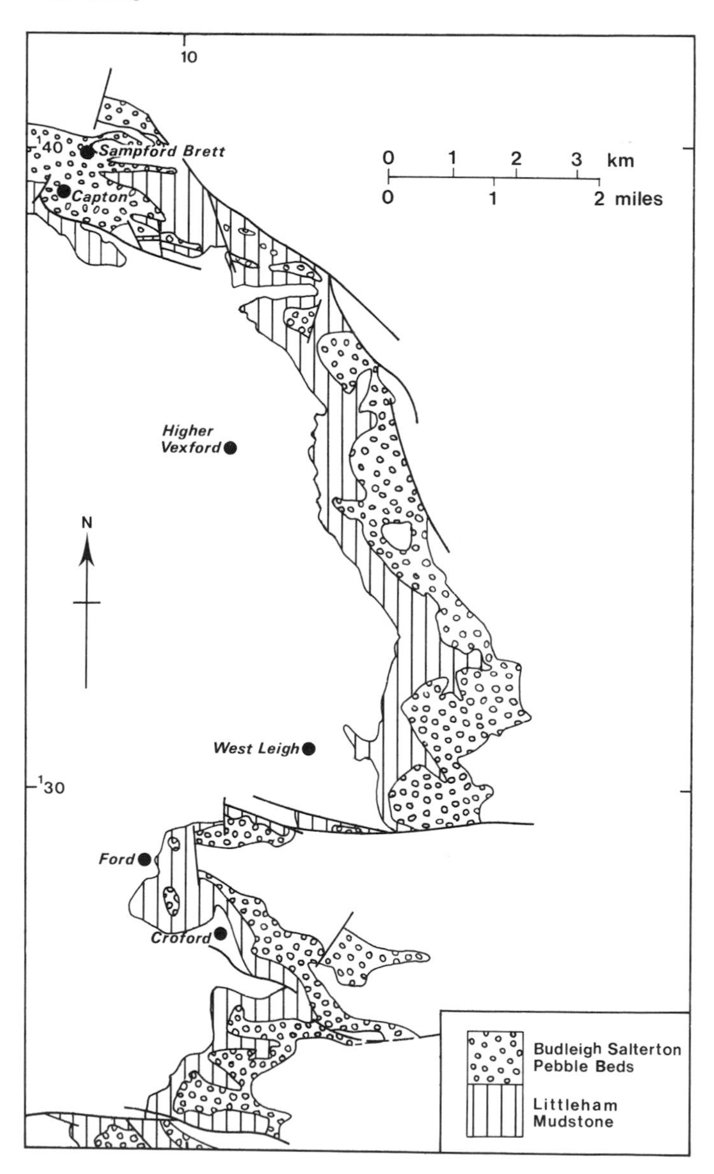

Figure 11 Outcrops of the Littleham Mudstone and the Budleigh Salterton Pebble Beds

Budleigh Salterton Pebble Beds (Figure 11)

Sampford Brett to Ash Priors

Degraded exposures [0770 4025] west of Sampford Brett show pebbles of both Devonian and Carboniferous limestone. Small pits [0807 4006] nearer the village are in 6 m of interbedded sandstones and sandy conglomerates. In a quarry [0902 4026] on the east side of the village, Otter Sandstone is faulted against a succession of boulders and cobbles of Devonian and Carboniferous limestones set in red sand 2.44 m, overlain by red coarse gritty pebbly sandstone 3.66 m, capped by yellow medium-grained sandstone with a few small pebbles 0.45 m. Exposures to the north show beds of small pebbles and coarse grit 1.22 m, about 2.4 m below pebbles cobbles and boulders of Devonian and Carboniferous limestones in red sands 2.13 m [0885 4055], and a 10-m-long face of sandy conglomerates containing bands of smaller pebbles [0892 4071].

The railway cutting [090 408] west of Castle Hill is in the following upward succession at the top of the formation: sandy conglomerate 1.82 m, massive sandstone with small pebbles 0.61 m, band of pebbles 0.15 m, soft sandstone 0.1 m, massive sandstone with small pebbles 0.75 m, soft red and yellow fine-grained sandstone (Otter Sandstone) 2.74 m. Two old quarries [0928 4069; 0930 4061] on Castle Hill show up to 10 m of sandy conglomerates with pebbles up to 0.45 m across. Mr Mitchell has identified the following Viséan fossils from limestone pebbles: *Lithostrotion martini*, a zaphrentoid, *Megachonetes* sp., an orthotetoid, a productoid, *Straparollus* sp., a smooth spiriferoid, *Spirifer* sp. and a fish tooth; he reports that an Arundian age is possible but not certain.

Woolston Quarry [0945 4015] contains the following succession:

	Thickness m
Otter Sandstone	
Sandstone, red and yellow, medium-grained, poorly bedded	4.27
Budleigh Salterton Pebble Beds	
Conglomerates with pebbles up to 25 mm across and subordinate sandstones	1.83
Sandstone, yellow, medium-grained, massive, with some pebbles at base	0.46
Conglomerates with pebbles up to 350 mm across and calcite veins and vugs	6.71
Sandstone, coarse-grained, with scattered pebbles; thin laminated sandstone at base	1.07
Sandstone and sand, coarse-grained; some lamination and cross-lamination; scattered pebbles in upper part	0.97
Sandstone, coarse-grained, gritty, with scattered pebbles	1.14
Conglomerates, locally passing into gritty sandstones	0.91
Sandstone, gritty, with thin calcite veins and a few pebbles	0.30
Conglomerates with pebbles up to 200 mm across	1.52
Sandstone, red	0.30
Conglomerate with pebbles up to 100 mm across	0.30
Sandstone, red, laminated, with a pebbly lens	0.36
Conglomerate with pebbles up to 200 mm across	1.22
Sandstone, red, laminated	0.20
Conglomerate	0.20
Sandstone, red, coarse-grained, cross-laminated at base	0.33
Conglomerate with pebbles up to 300 mm across	1.37

Mr Mitchell reports that limestone pebbles from the basal 3.35 m of the 6.71 m of conglomerates have yielded the following fossils, probably of Arundian age: *Koninckopora inflata*, *Fasciculophyllum* sp., *Lithostrotion martini*, *Siphonophyllia garwoodi?*, *Syringopora* cf. *reticulata*, *Gigantoproductus?* cf.θ, *Megachonetes* sp., an orthotetoid, *Productus?* (sensu stricto), a smooth spiriferoid, and *Syringothyris* sp. Water lying in the quarry suggests that the Littleham Mudstone is not far below. The railway cutting to the north-west is mainly in Otter Sandstone (p. 35).

The pebble beds around Capton contain a good deal of interbedded sandstone. A small knoll immediately south-west of Aller Farm shows 6 m of current-bedded sandstone and conglomerates [0772 3958]. Ussher (1908) recorded 20 ft (6.1 m) of evenly bedded red and greenish-white mottled brecciated sandstone south of Capton, probably in the quarry [0823 3906] now showing 4 m of purple, green and white sandstone and pebbly sandstone; traces of green films may be of malachite.

A prominent east – west ridge south of Woolston shows, at its western end [0872 3976], 3 m of sand with small pebbles overlain by 2 m of pebbly sandstone, and, near its eastern end [0961 3977], 3 m of massive and thickly bedded current-bedded pebbly sandstone. Interbedded conglomerates and sandstones are common in roadsides to the south, and Vellow Quarry [096 390] is in 12 to 14 m of massive conglomerates with subordinate sandstones; pebbles range up to 0.5 m across and include some of Carboniferous Limestone. Another large quarry [097 387], between Lower Vellow and Vellow, shows 17 m of coarse conglomerate with subordinate current-bedded sandstone. A nearby roadside exposure [0956 3883] shows traces of marl in pebbly sandstone near the base of the formation. An 'island' of pebble beds rising above the alluvial plain north-north-east of Vellow contains an old pit [0983 3908] in 5 m of interbedded conglomerates and current-bedded sandstones. Several small hills near and east of Newton mark outliers of pebbly rocks on Littleham Mudstone, but only one contains a good exposure [1151 3841], where 4 m of coarse conglomerates have been worked for limestone pebbles.

Roadside exposures [1210 3711] near Heddon Oak are of subrounded and subangular pebbles in sands of mixed grade. The lane from Leigh Farm to Crowcombe cuts through similar friable rocks [1250 3643], as does the West Somerset Railway to the west [128 360] and south [131 357] of Roebuck Farm. Pits [126 351] west of Heathfield Farm, now overgrown, were noted by Ussher (1908) to expose 25 ft (7.6 m) of gravelly material, with angular and subangular stones of various sizes in reddish brown earthy sand and loam, the only traces of bedding being three lenticular bands of earthy sand.

The railway cutting [1378 3417] south-east of Crowcombe Station cuts through pebbly sands at the top of the formation. A small bank [1372 3434] at the station is composed of unsorted, unbedded, soft stony sand, and Ussher (1908) noted the presence hereabouts of subangular sandstone fragments, of various (small) sizes, set in reddish brown loamy sand.

An old quarry [1420 3298] at Coursley is in more competent strata, 6.5 m mainly of red conglomerates, and another [1477 3247], at Nethercot and near the top of the formation, is in 7.5 m of massive and thickly bedded red conglomerates with some sandstones and a few thin marly bands. A railway cutting [147 322] to the south is in 10 m of massive and thickly bedded calcareous conglomerates with some interbedded calcareous sandstone, and an old pit [1476 3209] alongside the railway shows calcareous conglomerate 1.1 m, overlain by calcareous sandstone 0.2 m, capped by calcareous conglomerate 0.8 m.

A railway cutting [1505 3185] north of Combe Florey is in sandy conglomerates and pebbly sandstone, and one of several quarries in nearby woodland [1498 3160] shows hard, massive, calcareous conglomerate 5 m, overlain by calcareous sandstone with pebbles 1 m, capped by 2.5 m of rock that ranges from conglomerate to pebbly sandstone. Two old quarries south-east of the village lie at the top of the formation: one [1524 3108] shows weathered calcareous conglomerate, locally sandy, and the other [1553 3108] 6 m of massive conglomerates with friable red sandstone at their base and cut by vertical joints trending east-north-east and north-north-west.

Extensive overgrown quarries [143 304] in Ash Wood show up to 15 m of calcareous sandy conglomerates, in one place [1429 3043] capped by 3 m of bedded calcareous sandstone and pebbly sandstone of the Otter Sandstone. Three old quarries in the basal part of the formation to the west of Denbury Farm expose the following successions: massive conglomerate with pebbles up to 0.3 m across 3 m, overlain by current-bedded pebbly sandstone 1.1 m, and conglomerate with generally smaller pebbles and a little interbedded sandstone 5 m [1345 2958]; conglomerate 3.5 m, overlain by calcareous sandstone 0.9 m, pebbly sandstone 1.7 m, conglomerate 2.5 m, calcareous sandstone 3 m, and conglomerate 4 m [1364 2953]; and 15 m of interbedded sandy conglomerate and current-bedded pebbly sands [1385 2942]. Two quarries east of the farm lie near or at the top of the formation: one [1453 2965] shows 20 m of interbedded conglomerates and current-bedded pebbly sandstones, and the other [1466 2947], conglomerates and sandstones 4 m, overlain by conglomerates 3.5 m, current-bedded pebbly sandstone 1 m, and conglomerates 3 m. The conglomerates contain many large limestone pebbles.

Chapel Leigh to Cobhay Farm

Small patches of pebble beds south of Chapel Leigh contain old pits, in one of which [1289 2911] 1 m of pebbly sandstone is overlain by 5 m of conglomerate; in another [1237 2942], 8 m of conglomerates with interbedded pebbly sandstones show traces of faults trending east-north-east. Pits to the south of Hoccombe show 4 m [1158 2943] and 8 m [1147 2928] of thickly bedded conglomerates cut by vertical joints trending north and east. Hard massive conglomerates quarried [1103 2945] at Burrow Hill Farm are exposed to a thickness of 15 m and contain pebbles, many of which are of limestone, up to 0.4 m across.

Gould's Quarry [105 294] is a large disused working in which about 20 m of massive and thickly bedded conglomerates comprise pebbles of limestone, sandstone and quartz-pebble conglomerate set in a calcareous ferruginous sandy matrix. The lowest 2 m were those mainly worked for lime; they are overlain by thin sandstone, and further thin sandstones occur towards the top of the face. Another large quarry [098 292], now wooded, extends across much of the pebble beds outlier that caps Tipnoller Hill, north-east of Ford. About 20 m of massive and thickly bedded conglomerate are exposed, with pebbles of sandstone, limestone and quartz; the largest pebbles occur in the lower beds. A second outlier forms Castle Hill, east of Wiveliscombe, where 20 m of massive and thickly bedded conglomerates comprise large pebbles of limestone and sandstone, and smaller pebbles of quartz, set in calcareous sandstone. The upper beds are thinner and contain smaller pebbles, and the quarry faces carry extensive calcareous films.

A wooded scarp marks the pebble beds outcrop from north of Croford House to the valley north of Milverton. Densely overgrown excavations in and near Brimley Quarry [111 276] show up to 20 m of conglomerates with interbedded sandstones up to 1 m thick.

Plate 4 Budleigh Salterton Pebble Beds, Holywell Quarries, Preston Bowyer.
Conglomerates near the top of the formation are interbedded with current-bedded sandstones (A 13837)

Holywell Quarries are overgrown in the west [125 271], but farther east, show sandy rubbly conglomerate 4 m, overlain by hard massive conglomerate 3.5 m, pebbly sandstone 0.3 m, current-bedded sandstone with pebbly lenses 1.1 m, massive conglomerate 3 m, current-bedded sandstone 0 to 1 m, rubbly conglomerate 3.5 m [1270 2703], and conglomerates with interbedded thin sandstones 6 m, overlain by current-bedded pebbly sandstone 1 to 2 m, and conglomerates 32 m [1282 2698]. The pebbles are of sandstone, limestone and quartz.

Haywood Quarry [1206 2655] contains conglomerates with thin sandstones 4 m, overlain by current-bedded sandstone 1 m, and conglomerates 3 m. Ford Bridge Quarry [1250 2635] is now partly filled, but Ussher (1908) recorded a 30-ft (9.1-m) section comprising 18 beds of conglomerate, with pebbles of limestone, sandstone and quartz; the beds were thicker, over 5 ft (1.5 m) on average, in the lower part of the face. Near the entrance to the quarry the junction of conglomerates on red marls is exposed [1256 2624].

About 12 m of conglomerates, with interbedded sandstones up to 1 m thick, have been worked in Park Kiln Quarry [116 264], alongside the Wiveliscombe road north-west of Milverton. Some slipping of the beds has occurred, which Ussher (1908) thought might be due to undermining of the face in search of limestone. Poole's Kiln Quarry [104 258], near Farthing's Farm, shows similar effects. Removal of large limestone pebbles from the lower part of the face has brought about collapse along vertical joints. Cave-like fissures are present, probably the result more of movement than of solution, although the 20 m of conglomerates exposed are calcareous and commonly covered by limy films.

Conglomerates are exposed at Lower Lovelinch [112 249]. Old quarries east of the farm are at or near the top of the formation; one [1150 2485] shows massive conglomerates 10 m, overlain by pebbly sandstone, possibly Otter Sandstone, 2 m; another [1140 2471] exposes massive conglomerates with pebbles up to 0.3 m across, 10 m, overlain by pebbly sandstone, possibly Otter Sandstone, 0.9 m, the rocks cleft by a large north–south fissure; a third quarry [1141 2465] is in 7 m of massive conglomerates with pebbles up to 0.3 m across, overlain by flaggy sandstone with pebbles (Otter Sandstone) 1 m. Both conglomerates and sandstones are calcareous.

Partially grassed-over old pits [0912 2461] to the south of Cobhay Farm show up to 4 m of conglomerates with pebbles up to 0.3 m across.

Holford

Red sandy conglomerates or breccias exposed [1554 4123] in the stream below Holford contain fragments of local Devonian rocks and are thought to be Budleigh Salterton Pebble Beds. They are faulted against Devonian sandstone and tuff to the south-west. About 7 m of sandy conglomerate crop out alongside the stream to the north-east [1561 4128].

Otter Sandstone (Figure 12)

Williton to Bishop's Lydeard

Williton Quarry [0790 4065], now largely obscured, shows 7 m of fine-grained sandstone, brick-red with yellowish white patches, locally friable, poorly bedded or massive, with a few scattered quartz pebbles, and bands and lenses of small pebbles and soft sandstone pellets. Union Quarry [0832 4066] exposes 2.4 m of mottled red and yellow sandstone with scattered pebbles, overlain by 0.6 m of pebbly sandstone. At Sampford Rocks [0861 4027] the road cuts through massive red and yellow mottled sandstone with scattered pebbles of quartz and sandstone 3.8 m, overlain by sandy marls and sands 1.1 m, massive red and yellow mottled fine-grained sandstone 1.5 m, coarse sand with bands of small pebbles 0.3 m, and fine-grained sandstone 0.3 m. A small quarry [0885 4039] to the east is in 4.3 m of poorly bedded mottled red and yellow fine-grained sandstone; the rock is colour banded in places, locally friable, and contains small pellets of red sandstone and a few lenses of pebbly coarse sand.

A railway cutting [092 403] east of Sampford Brett displays the following section:

	Thickness m
OTTER SANDSTONE	
Sandstone, red and yellow, fine-grained, soft and poorly bedded	1.83
Sandstone, coarse-grained, with pebbles up to 40 mm across	0.46
Sandstone, red and yellow, fine-grained, soft and nodular	0.76
Sandstone, purplish yellow, massive, with small pebbles	1.68
Sandstone, red and yellow, rubbly	1.07
Sandstone, coarse-grained, massive, with few pebbles	0.41
Sandstone, red and yellow, soft; pebbly lenses near base	1.52
Sandstone, buff-white, coarse-grained, pebbly, with bands and lenses of soft yellow sandstone	2.44
Section obscured	3.05
Sandstone, red and yellow, massive	0.15
Sandstone, red, rubbly	0.15
Sandstone, coarse-grained, with pebbles up to 50 mm across	0.86
Sandstone, coarse-grained, friable, with pebbles up to 150 mm across	2.13
Sandstone, massive, with a few pebbles	0.46
BUDLEIGH SALTERTON PEBBLE BEDS	
Sandstone, red, coarse-grained, with pebbles up to 370 mm across	1.83

A small pit [0963 4011] to the east of Woolston Quarry shows the basal beds of the Otter Sandstone as massive yellow medium-grained sandstone with a few quartz pebbles 0.9 m, overlain by poorly bedded red, yellow and grey soft marly sandstone 0.86 m, and massive red sandstone with bands and lenses of small pebbles and a few larger pebbles near the base 0.76 m.

A small faulted outlier at Aller Farm, north-west of Capton, contains an exposure [0790 3974] of 5 m of thickly bedded and massive friable sandstone, locally calcareous, with scattered pebbles, and cut by steep joints trending 030°. A second outlier of pebbly sand caps a rise [091 392] north of Vellow Wood Farm, but the distinction in this area between sandy conglomerates and overlying pebbly sands is arbitrary. Buff fine-grained sandstones crop out alongside the railway [1052 3857] west of Newton, and friable yellow and brown sandstone in a nearby lane [1068 3848].

A large quarry [135 363] just south of Lawford is now much overgrown but shows 9 m of thickly bedded and massive reddish brown calcareous sandstone weathered to a nodular appearance. Ussher (1908) saw 12 to 15 m of beds comprising an upward succession of grey corrugated calcareous sandstone with gravelly lenses, red and buff mottled sandstone, rubbly sandrock fractured cuboidally, and evenly bedded red sandstone. H. H. Thomas (*in* Ussher, 1908) described dull red calcareous sandstone from west of Crowcombe as containing grains of chert and other siliceous sediments.

The railway south-west of Rich's Holford cuts through 6 m of sand, sandrock and thickly bedded nodular calcareous sandstone [141 337]. Old quarries on the north-east side of the line show 8 m

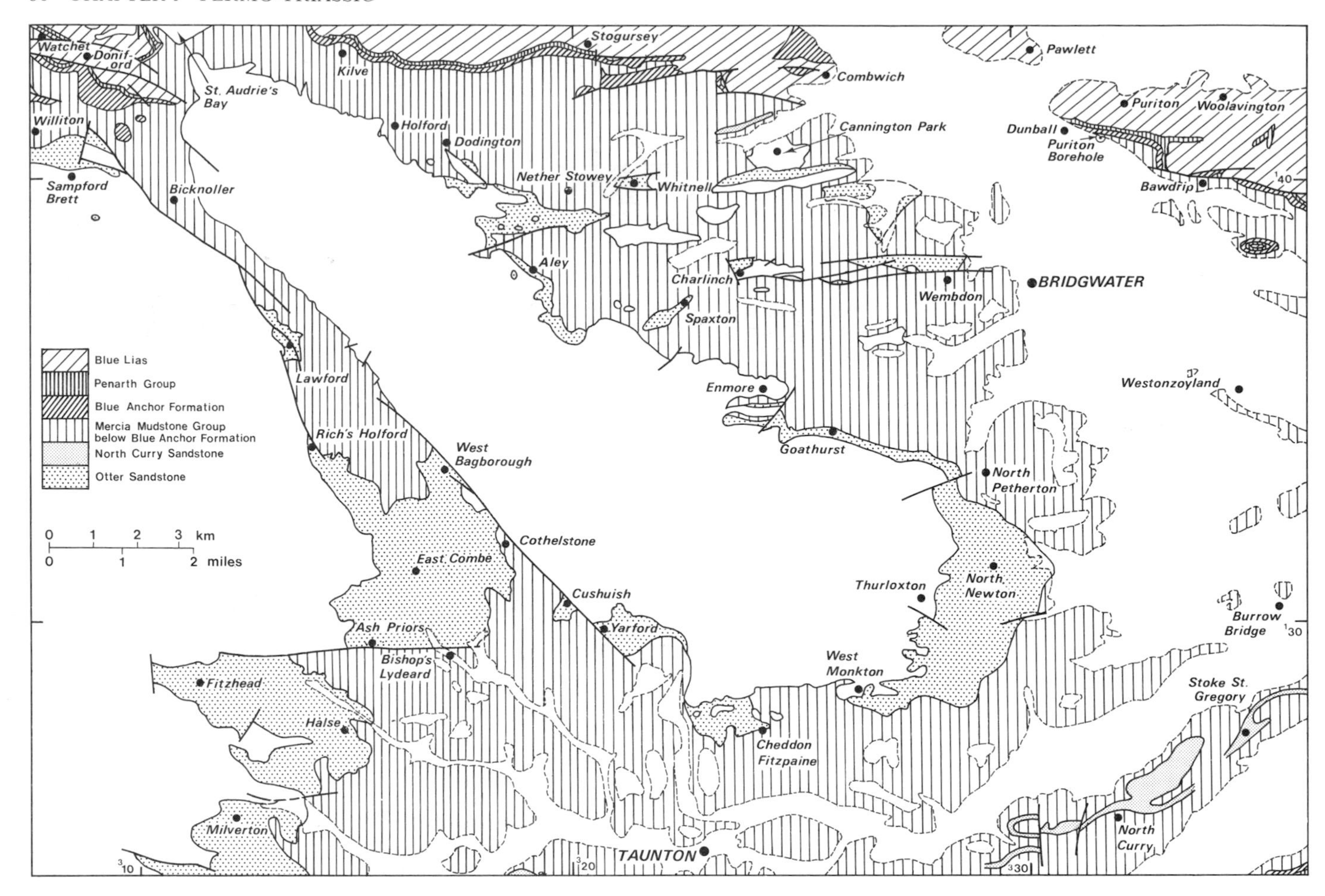

Figure 12 Outcrops of the Otter Sandstone, Mercia Mudstone Group, Penarth Group and Blue Lias

of thickly bedded sandrock and calcareous sandstone [1429 3362] and 6.5 m of thickly bedded red, buff and grey nodular calcareous sandstone [1453 3344]. Current-bedded red sandrock and calcareous sandstone crop out in another railway cutting [1456 3310] to the south.

Large quarries [157 323] at Yarde Farm show 5 m of brown and red sandstone with some sandrock and a little soft sand, the difference being due to the distribution of calcareous cement. A small pit [162 321] farther east, now filled, exposed 6 m of calcareous sandstone and sandy limestone when seen by Ussher (1908). Red and purple sands with hard calcareous sandstones crop out in roadsides at West Bagborough.

Sand and sandrock with beds of calcareous sandstone are seen in roadsides at East Combe [161 311]. Ussher (1908) noted grey, purple and red sandy limestones and sandrock in a quarry at the crossroads [167 316] north-east of the village; no trace remains. Perhaps he was referring to a quarry [1652 3114] east of the hamlet; it too has been obliterated. A lane north of Watts House cuts through red and brown sand and thickly bedded sandrock with thin bands of marl and silty marl [164 302].

A large quarry [166 300] just north-west of Bishops Lydeard marks the digging of building stone for, among other uses, restoring the village church. Sands, sandrock and calcareous sandstone are extensively exposed, but degraded and overgrown. Ussher (1908) examined the (disused) quarry in 1906; he noted brecciated sandstone, overlain by reddish brown coarse-grained sandstone containing small fragments of quartz and slate and cut by a network of calcareous veins, rubbly sandstone and sandrock, red, brown and green mottled sandstone, and shaly sandstone with marl. H. H. Thomas (*in* Ussher, 1908) described dull red calcareous sandstone, with grains closely cemented, probably from this quarry; plentiful spangles of white mica were noted, as was secondary anatase growing on ilmenite and leucoxene. The junction between Otter Sandstone, red, brown, yellow and green sand and calcareous sandstone, and red Mercia Mudstone may be located [1628 2947] alongside the railway west of Bishops Lydeard (p. 27).

A roadside exposure [1483 3012] north-west of Ash Priors shows 1.6 m of current-bedded sandstone, and outcrops in the village comprise 4 m of calcareous sandstone with scattered small pebbles and marly bands [1513 2951] and 3 m of calcareous sandstone with scattered pebbles up to 100 mm across [1521 2948].

Fitzhead to Bickleigh Farm

Sand and sandrock in roadsides [112 289] north-west of Fitzhead contain scattered small pebbles. Similar exposures in the village show 2 m of sand and calcareous sandrock [1131 2847] and 3 m of sandrock with marly bands and ramifying iron oxide [1135 2835]. About 2 to 2.5 m of nodular calcareous sandstone are exposed in roadsides [124 287] north-east of Fitzhead. A small quarry [1256 2780] at Dean Farm, near the base of the formation, shows current-bedded sandstone with scattered pebbles 2 m, separated by a lens of pebbly sandstone 0 to 0.5 m, from overlying sandstone with scattered pebbles 1 m.

About 3.5 m of calcareous sandstone, with a few pebbly patches, are exposed in a roadside pit [1336 2769] west-south-west of Halse, and up to 2 m of massive red sandrock, locally current-bedded, in roadsides in and near the village. A quarry [1370 2737] in the

Plate 5 Otter Sandstone, Bishop's Lydeard.

Calcareous sandstone, worked for building stone, overlies friable sandrock (A 13843)

valley south-south-west of Halse shows conglomerates of the Budleigh Salterton Pebble Beds overlain by pebbly sandstone 2 m, and current-bedded sandrock with scattered pebbles 6 m.

Scattered exposures of red sandrock and calcareous sandstone, locally with a few small pebbles, occur alongside roads west-north-west of Preston Bowyer. Road cuttings in the village show thinly interbedded calcareous sandstone and micaceous siltstone [1318 2649], 5 m of current-bedded sandrock with marly partings and thin pebbly lenses [1331 2643], and 5.5 m of locally pebbly sandrock [1335 2642]. H. H. Thomas (*in* Ussher, 1980) examined red calcareous sandstone from Preston Bowyer and reported that many of the grains were of sedimentary rocks.

Milverton contains several road cuttings in Otter Sandstone. In Mill Lane 2 m of current-bedded sandrock [1227 2605] overlie silty marl [1226 2607], and other traces of marl occur in the lower sandstones thereabouts. Butts Way traverses sand and sandrock, and at its lower end [1191 2568] 3 m of red current-bedded calcareous sandstone, weathered to a nodular appearance, contain thin beds of soft sand. Calcareous sandstone with a few pebbly bands crops out alongside Sand Street nearby [1194 2562]. Ussher (1908) recorded locally pebbly calcareous sandstone beneath near-white and pale red sandrock at Houndsmoor [126 254]. Old pits [108 244] east-south-east of High Lovelinch show traces of silty and sandy marl in the lower beds of the formation, and ponds [120 245] and surface rubble in an orchard to the west of Baghay Farm suggest the presence of thin red marls at a slightly higher stratigraphic level. Roadside exposures at the western end of the orchard show 3.5 m of sandstone and pebbly sandstone, generally calcareous [1162 2481], and 4 m of current-bedded sandstone and calcareous sandstone with pebbly bands and lenses [1165 2472].

Cushuish to Cheddon Fitzpaine

A roadside quarry [196 302] south of Cushuish is mainly in massive and thickly bedded clean friable sandstone, generally pale buff but locally red, up to 4.5 m thick; traces of current bedding occur, and reddish brown sandrock with calcareous bands is exposed in the north-east corner of the pit. Ussher (1908) noted sandy marls and shaly sandstone at the top of the face, and considered them to be basal 'Keuper Marl' (Mercia Mudstone Group). The southerly road through Cushuish cuts through 4.5 m of massive and thickly bedded red and cream sandrock [197 304].

Quarries at Yarford, near the top of the formation, show 2 m of massive and thickly bedded sandstone [2033 2991] and a 4-m face of buff and white sandrock overlain by massive red calcareous sandstone [2036 2986]. Nodular red calcareous sandstone with sandy limestone crops out alongside the road at and south of Tarr Farm [2146 3002 to 2141 2991], and 1.5 m of massive and thickly bedded sandstone at the road junction [2140 2965] to the south.

A lane [2308 2740] east of Pyrland Hall affords an overgrown section in sands and calcareous sandstone, and similar strata up to 1 m thick crop out alongside a road to the east [2355 2755].

Holford to Cannington

A streamside exposure [1548 4118] below Holford shows Devonian slates overlain by sandstones that are locally marly but in places pebbly, and are thought to lie near the top of the Otter Sandstone; 180 m to the north-east [1563 4129] red sandstones that appear to overlie pebbly rocks are thought to be basal Otter Sandstone. Ussher (1908) recorded a patch of sands and gritty sands west of Holford [about 153 410].

Roadside pits [176 403] south-east of Dodington are in massive and thickly bedded sandrock. Another [1744 3984], to the south, shows much-degraded faces of purple speckled fine- to medium-grained sandstone.

The road north-east of Friarn traverses thinly bedded sandstones and red marly sandstones [1805 3868] and sandrock [1818 3882] at the top of the formation. At 450 m south of St Mary's Church, Nether Stowey, 5 m of friable thickly bedded red-stained cream sandstone and sandrock are exposed in an old quarry [1964 3920]. Farther east, at Stowey Rocks [2029 3900], 7 m of thickly bedded and massive rusty brown medium-grained sandstones have been worked for building stone. Exposures just east of Stowey Rocks show 2 m of massive and thickly bedded brown sandstone beneath red marl of the Mercia Mudstone Group in an old pit [2047 3905], and 2.5 m of thickly bedded reddish brown sandstone in a roadside [2053 3916].

Red and grey medium-grained sandstones, thickly and thinly bedded, crop out in roadsides at Whitnell [2134 3997; 2142 3977; 2153 3977].

Two boreholes on the southern side of the Swang Farm Carboniferous inlier, Swang Farm No. 1 [2295 3891] and No. 2 [2296 3891], proved Otter Sandstone at a little over 10 m depth.

About 1 to 1.25 m of thin, conglomeratic beds resting on Palaeozoic strata at 17.17 m and 18.44 m respectively probably belong to the Otter Sandstone rather than to the Budleigh Salterton Pebble Beds as suggested by Whittaker (1978).

Roadsides south-west of Cannington Park show horizontal red sandstone [2409 3992] and 1.5 to 2.4 m of purplish red friable fine-grained sandstone [2411 4002]. A pond [2461 3992] to the east contains large blocks, possibly tipped, of red pebbly sandstone, and roadsides [2487 3997] show red sandstone and purple pebbly sandstone. H. H. Thomas (*in* Ussher, 1908) described non-calcareous sand and sandstone from the Cannington area.

Aley to Spaxton and Wembdon

Red, grey and green sandstones, commonly friable, crop out by the roadside in Plainsfield [1947 3675; 1951 3667; 1957 3665]. Sandrock has been dug farther east [1994 3639], and medium-bedded red sandstone [2003 3671] underlies red marls at the top of the formation. H. H. Thomas (*in* Ussher, 1908) described sand from east of Plainsfield as feebly cemented, non-calcareous and fine-grained with baryte probably acting as a cementing medium.

About 3 m of red sands have been dug [2162 3662] south-east of Absley Farm, and similar sands with beds of calcareous sandstone crop out [2192 3686] alongside a road to the north-east. A quarry [226 372] on the north-eastern edge of Spaxton shows 3 to 4 m of thickly bedded reddish brown calcareous sandstone.

Red sandstone is exposed in a footpath [2362 3805] north-west of Charlinch, and thickly bedded calcareous sandstone and red pebbly sandstone by the roadside [2412 3765] to the south-east. Farther east along the same road, in a hedge bank within a cottage garden [2487 3766], 2 m of massive and thickly bedded red pebbly sandstone lie near the top of the formation. EAE

Field fragments immediately to the west of Clayhill House [262 376] provide the only evidence of a small patch of Otter Sandstone. In the fault-bounded area north of Wembdon, field fragments suggest that much breccia is present in the western part. In a quarry [2703 3815] near Sandford Farm reddish brown fine-grained sandstone with pale brown irregularly disposed patches of calcareous sandstone apparently rests on an angular breccia containing fragments of slate, sandstone, quartz and some limestone, the last possibly of Cannington Park type. An old quarry [2778 3805] 800 m to the east contains 3.05 m of hard reddish brown and pale brown fine-grained sandstones, calcareous and with lenses of angular breccia, overlain by 2 m of horizontal pale buff, soft, fine-grained sandstone. An old flooded quarry [2825 3788] at Wembdon contains 3.2 m of reddish brown and pale buff fine-grained sandstones, calcareous in places and apparently resting on breccia with a reddish brown sand matrix and thin sand courses.

Enmore – North Newton – West Monkton

A silage pit [2335 3456] at Smocombe Farm is in 3 m of buff and red sands. Large doggers of red calcareous sandstone occur at the foot of the face. Up to 3 m of sands and calcareous sandstones are exposed in and alongside roads and tracks to the east [2375 3449; 2377 3455; 2393 3450].

Around Goathurst surface debris suggests that breccias make up a large proportion of the Otter Sandstone, and boulders of indurated breccio-conglomerate are found in a field [263 340] to the east of the village. At North Petherton, however, the sequence appears to consist predominantly of sandstone, and 3.5 m of horizontal greyish green calcareous fine-grained sandstone were seen in a quarry [2836 3348] north-west of the village. A large old sandpit [281 326] west of North Petherton shows soft red fine-grained sandstone with thin calcareous bands some of which are greyish green. To the south, towards Shearston, red sandy breccias near the base of the formation crop out [2830 3122]. At Shearston itself [2824 3655] 3.85 m of reddish brown fine-grained sandstone with pale buff calcareous sandstone bands are seen.

An exploratory borehole [2955 3196] for the M5 motorway south-south-east of North Petherton provided the following succession:

	Thickness m	*Depth* m
Top soil	0.20	0.20
Otter Sandstone		
Sand, reddish brown, silty and clayey (weathered sandstone)	1.80	2.00
Sandstone, reddish brown and grey, fine-grained	3.00	5.00
Sandstone, reddish brown, moderately strong; occasionally greyish green and fine-grained, with irregular calcitic cemenattion and some poorly cemented layers	5.90	10.90
Sandstone, reddish brown, fine-grained, moderately weak, with a little calcitic cementation and a few poorly cemented layers, tending towards siltstone in the basal 1.4 m	7.30	18.20

A roadside cutting [294 309] to the west of North Newton reveals 6.2 m of pink and buff calcareous fine-grained sandstones with soft reddish brown marly lenses and beds. The sandstones are honeycomb weathered. At the centre of the village [2989 3105] 2.2 m of horizontal red fine-grained sandstone with irregular pale buff harder calcareous bands are exposed, and south-west of the village [2922 3051] thinly bedded brownish red fine-grained sandstone with thin cream calcareous bands is seen.

A motorway borehole [2909 3078] gave the following section:

	Thickness m	*Depth* m
Top soil	0.50	0.50
Otter Sandstone		
Sand, reddish brown, fine- to medium-grained, clayey and silty	2.50	3.00
Sandstone, reddish brown, moderately weak; in places fine-grained or tending towards a breccia consisting of angular fragments of slate and quartz within a sandstone matrix	8.55	11.55

Three boreholes [2877 3010; 2887 3039; 2893 3039] between North Newton and Thurloxton reached Morte Slates beneath Otter Sandstone with a basal breccia. The sequence in the third borehole [2893 3039] is representative:

	Thickness m	*Depth* m
Top soil	0.60	0.60
Otter Sandstone		
Sand, reddish brown, fine- to medium-grained, slightly clayey	2.40	3.00
Sandstone, reddish brown, occasionally greyish green, fine- to medium-grained	2.40	5.40
Sandstone, reddish brown to pale green, fine- to medium-grained, with irregular calcitic cementation and a little dolomite	8.35	13.75
Breccia, moderately strong, consisting of angular fragments of slate and quartz in a calcitic sandstone matrix	1.25	15.00

	Thickness m	Depth m
MORTE SLATES		
Siltstone, strongly cleaved, micaceous; cleavage dips at 70°	3.00	18.00

At Tuckerton a roadside exposure [2974 3005] shows 2.25 m of brownish red soft fine-grained sandstones with honeycomb-weathered pale buff and greenish grey fine-grained calcareous sandstone in beds and nodular stringers. Scattered small exposures around West Newton, include 3 m of reddish brown nodular sandstone [2886 2967], 2.2 m of pale grey and cream fine-grained sandstone [2886 2948] and 2.2 m of rubbly reddish brown sandstone [2864 2885]. A motorway borehole [2834 2912] 0.5 km west of West Newton provided the following record:

	Thickness m	Depth m
Top soil	0.30	0.30
OTTER SANDSTONE		
Sand, reddish brown, slightly clayey	1.95	2.25
Sandstone, reddish brown to greyish green, fine- to medium-grained	1.45	3.70
Sandstone, reddish brown, locally mottled greyish green or buff, fine- to medium-grained with irregular calcitic cementation	3.00	6.70
Sandstone, reddish brown and greyish green, fine- to medium-grained, with irregular calcitic cementation; a few layers contain angular inclusions of slate and there are some dolomite-coated fissures	3.50	10.20
Sandstone, as above but with very little calcitic cementation, and with angular slate and quartz fragments comprising a breccia in places	4.05	14.25

Evidence that much breccia is present in the sequence around Walford House is provided by the field fragments.

Two small outliers of Otter Sandstone occur one on each side of Coombe Bottom, on the Morte Slates; the western one [267 293] is based on the presence of field fragments of red sandstone but in the eastern one 2 m of horizontal red rubbly sandstone are exposed [2700 2960] and 0.2 m of sandstone is seen adjacent to underlying Morte Slates [2688 2956] in small exposures in pasture fields. At West Monkton 3.5 m of reddish brown sandstone are seen at the roadside [2627 2820]. BJW

Mercia Mudstone Group

Watchet to St Audrie's Bay

The following succession in the Blue Anchor Formation is exposed on the foreshore [0770 4355] near Watchet. Sequences identified by the same capital letters in this and the succession on p. 39–40 correlate with each other. The section is given in greater detail by Whittaker and Green (1983).

	Thickness m
Marl and shale, greenish grey, commonly blocky, locally silty	2.16
Siltstone and silty marl, greenish grey, shaly near base	1.14
Strata mainly obscured	3.05
Marl, greenish grey, shaly and hard	0.69
C Marl, interbedded grey and dark grey, blocky	3.58
Marl, greyish green, grey and greenish buff, locally shaly or silty, a few thin siltstones and mudstones	5.53
B Marl, interbedded hard green and dark grey, disturbed	6.25
Marl, banded green and grey	1.83
Siltstone, greenish grey, hard, laminated with thin marl	0.76
A Marl, grey and green, with a thin red band about midway, laminated and silty in the lower part	1.92
Marl, green and grey	3.03
Marl, mainly pale green, some greyish green, locally silty and hard, laminated at top	5.91

The bottom 5.91 m are 'Tea Green Marl', and the strata above are 'Grey Marl'.

From Watchet to the Doniford Bay Fault [0786 4336] the coastal exposures show about 40 m of red marls with green siltstone bands at the top of the Group. Dark grey mudstones, green blocky mudstones and greyish green siltstones in a cave [0777 4340] are an example of 'Grey Marl' type lithologies below the Blue Anchor Formation.

An old pit [0980 4196] to the south of Rydon shows 1.22 m of grey marl.

The following succession in the Blue Anchor Formation is exposed in the cliff west of The Slip [1053 4314] at St Audrie's Bay (see also Whittaker and Green, 1983).

	Thickness m
Siltstone, grey, hard, calcareous and laminated in the upper part, with wisps of marl	0.45
Marl, dark grey, blocky, with black shale	0.43
Siltstone, grey, hard, with subordinate black shale and marl	0.34
Marl, grey, on black shale; hard siltstone at base	0.46
Marl, greenish grey, locally dark grey, commonly blocky, locally silty or shaly; black shale at base; top 2.06 m contain *Gyrolepis*, *Hybodus* cf. *cloacinus*, '*Sargodon*' and '*Sphaerodus*'-type teeth, fish fragments, gastropod fragments and *Mytilus?*	3.27
C Marl, dark grey or black, shaly, with lens of silty marl	1.60
Marl, greyish green, grey or black, locally shaly, silty, blocky or laminated	2.03
Siltstone, grey, hard, with black marl band midway	0.14
Marl, grey or greenish grey, with subordinate black shale, commonly blocky, locally laminated	4.28
B Marl, green and buff, blocky, with thin hard pinkish buff and grey lenticular siltstone in upper part	4.95
Marl, greenish grey, blocky with interbedded black shale	1.07
Marl, banded greenish grey and buff, blocky with hard pinkish buff siltstone about midway	1.57

	Thickness m
A Marl, green, blocky, with abundant cavities; thin red band near top, hard greenish grey siltstone at base	0.91
Marl, dark greenish grey but green at top, blocky, interbedded with dark grey shaly marl	2.64
Marl, green, locally greenish grey, blocky, silty in places, locally laminated	5.19

The bottom 5.19 m are 'Tea Green Marl'; the overlying beds are 'Grey Marl'. Bristow and Etheridge (1873) recorded fish scales, annelid burrows and '*Gervillia*' *praecursor* from a bed 1.52 m below the top of the section.

The preceding succession is continued in the cliffs in St Audrie's Bay [1055 4312 to 1200 4375], which show about 69 m of strata below the Blue Anchor Formation. The section below is given in greater detail by Whittaker and Green (1983):

	Thickness m
Mudstone, red above, green and harder below	0.81
Siltstone, greenish grey, massive above and laminated below; siltstone nodules in basal 0.02 m	0.24
Mudstone, green, greyish green and red; commonly blocky, locally fissile and shaly; a few silty wisps and partings	9.23
Siltstone, greenish grey, hard, with cavities	0.28
Mudstone, red, green and grey; locally blocky, locally silty with a few siltstone laminae	2.83
Siltstone, grey, hard	0.11
Mudstone, green and grey; some blocky, some fissile	1.24
Siltstone, grey, hard and poorly laminated	0.41
Mudstone, green, greenish grey and red; silty at top; locally blocky	1.94
Siltstone, greenish grey, very hard	0.13
Mudstone, green and red, locally blocky, locally silty with a few siltstone wisps	2.17
Siltstone, green and greyish green, commonly laminated and locally blocky, interbedded with red, purple and green mudstone, locally faintly laminated	1.37
Mudstone, red and green; locally blocky, locally slightly fissile	2.95
Siltstone, green and red	0.69
Mudstone, red with green patches, green mottled at base	3.14
Siltstone, green and hard, interbedded with red and green mudstone	1.36
Mudstone, red and green; locally blocky, rarely laminated, rarely silty	4.03
Siltstone, green, hard and marly	0.20
Mudstone, red and green; locally blocky, locally with 'fish eyes'	3.16
Siltstone, green, laminated	0.08
Mudstone, green and red; locally silty and blocky	0.76
Siltstone, green, laminated in lower part	0.15
Mudstone, red and green; commonly blocky, 'fish eyes' locally, silty in places	21.04
Siltstone, green, hard and sandy; red mottles near base	0.22
Mudstone, red, mottled near top, blocky	0.20
Siltstone, green with red mottles, hard and sandy	0.09
Mudstone, red, blocky, with small 'fish eyes'	0.41
Sandstone, green, hard and silty	0.04
Mudstone, mainly red, some green; commonly blocky, locally silty or sandy, green 'fish eyes' in lower part	9.55

The Blue Anchor Formation is taken to commence above the highest prominent red band in the section. Dark grey mudstones, 0.06 m and 0.13 m thick at 13.39 m and 13.79 m respectively below that level, resemble lithologies in the overlying Blue Anchor Formation and are the lowest beds in the section to yield indigenous Triassic miospores (Warrington, 1974, 1978). An assemblage of reworked late Permian palynomorphs has been recorded from 16.84 m below the top of the Blue Anchor Formation (Warrington, 1970).

Bicknoller to West Bagborough

The A358 road near Bicknoller cuts through red and greyish green marls [1116 3882]. About 1.5 m of red marl with a few green bands and patches were noted in a newly dug grave in Crowcombe churchyard [1407 3673]. Sand occurs with red and green marl in the lane [1440 3660] from Crowcombe to Little Quantock Farm, and 3.5 m of red marl with pale greyish green spots and showing conchoidal fracture in a lane [1440 3627] west-south-west of the farm. In the farmyard at Flaxpool [1404 3548] 3 m of red marl, locally greyish green, are overlain by 1 m of stony clay Head.

Roadside exposures [1431 3408 to 1447 3403] at Rich's Holford show red and greenish grey marl. Similar rocks near Stockham Cross [e.g. 1578 3415] are of locally silty marls showing conchoidal fracture, and red marls with greyish green spots have been dug farther east [1611 3430; 1633 3427]. Silty marls near the base of the formation at Shopnoller [1644 3289] are purple and red with pale green spots and with thin purple siltstones.

Cothelstone – Taunton – Stoke St Gregory

Red and green silty marls [1793 2992] near the base of the formation at East Lydeard contain a little interbedded sandrock. Marly debris from a gas main trench to the south showed a little sandstone [1825 2934] and greyish green siltstone [1745 2906].

Marls with sand and sandrock in roadsides [1513 2681] to the North of Hillcommon lie near the base of the formation. A borehole [1503 2635] to the east of the hamlet proved Otter Sandstone at about 35 m depth, suggesting an easterly dip of about 4°. South of Tone Vale Hospital the A361 road cuts through red and greyish green marls [171 266], and still farther south up to 1.6 m of red and greenish grey marls crop out in an old degraded railway cutting [1697 2570].

A large old marlpit [1631 2426] south-west of Hillfarrance, a few metres outside the district, is in red and greyish green marl. To the east, just south of Hele Manor, the hamlet of Hele stands on pale greyish green and red marls and silty marls interbedded with pale greyish green thinly bedded siltstones and sandstones. The siltstones and sandstones are much in evidence in walls; they crop out in the remains of an old pit [1877 2434], and other pits near by are now grassed over. It is possible that these arenaceous rocks correlate with those at North Curry (p. 41).

Knowle Hill [186 271], at Norton Manor, appears to comprise a cap of sandstone on red and greyish green marls, but there is much tipped rubble about. A borehole [2009 2746] to the east proved the base of the Mercia Mudstone Group at 29 m depth.

Roadside sections [2047 2495] in Bishop's Hull show up to 4 m of red marl, locally tinged greyish green, and the footpath along the river passes, at Tytherleigh House, a 10-m face of similar rocks [2070 2493]. Excavations for a new road [2080 2488] immediately to the east are in 6 m of red marl.

Roadworks [2373 2529] at Lambrook, Taunton, exposed grey finely laminated silty sandstones with a little medium-grained sugary-textured sandstone; these rocks may correlate with the sandstones of North Curry. Farther east along the roadworks, cuttings [2461 2562; 2483 2556] show up to 10 m of red marl, spotted pale greyish green.

An excavation [2442 2774] at Cheddon Fitzpaine was reported by the farmer to have been 4.6 m deep and to have shown clay overlying sands. It adjoins an inlier of Morte Slates and may have penetrated marginal sands of the Mercia Mudstone Group. EAE

A few small exposures of red Mercia Mudstone comprising reddish brown silty calcareous mudstones occur south and east of Ruishton.

A trial borehole [2625 2581] to the east of Hyde Farm, made for the M5 motorway, proved the following sequence:

	Thickness	*Depth*
	m	m
Top soil	0.30	0.30
Clay, reddish brown, sandy and silty	2.80	3.10
Clay, reddish brown, with some black-stained fissures	1.00	4.10
Clay, reddish brown, with a few greyish green spots, slightly silty and calcareous	4.60	8.70
Siltstone, reddish brown with a few greyish green spots; friable and occasionally calcareous	5.05	13.75

The record of a motorway borehole [2795 2813] sited to the east of Walford is representative of others in the series:

	Thickness	*Depth*
	m	m
Top soil	0.30	0.30
Clay, reddish brown, silty	1.25	1.55
Clay, reddish brown, with grey, green and black speckles, silty and stiff	1.25	2.80
Clay, reddish brown, very silty and calcareous, becoming hard below 5 m	2.70	5.50
Siltstone, reddish brown, with very scattered greyish green mottling; calcareous and argillaceous; finely laminated in parts	8.60	14.10

Old brick pits [307 283] at Durston Station are now overgrown but reveal some 3.5 m of red and reddish brown silty calcareous mudstone, with greenish silty and sandy mudstone.

In a water borehole at New Barn [2974 2439] the driller's log recorded 5.49 m of red marl, on 3.35 m of grey sandstone, on 5.80 m of grey marl, on 9.75 m of red marl. The 3.35 m of grey sandstone, and perhaps some of the underlying grey marl, are thought to be the North Curry Sandstone, and form a faint feature north of New Barn and around the knoll-like hill at Knapp. A borehole [3058 2431] near Borough Post revealed (driller's log) 25 m of red, grey and green marl, on 4.57 m of greyish green sandstone becoming red to grey in the top 1.22 m, on 2.44 m of red marl; the 4.57 m of sandstone probably represent the North Curry Sandstone. The latter crops out in several places between Lower Knapp and North Curry, and is met with in a roadside exposure [3185 2557] near North Curry church as rubbly bluish green fine-grained sandstone; 50 m to the north [3184 2552] 1.5 m of blue and reddish brown mottled mudstone are overlain by 2.5 m of pale blue mudstone; these beds are about 5 m below the base of the sandstone.

The best exposures of the North Curry Sandstone occur around Moredon; in the track leading northward [3245 2626] the following section was recorded:

	Thickness
	m
NORTH CURRY SANDSTONE	
Sandstone, greyish green, flaggy	1.0
Sandstone, greyish green, hard and nodular	*to* 0.2
Mudstone, pale brown, sandy	0.5
RED MERCIA MUDSTONE	
Mudstone, chocolate, reddish brown and bluish green, blocky and calcareous	*seen* 15

The road [3253 2586] south of Moredon shows the following sequence:

	Thickness
	m
NORTH CURRY SANDSTONE	
Sandstone, greenish grey, fine-grained, thickly bedded, with greenish grey mudstone intercalations	2.00
Mudstone, greenish grey, soft, earthy and sandy	0.14
Sandstone, greenish grey, fine-grained, hard and current-bedded	0.36 *to* 0.55
Sandstone, brown, fine-grained, with thin greyish brown sandy mudstone beds and thin bluish green mudstones with mud cracks	1.42

The beds seen in another exposure 75 m to the south comprise nearly 2 m of thin- to medium-bedded brownish grey sandstones, with mudstone inclusions and thin beds, and these probably directly overlie the previous section.

The North Curry Sandstone caps the hill north-eastwards towards Mare Green, where it is sporadically exposed. Around Huntham, the outcrop of the sandstone is difficult to follow, and it may locally be absent, but in a roadside exposure [3511 2773] near Dyke's Farm 1.03 m of grey thinly bedded sandstone and shale rest on 0.25 m of rubbly bluish grey nodular sandstone, and 1.5 m of overlying red Mercia Mudstone are seen 50 m to the east. At Churley Farm [3569 2814] the North Curry Sandstone is represented by 2 m of greenish grey fine-grained sandstone with greenish grey mudstone bands. The sandstone is last seen in the railway cutting [3640 2820] at the edge of the district, where 2.5 m of strata are composed of greenish grey mudstones predominating over fine-grained sandstones. BJW

Kilve

The Blue Anchor Formation crops out in a stream at Kilve [1500 4336] and in the valley sides south of that locality. About 4.6 m of greenish grey and buff grey marly siltstones are exposed [1507 4298] behind an old mill. An old pit [2513 4240] and the adjacent road cutting [2516 4229] west of Combwich show greyish green and buff marls and siltstones up to 3 m thick, also of Blue Anchor Formation.

Nether Stowey to Charlinch

An old marlpit [2068 4167] north-east of Peadon Farm contains traces of red sandy marl and green sandstone. A lane [2256 4101] south of Wood Farm cuts through 2.37 m of blocky red marl with green patches, with a 12-mm greenish grey siltstone at 0.71 m from the base and a 25-mm greenish grey fine-grained sandstone at 1.41 m from the base, overlain by 0.08 to 0.18 m of lensoid greenish grey fine-grained sandstone, 0.15 to 0.25 m of hard green marl with red mottles and siltstone wisps, 1.3 m of blocky red marl, 0 to 0.03 m of hard greenish grey fine-grained sandstone and siltstone, 4.27 m of red marl with green patches, 0.23 m of hard greenish grey sandstone, some fine-grained, some gritty with pebbles of green mudstone, and 1.83 m of red marl with green patches. These strata lie roughly on strike with a narrow east-north-east-trending ridge 1.5 km long south of Beere Manor Farm, which is capped by green sandstone, usually in evidence only as surface brash but in one place [2395 4121] exposed as greenish grey flaggy sandstone, generally fine grained but with some coarser ribs, with some interbedded red, purple and green marl.

The stream north of Inwood Farm has been dug out to expose red and grey marl beneath drift [207 397]. Red marl seen in a lane [2301 3976] near Oatley Farms lies near the base of the formation and contains red medium-bedded medium-grained sandstone exposed [2307 3971] to a thickness of 2 m. Small pits [1954 3767; 1979 3784] north of Plainsfield show red and greyish green variegated marl and contain a few sandstone fragments.

Exposures near Four Forks include 2 m of red marl in a roadside [2322 3649] and silty marl in an old marlpit [2379 3690]. Others near Charlinch include roadside sections in sandy marl with blocks of sandstone [2400 3759] and shaly sandstone [2413 3764], and an old pit [2430 3773] in red and variegated red and green marl and silty marl with some silty sandstone. EAE

Bridgwater to North Petherton

Exposures in the Mercia Mudstone Group are few and poor in the area west and south of Bridgwater. Reddish brown silty calcareous mudstone floors the old flooded brick and tile works pits on the north and east side of Chilton Trinity. An old marl pit [289 354] south of Bridgewater contains 3 m of red and reddish brown calcareous silty mudstone with thin harder pale greenish grey bands. A borehole [3082 3635] in Bridgwater proved the following sequence:

	Thickness m	*Depth* m
Made ground	0.91	0.91
ALLUVIUM		
Clay, grey and blue	3.36	4.27
Peat	0.30	4.57
Clay, blue, soft	6.40	10.97
Peat, brown	0.92	11.89
Clay, blue, sandy, soft	3.65	15.54
Sand, fine-grained	6.41	21.95
MERCIA MUDSTONE		
Marl, red	3.96	25.91
Marl, red, and sandstone	7.31	33.22
Marl, red	1.22	34.44
Marl, red, with thin sandstone bands	4.27	38.71
Marl, red	12.50	51.21
Marl, red, with hard sandstone beds	12.80	64.01
?OTTER SANDSTONE		
Sandstone, red, hard	11.88	75.89
Marl, red	0.31	76.20

This record indicates the sandy nature of the basal strata in the group. About 2 km to the north, another borehole [3116 3824] proved 25.6 m of alluvial deposits overlying red Mercia Mudstone to 76.2 m; the solid deposits comprise red marl and red and blue mottled marl, and are above the sandy beds at the base of the Group.

Some of the site investigation boreholes for the M5 motorway were cored in part of the red Mercia Mudstone. One [3057 3413] proved a succession typical of those boreholes in the Huntworth area:

	Thickness m	*Depth* m
Top soil	0.46	0.46
MERCIA MUDSTONE		
Clay, red, silty, stiff and slightly shaly	1.83	2.29
Clay, stiff, hard in places, red and green patches below 3 m, with a 0.15-m silt layer at 3.28 m	1.67	3.96
Mudstone, red and green, silty and calcareous	1.53	5.49
Mudstone, red, silty, slightly shaly, calcareous; very silty and calcareous below 7.62 m	2.59	8.08
Mudstone, red, silty and calcareous	0.99	9.07
Mudstone and siltstone, red and calcareous	1.60	10.67

About 1 km to the south-west a borehole [3002 3340] proved the following succession:

	Thickness m	*Depth* m
Top soil	0.30	0.30
MERCIA MUDSTONE		
Clay, reddish brown, silty, sandy and gravelly in parts	3.40	3.70
Clay, reddish brown with some greyish green spots and black or pink staining, silty	1.60	5.30
Clay, reddish brown with a few greyish green spots and some black and pink staining; hard, silty and calcareous in places	2.90	8.20
Siltstone, reddish brown, slightly calcareous and argillaceous, with blocky fracture and black staining on fissure surfaces	3.10	11.30

The sandy basal beds of the formation are seen in a borehole [2968 3223] south-east of North Petherton:

	Thickness m	*Depth* m
Top soil	0.50	0.50
MERCIA MUDSTONE		
Clay, reddish brown, silty, friable slightly sandy and calcareous in places	2.00	2.50
Clay, reddish brown, silty, friable and calcareous	2.30	4.80
Siltstone, reddish brown, greyish green mottled in places, calcareous and argillaceous, with some black staining on fracture surfaces and inclined joints	4.25	9.05
Siltstone, reddish brown, greyish green and buff, variably sandy and argillaceous; fine-grained sandstone in basal 0.25 m	1.15	10.20

Bawdrip – Westonzoyland – Burrow Bridge

To the east of Bridgwater the Mercia Mudstone Group is almost entirely obscured by a cover of alluvium, peat and Burtle Beds, and exposures are very rare. Ussher (1908) noted that an examination of the railway cutting [3134 4110] at Dunball, south-west of Puriton, in 1868, showed about 25 ft (7.6 m) of 'Grey Marls' (Blue Anchor Formation) comprising greenish grey sandy clays and limestones interbedded with cream-coloured marls and shales, at the base of a section that extended up into Lias strata. At the northern end of the outcrop of Burtle Beds near Chedzoy, small tracts of red Mercia Mudstone [334 392; 340 390] rise only a metre or so above the top of the alluvium and, farther south, two small areas [350 320; 365 325] east of Northmoor Green are also mere low rises above the alluvial flat. The top of Burrow Mount [359 305] is some 25 m above the alluvium, but the hill has been disturbed to make fortifications and building foundations of various ages and no solid exposures can now be found. BJW

Penarth Group

Strata of the Westbury Formation are exposed on the foreshore [0765 4362] east of Watchet harbour to a thickness of 13.5 m. They comprise interbedded grey shales and argillaceous limestones with a few beds of sandy limestone, sandstone, marl and mudstone; bone-beds and shells occur. A few of the limestones and sandstones are pyritic, and one such sandstone contains calcite and gypsum. Fibrous calcite ('beef') is common in the upper part of the sequence. Whittaker and Green (1983) gave the succession in detail, cross-referenced to the description by Richardson (1911).

In Doniford Bay [0827 4345] the whole of the Penarth Group is exposed on the foreshore. The succession, summarised from Whittaker and Green (1983), is as follows:

	Thickness m
LILSTOCK FORMATION	
Langport Member: Mudstone, greenish grey, with lenticular limestones; on limestone, typically pale brownish grey, mostly fine-grained but ranging from porcellanous to coarse and crystalline, locally silty, with shells in places, interbedded with grey blocky mudstones	1.82
Cotham Member: Mudstone, greenish grey, with limestone lenticles; on limestone, greenish grey, lenticular, fine- to medium-grained with traces of marl and sandstone; on siltstone, greenish grey, hard, calcareous, ripple-marked, locally contorted and of variable thickness; on mudstone, green and marly	1.24
WESTBURY FORMATION	
Limestone, grey, shelly, generally earthy, locally medium- or coarse-grained, commonly lenticular or nodular, interbedded with black shales, a few beds of siltstone and a thin sandstone containing limestone pebbles; pyrite commonly locally; 'beef' mainly in the upper beds	12.70

The siltstones of the Cotham Member yielded *Cardinia* cf. *regularis*, *Chlamys valoniensis*, *Dimyopsis intusstriatus*, *Eotrapezium concentricum*, '*Gervillia*' *praecursor?*, *Placunopsis alpina*, *Protocardia rhaetica*, *Tutcheria cloacina*.

The Westbury Formation yielded *Cardinia* sp., *C. valoniensis*, *E. concentricum*, *E. elongatus*, *E.* sp. nov.?, '*G*'. *praecursor*, *Lyriomyophoria postera*, *Modiolus* cf. *hillanus*, '*Modiolus*' *sodburiensis*, *P. alpina*, '*Pleurophorus*' *elongatus*, *Pteromya* cf. *crowcombeia*, *P. rhaetica*, *Rhaetavicula contorta*, *T. cloacina*, '*Natica*' *oppelii*, *Ophiolepis* sp., and fish fragments including *Acrodus minimus*, *Gyrolepis alberti* and *Hybodus minor*.

The following section at the foot of the cliff [1032 4327] in St Audrie's Bay has been summarised from Whittaker and Green (1983):

	Thickness m
LILSTOCK FORMATION	
Langport Member: Mudstone, greenish grey, with impersistent limestones; on limestone, pale brownish grey or grey, fine-grained or porcellanous, locally silty, with a little pyrite and calcite stringers, interbedded with grey blocky mudstone, locally shaly or silty	1.46
Cotham Member: Interbedded greenish grey shale, mudstone, marl, siltstone and sandstone, locally calcareous; the argillaceous rocks are locally blocky or laminated, with small cavities and minor contortions and slump structures; desiccation cracks filled with sand extend down 0.46 m from the topmost sandstone bed of the member	2.13
WESTBURY FORMATION	
Black shale with beds of grey earthy limestone; calcite 'beef' is common; silty calcareous marl at base of top shale	*seen* 2.45

In the following cliff section [1043 4306] the Cotham Member is affected by faulting and may not be complete:

	Thickness m
LILSTOCK FORMATION	
Langport Member: Mudstone, greenish grey or grey, with impersistent limestones; on limestone, grey, fine-grained or porcellanous, commonly lenticular or nodular, locally silty, interbedded with grey shale and marl	1.50
Cotham Member: Interbedded marl and siltstone, mainly greenish grey but buff in places; marl, blocky or laminated, locally with lenses of sandstone; uppermost siltstone contorted and penetrated from above by small sand-filled pipes	1.56
WESTBURY FORMATION	
Interbedded black shale and grey earthy limestone; 'beef' is common	*seen* 3.81

The upper part of the Langport Member yielded *D. intusstriatus*, *Liostrea hisingeri*, *Plagiostoma* sp., *Meleagrinella?*, *Modiolus hillanoides*, *Pleuromya?* and *Protocardia?*. The Westbury Formation yielded *Cercomya?*, *C. valoniensis*, *E. concentricum*, *Modiolus* sp., *Liostrea?*, *Placunopsis alpina*, *Protocardia rhaetica*, *R. contorta* and *T. cloacina*. Whittaker and Green (1983) gave the detailed succession, together with Richardson's (1911) record of Westbury Formation strata now hidden by landslip.

Limestones of the Langport Member crop out in a railway cutting [0853 4276] south-west of Doniford. At East Wood [1410 4347], to the east of East Quantoxhead, a band of black shales can be traced round the southern scarp slopes of a hill. Faulted patches of the Penarth Group occur hereabouts [1438 4328], but the main crop can be followed into the valley at Kilve where Westbury Formation shales are exposed in the stream bed [1500 4339].

Ussher's (1908) record of the railway cutting [3135 4120] at Dunball, south-west of Puriton, examined in 1868, shows the following succession between the Blue Anchor Formation and the Lower Lias: sands and shales 0.6 m, overlain in sequence by black shales with selenite 5.18 m, calciferous sandstone bone-bed 0.06 m, black shales with thin limestones 4.57 m (Westbury Formation), white and grey limestones and shales with hard striped limestone near base 2.44 m, capped by the Sun Bed (Lilstock Formation). The black shales (Westbury Formation) yielded *C. valoniensis*, '*P*'. *elongatus*, *P. rhaetica* and *R. contorta*, and the bone-bed contained *A. minimus*, *G. alberti* and *Hybodus*.

In the railway cutting [356 407] near Cossington Station, Ussher (1908) recorded Penarth Group strata as follows in upward order: dark blue or black paper shales, rusty at top, with limestone beds and nodules 4.88 m; hard banded limestone 0.33 m; bluish grey and yellow shaly clay with small calcareous concretions 1.37 m; four beds of pale grey compact limestone, the lowest resembling Cotham Marble, with clay partings 1.45 m; Lower Lias. The 1.45-m limestone sequence yielded *Pleuromya*, *P. rhaetica* and '*G*' *praecursor*.

EAE

Plate 6 Shrinkage cracks in Penarth Group strata, St Audrie's Bay.

Polygonal cracks in beds of the Cotham Member have been filled with material similar to that forming the overlying bed (A 11718)

CHAPTER 5
Jurassic

GENERAL ACCOUNT

The youngest 'solid' rocks of the district belong to the Lower Lias, and the following description of them is based largely on the work of Whittaker and Green (1983). The Triassic–Jurassic boundary is defined (Warrington and others, 1980; Cope and others 1980) as lying immediately below the first occurrence of *Psiloceras*, and in this district it is about 5.5 m above the base of the Lias. The Lower Lias strata here comprise interbedded limestone and shale or mudstone almost entirely of the Blue Lias, and their total thickness is between about 160 and 200 m, compared to a thickness of 29 m on the Dorset coast.

Cyclic sedimentation is evident, with repetition of the (upward) sequence: shale, mudstone, limestone, mudstone. The shales are locally bituminous, with thin alternations of carbonaceous and clay laminae and ramifying calcite stringers. Pyrite is common, and selenite deposited on the bedding planes during weathering gives rise to the typical weathered 'paper shales'. The base of the shales is generally sharp, but the top locally contains *Chondrites* mottles. Fossils include ammonites, fish fragments and a few small thin-shelled bivalves. Sulphides and the absence of burrows point to anaerobic conditions of deposition, possibly in fairly deep water.

The mudstones are grey, blocky and calcareous, rarely fissile, with a benthonic fauna and trace-fossil mottling. Most of the limestones are dark bluish grey, hard, compact and splintery, generally persistent but locally lenticular or nodular. A minority are very fine grained or porcellanous, like some beds in the underlying Langport Member. Fossils are commonest in or near thin (about 0.03 m) transitional lithologies at the tops and bottoms of limestones.

The sharp base to the shale of each cycle betokens transgression, with deepening water, followed by deposition and a passage to aerobic conditions marked by mudstone. Shallow water facilitated the formation of limestone, and slightly deeper water that of the succeeding mudstone.

Five divisions may be distinguished on the coast, and are given in Table 4, with their palaeontological zones and generalised thicknesses.

DETAILS

Doniford to St Audrie's Bay

The following succession, exposed in offshore reefs [0870 4355] north of the Doniford Bay Fault, includes strata of the lowest four divisions (Table 4):

		Thickness m
4	Interbedded shale, mudstone and limestone; limestone locally lenticular or nodular; 1.06-m limestone at base with thin mudstone partings; *conybeari* Subzone	6.65
3	Interbedded mudstone, shale and limestone; the limestones are commonly massive and persistent in the upper part, and some are lenticular and nodular below; mainly *angulata* Zone but the top 0.83 m are *conybeari* Subzone and the basal 10.3 m are *liasicus* Zone	51.19
2	Mainly shale and mudstone; a few thin limestones, mostly nodular; *liasicus* Zone except for the basal limestone (about 0.14 m thick) which is *planorbis* Zone	24.87
1	Interbedded mudstone, shale and limestone; the top 8.94 m are *planorbis* Zone and the basal 7.57 m are Pre-planorbis Beds of Rhaetian age	16.51

Whittaker and Green (1983) gave the succession in greater detail.

Immediately south of the Doniford Bay Fault the strata are predominantly shales and mudstones. Reefs of fissile shale and nodular limestone with *Arnioceras* sp. and *Coroniceras* sp. occupy an east – west belt of foreshore close to the beach; the succession lies in the topmost lithological division, is of *semicostatum* Zone age, and comprises 38.3 m of interbedded shales, mudstones and thin locally nodular limestones (see Whittaker and Green, 1983). Beds that are correlated with the top half of this sequence are exposed in the cliff section south of the Doniford Bay Fault where this passes near the steps in Helwell Bay [0783 4325 to 0780 4337]; the 50-m succession comprises shales with thin limestones, overlain by mudstones and shales, and includes the youngest Jurassic rocks in the district (see Whittaker and Green, 1983). The youngest rocks in the cliff are mudstones; they are repeated on the foreshore close to the fault [0817 4337 and 0832 4333], where they have yielded *Coroniceras* sp. A small faulted inlier of *semicostatum* Zone strata [0866 4324] has yielded *Arnioceras* and *Coroniceras*, and shales and limestones of the *bucklandi* Zone in a faulted syncline offshore [0915 4355] have yielded *Coroniceras* sp.

The cliff section east of Doniford Camp is summarised below; topmost *planorbis* Zone strata are repeated on the foreshore by strike faulting [1013 4334], and other beds in the cliff by low-angle thrust faulting [1029 4319].

		Thickness m
3	Shales with limestones; the limestones are generally thin and locally lenticular; the top 31.81 m are *angulata* Zone, the basal 10.38 m are of *liasicus* Zone age	42.19
2	Mainly shale and mudstone, with thin, commonly nodular limestones; *liasicus* Zone except for the basal ?0.21 m, which is of *planorbis* Zone age	20.55

1 Interbedded shales and limestone; the uppermost ?7.65 m are of *planorbis* Zone age and the basal ?5.62 m are Triassic Pre-planorbis Beds — 13.27

Whittaker and Green (1983) gave the succession in detail.

Watchet to Combwich

Limestones in a small pit [0978 4227] south-west of Rydon lie close to a fault trending north-west – south-east and dip at 50° westward.

Old quarries [1430 4346] in East Wood, east of East Quantoxhead, are much overgrown but show limestones and shales. Stream sections [1497 4350] near Kilve include 0.64 m of shales overlain by 0.3 m of dark grey limestone. Both exposures probably belong to the *planorbis* Zone.

East of Stogursey *planorbis* Zone strata form a north-facing dip slope, and shales and limestones crop out alongside the road [2057 4276; 2104 4271; 2110 4267]. Two old quarries [2261 4256; 2261 4287] near Cockwood show up to about 2 m of interbedded shales and limestones yielding *P. planorbis*. The more northerly quarry shows limestone 0.05 m, overlain by blocky grey shale 0.29 m, splintery bluish grey fine-grained limestone 0.09 m, fissile grey shale 0.43 m, massive bluish grey limestone 0.25 m, fissile bluish grey shale 0.58 m, and massive well-jointed bluish grey limestone 0.33 m.

An old quarry [2344 4211] west of Knaplock Farm exposes massive well-jointed limestone 0.32 m, overlain successively by fissile shale 0.46 m, massive blue-hearted well-jointed limestone 0.32 m, shale probably of *planorbis* Zone age 1.83 m, slightly flaggy limestone 0.16 m, shale 0.38 m, and well-jointed limestone with vertical calcite stringers 0.18 m. An old pit [2474 4221] south of Hill Farm contains massive bluish-grey-hearted well-jointed limestone 0.33 m, overlain by shale, blocky and calcareous in its lower part and fissile in its upper part 0.49 m, massive well-jointed limestone with vertical 'beefy' calcite stringers 0.25 m, shale with *P. planorbis* 1.04 m, flaggy calcareous mudstone or argillaceous limestone 0.25 m, fissile shale 0.36 m, blocky calcareous mudstone 0.23 m, and fissile shale 0.23 m. Shales and limestones in a similar pit [2480 4211], little more than 100 m to the south-east, contain *Coroniceras* and may belong to the *bucklandi* Zone. Possibly the two localities lie on either side of a fault.

Pawlett to Woolavington

Rubble capping the clay slopes of Pawlett Hill [292 432] is of limestone with *Gryphaea*, and limestone blocks used in a wall [2866 4282] at Gaunt's Farm contain a large arietitid ammonite and were possibly collected locally. The predominant lithology around Pawlett appears to be mudstone, and the local strata may belong to the upper part of the *bucklandi* or to the lower part of the *semicostatum* Zone.

Ussher (1908) recorded 6 m of interbedded shales and limestones in a cement works adjoining the railway cutting [314 417] west of Puriton; he noted that Bristow and Etheridge (1873) had seen 9 m of strata with *P. planorbis* at Puriton, and speculated that the *angulata* (now *liasicus* and *angulata*) and *bucklandi* zones might contain relatively little limestone in that neighbourhood. Limestones in a large old quarry [316 411] south-west of Puriton have yielded *P. planorbis*, and a small pit [3377 4039] east of Knowle Hall shows 0.66 m of interbedded limestones and shales. Evidence from shallow excavations in a housing estate [346 408] to the south of Woolavington suggest a thin Lias cover on Penarth Group. In old railway cuttings west [353 404] and north-east [3620 4086] of Cossington, shales and limestones with *P. planorbis* are now poorly exposed, but Ussher (1908) saw 4.5 m of shales, clays and argillaceous limestones.

EAE

Table 4 Jurassic stratigraphic divisions

Lithological divisions	Generalised thickness (m)	Subzone	Zone	Stage
5 Mudstones and shales; some argillaceous limestones	80	*resupinatum* *scipionianum* *lyra*	*semicostatum*	SINEMURIAN
4 Fissile shales and mudstones; a few limestones in the upper and middle parts, alternating shales and limestones in the lower part	40	*rotiforme* *conybeari*	*bucklandi*	
3 Limestones and shales; beds are thicker towards the top	50		*angulata*	HETTANGIAN
2 Dark grey shales and mudstones; some nodular limestones	20	*laqueus* *portlocki*	*liasicus*	
1 Limestones and shales	13	*johnstoni* *planorbis*	*planorbis*	
				RHAETIAN (Triassic)

CHAPTER 6

Intrusive igneous rocks

Ussher (1908) chronicled the discovery, in 1814, of a block of igneous rock in the village of Cheddon Fitzpaine, the location of the quarry whence it had been brought, and the naming of the rock as the 'Hestercombe Syenite'. He noted that the quarry was seldom worked, and quoted J. S. Flett's identification of the rock as a diorite. The rock has been intruded into Morte Slates.

Dr J. R. Hawkes, with access to better specimens than were available to Flett, has provided the following description. The rock (e.g. E 54055) is medium grained and consists chiefly of randomly-oriented lamellar-twinned subhedral crystals of sodic oligoclase, with clots and dispersed groups and radiating clusters of fibrous chlorite crystals. Small quantities of limonitic iron oxide are associated with most of the chlorite crystals. Dispersed 'subhedral' aggregates of opaque oxide, possibly mainly goethite, may mark the sites of original olivine or perhaps pyroxene crystals. Many of the chlorite fibres are rectilinear and probably have replaced biotite; more finely divided aggregates have partially replaced some feldspar crystals. Other aggregates of fibrous chlorite may have resulted from alteration of pyroxene, but this has not been confirmed from outline shapes. There is no evidence for the presence of amphibole, and sodium cobaltinitrite staining confirmed that no potassium feldspar is present. The rock contains abundant accessory apatite and also rare random patches comprising interlocking anhedra of strained quartz. Some quartzose patches contain irregularly shaped aggregates of opaque oxide, possibly goethite, with which are associated minute needles of ?rutile. The freshness of most of the feldspar suggests that alteration of other constituents was probably due to contained magmatic fluids. The rock is a lamprophyre similar to the kersantite-lamprophyre at Fremington (Edmonds and others, 1984), except that the latter contains a good deal of calcite and has a vesicular texture; possibly the Hestercombe dyke is exposed at a deeper level of emplacement.

The intrusion was examined by Evens and Wallis (1930), who also located three quartz-diorite sills up to 1.5 m thick, and two quartz-diorite dykes up to 0.45 m wide in large quarries at Coombe [271 290], which had been opened in slates, siltstones and sandstones. Their view that all the minor intrusions were probably offshoots of a single larger concealed body was challenged by Webby (1966a), who thought the evidence from surface debris was inadequate and regarded the dykes at Coombe as not in alignment with the Hestercombe rock.

The type locality of the lamprophyre lies on the west side of a wooded combe about 0.5 km at 013° from Hestercombe House. The northern bay [2428 2928] and southern bay [2428 2925] of the quarry are separated by a narrow spur. No slates crop out in the spur, but some slaty rubble is present and the igneous rock near the spur is more fractured than that within the bays. Slaty rubble is much in evidence immediately south of the south bay and north of the north bay. It is presumed that the two bays have been opened in two separate but closely adjacent dykes, the northern one 12 m wide and the southern one 10 m wide. Should there be no slate between the bays, then the total width of igneous rock is 24 m and the quarry would be in a single dyke with a narrow zone of closely spaced joints about midway, or possibly in two dykes in contact one with the other.

The massive rock is cut by joints trending east-south-east – west-north-west, some near vertical, some inclined fairly steeply to south-south-west. Others trend north-east – south-west. The direction of working was west-north-west, probably following the trend of the dyke.

A larger quarry in slates with sandstones lies a short distance to the south-west, and on its northern edge [2424 2920] a dyke 1 m wide trends 120°. Baked slates adjoin the dyke and in places have been converted into fine-grained pale creamy buff rock lacking any cleavage. About 200 m to the west, another quarry in slates and silty slates with sandstones contains a poorly exposed narrow dyke at its northern end [2405 2920].

No other exposures of dyke have been found in the Hestercombe area. Traces of rubble to the west [238 294; 233 294; 228 292; 227 295; 225 299; 215 304] are too ill defined and scattered to map, but confirm a west-north-westerly trend. Patches of debris permit the tracing of dykes for short distances east of the combe, but a large quarry [247 291], much overgrown, appears to be entirely in slates with quartzitic sandstones although its position is such that one or more dykes might have been expected to be present. The implication is that the Hestercombe dykes at outcrop do not extend for more than a few hundreds of metres, unless perhaps as thin and impersistent stringers. The small dykes at Coombe are not in line with those at Hestercombe but nevertheless trend in the same direction and must surely be of similar age and origin. Fragments of the rocks have been found in weathered Otter Sandstone in an old pit [251 293] (Evans and Wallis, 1930), and the intrusions postdate the development of cleavage in the Morte Slates. A probable Variscan age of intrusion is indicated, and rubidium-strontium determinations suggest a figure of 264 ± 36 Ma.

The nearest rocks in some ways comparable include lamprophyres such as the biotite-minette of Rose Ash, east-south-east of South Molton, almost 50 km distant, and the kersantite of Fremington, over 70 km away. Permian lavas showing many of the characteristics of lamprophyres occur north-west of Tiverton, about 35 km from Hestercombe. The andesitic lavas north-east of Shepton Mallet, about 40 km from Hestercombe, are of Silurian age.

Lamprophyres cutting the Carboniferous rocks of Devon, and probably of late Carboniferous or early Permian age, may occupy feeder channels of the Permian lavas. Tidmarsh (1932) suggested that some of these lavas were end products of the mixing of acid and basic partly crystallised melts. Edmonds and others (1968) considered the possible generation of basic magma by sub-crustal melting during the rise of the Dartmoor Granite. Such a magma would require some modification to produce many of the known extrusives.

The lamprophyres, therefore, originated as small specialised magma fractions, and are to that extent abnormal intrusives. This is equally true of the dykes at Hestercombe, which are more likely to have resulted from processes of hybridisation or assimilation than from uninterrupted crystallisation of a basaltic liquid. There is no evidence of the existence of basic igneous rock or calcareous sediments in such quantities as to convert a magma from granitic to dioritic, or of acid igneous rock to convert a magma from gabbroic to dioritic. A possible explanation lies in the ascent of a basic magma through great thicknesses of sandstone, mainly Hangman Grits. However, no pluton is known beneath the area; nor can the existence of one be inferred, except as a theoretical parent body of the dykes. Brooks and Thompson (1973) and Edmonds and others (1979) have discussed the possible presence of such a body at depth in the Lundy area. The relatively wide but short dyke outcrops of Hestercombe suggest that they may lie above a small boss or cupola, and this possibility is supported by aeromagnetic evidence (p. 78). EAE

CHAPTER 7

Quaternary

No known material relics remain in the district of Pleistocene stages before the Wolstonian (about 200 000 to 100 000 BP), although earlier local ice caps may be presumed to have existed on high ground. Kellaway (1971) thought that Anglian ice might have swept across south-west England, but there is no evidence of such a glaciation in the present district.

Deposits mapped as 2nd Terrace occur in the Vale of Taunton Deane and in the north-west of the district, and by analogy with river deposits farther west (Edmonds and others, 1979; 1984) they are considered to be of Wolstonian age. Kellaway (1971) has suggested that the Burtle Beds, patches of sand and gravel rising only a few metres above the alluvial flats of the River Parrett, are outwash sediment from a Wolstonian, or possibly even Anglian, ice sheet rather than marine beach deposits as generally thought. Wolstonian ice, which left behind the boulder clay of Fremington to the west, is thought to have blocked the Bristol Channel and created 'Lake Maw' (Maw, 1864; G. F. Mitchell, 1960), and a sandstone boulder found at Hillfarrance may have got there on an ice floe in the lake at that time. Ice built up on the Quantock and Brendon hills, and resultant meltwaters further eroded valleys already worn in Anglian times and perhaps cut initially in the Permo-Triassic (Chapter 4).

If, as seems likely, the Burtle Beds are of marine origin, they probably equate with the raised beach of Weston-super-Mare and Saunton. The latter is considered to be Ipswichian (Edmonds and others, 1979), and grades into the 1st Terrace, and it is suggested here that the Burtle Beds and the 1st Terrace deposits of the Taunton district are interglacial sediments of Ipswichian age.

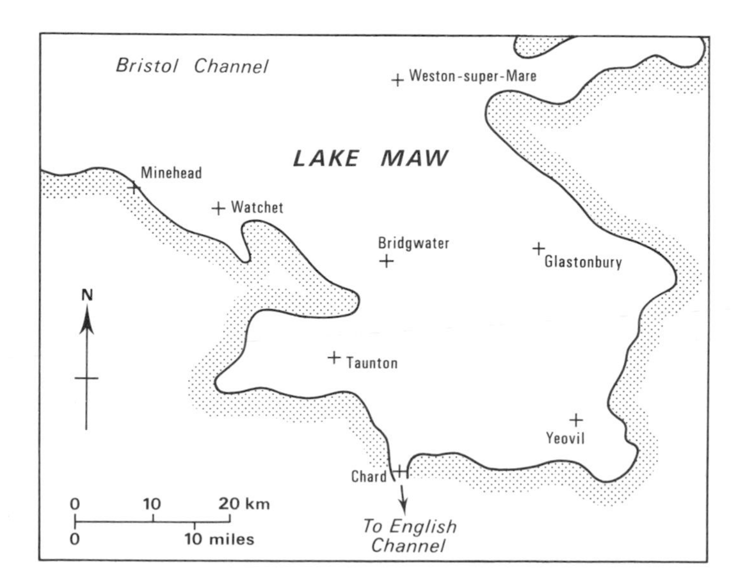

Figure 13 Approximate maximum southward extent of Lake Maw

Devensian ice advanced southwards only as far as South Wales. Sea level may have fallen to 100 m or more below OD (Godwin and others, 1958), and the Taunton area, in common with the rest of south-west England, lay within a periglacial zone. Snow probably lay long, or permanently, on the hills. The only remaining deposits of this age are those forming the mantle of stony clay Head. Over most of the district they form a widespread cover, removed by erosion from the steeper slopes but otherwise unrelated to topography. In the north-west, Head forms valley fill; some uncertainty exists as to the distinction between Head and river deposits, and it is likely that representatives of both alluvium and 1st Terrace are present between Williton and Doniford.

Head is here taken to include the weathered mantle of Pleistocene or Recent age, irrespective of whether, or how, or how far it has moved. There is no practicable alternative for the purposes of geological survey. Other Recent sediments comprise peat, the clays, silts, sands and gravels of river or estuarine alluvium, and modern beach deposits.

Pleistocene

The impression gathered in traversing valleys that run down from the Quantock and Brendon hills, except for those of some short coastal streams, is that many are too large for the waters they currently carry. Examples include the north-south valley [205 353] near Lower Aisholt. A history of valleys excavated by Permo-Triassic torrents (Chapter 4), and by Anglian and Wolstonian ice and meltwater, affords an adequate explanation.

The damming of the Bristol Channel by ice, first suggested by Maw (1864), was considered in more detail by G. F. Mitchell (1960) and Stephens (*in* Lewis, 1970). Present topography shows that the resultant lake would have had a southerly outflow near Chard to the River Axe, at a level of 85 to 90 m above OD (Figure 13). The divide between the Doniford Stream and Weacombe is capped by three patches of pebbly drift (p.52) mapped as 2nd Terrace. They range in altitude from about 85 m to 100 m above OD, a level, given the uncertainty in delineating a thin drift cover, which may be taken as coincident with that of the surface of 'Lake Maw', suggesting that the material may be a beach deposit.

The deposits of the 2nd Terrace south of Fiddington [212 395; 218 401] slope downstream from 76 m above OD to 45 m. Similar drift in the south of the district occurs on rises alongside the River Tone and its tributaries between Norton Fitzwarren and Bishops Lydeard, at just over 60 m above OD near the latter village, falling to about 45 m at the former.

A rounded boulder [1691 2445] at Court Farm, Hillfarrance, measures about 0.9 × 0.5 × 0.5 m. It lies, lichen-encrusted, in a private garden alongside an ornamental pool, and has not been properly sampled for examination. However, the rock appears to be a fairly clean, buff or fawn, fine- to medium-grained hard quartzitic grit, quite unlike any Permo-Triassic rock of the district and probably of Palaeozoic age. A previous occupant of Court Farm recalls that in about 1900 the boulder was alongside the garden gate, upright with its broader end sunk in the ground. The rock is water worn, in appearance a typical beach boulder, and must weigh more than half a tonne. No obvious reason exists why anyone should transport such a stone from the coast to Hillfarrance, an exercise more difficult in the 19th century than today. The only natural agency capable of the move is ice. A local glacier would probably have left other debris. An ice sheet would have left even more, and widespread, sediment. Both conjectures leave us with the problem of explaining the removal or concealment of much evidence. Two exotic boulders of conglomeratic quartzite at Shebbear, in north Devon, have been thought to be possible remnants of a differentially cemented ?Tertiary cover (Freshney and others, 1979). They lie at 143 and 168 m above OD respectively, too high for any but a major glaciation, but the Hillfarrance boulder rests at just over 30 m. It will be recalled that the conjectural 'Lake Maw' probably stood at 85 to 90 m above OD, and the most likely mechanism by which a small quantity of debris, including a single boulder, reached Hillfarrance was transport across the lake by an ice floe in Wolstonian times.

A boulder 0.6 to 0.9 m across, found in a cutting for the M5 motorway about 3 km south of Taunton, was described by Mr R. K. Harrison in 1974 as pale grey, hard, fine-grained, quartzitic sandstone, locally and superficially stained with iron oxide. He commented that the rock had not been matched with a source in south-west England but might have come from Namurian strata of south Wales or from a submarine source. The exact altitude at which this boulder lay is uncertain but may have been about 45 m above OD. It is suggested that it too probably drifted southwards on a Wolstonian ice floe.

Deposits of the 1st Terrace remain alongside the River Tone and other smaller tributaries of the River Parrett. Some adjoin the alluvium, others cap very low rises of Mercia Mudstone a metre or two above the flood plain. Much of the town of Taunton stands on alluvium or 1st Terrace. Remains of Irish elk in Taunton Museum, recovered from gravels, may be from the 1st Terrace. Ussher (1906) referred to rhinoceras bones from excavations on the northern edge of the Wellington district at Taunton Gaol, possibly in gravels of the 1st Terrace sand and gravel on the northern outskirts of the town, that skirting and underlying Kingston Road has yielded reindeer and bison remains, now in Taunton Museum; as with the other old records, the precise location is not known.

The Burtle Beds occur in the east of the district, as 'islands' rising above the surrounding alluvium to a maximum of just over 7 m above OD, and hence they are of historical importance in affording sites for settlement; they also rest directly on Mercia Mudstone, as just north-west of Bridgwater. At the surface the deposits most commonly seen are sands, usually cross-bedded where stratification can be distinguished. Silts and loams, commonly shelly, and some gravels, also occur. The sands are composed of fine grains of quartz with shell material in layers, and the gravels contain flints, quartz, water-worn sandstone, chert, red marl (Mercia Mudstone) and Blue Anchor Formation silts. In many places the sands and the gravels have a hard calcareous cement derived from the shelly content. Fossils include elephant, rhinoceras, horse, bear, red deer, fallow deer, roe deer, hyaena, wolf and shells of marine, freshwater and land organisms.

Bulleid and Jackson (1937; 1941) suggested a marine origin within the tidal zone. Possibly the beds are beach deposits, with non-marine fossils being washed down in rivers from adjacent land. Kidson (1970; 1971) supported the theory of a marine origin. He disregarded C^{14} dates on shells as unreliable, noted an occurrence of Burtle Beds beneath Head, and suggested a stratigraphical position similar to that of the raised beach at Saunton (Edmonds and others, 1979) and an Ipswichian age. Kellaway (1971) interpreted the Burtle Beds as glacial sand and gravel washed out from a Wolstonian ice sheet. He based his argument on the presence of Devonian, Carboniferous, Permo-Triassic, Jurassic and Cretaceous 'erratics', including the large 'Devil's Upping Stock' of Westonzoyland, which unfortunately was cut up for use and so lost. Kidson and Haynes (1972) found gravels from the Burtle Beds to be indistinguishable from several others in the Parrett estuary. They reasserted the idea of a marine, or possibly estuarine, origin but suggested a sand-bank rather than a beach. Kidson (1970) proved clays at the base of the Burtle Beds east of the present district. Kidson and others (1974) dug through the sands and these underlying clays to reach Lias clay and found, near the base of the Burtle Beds, hazel wood which yielded a C^{14} date of 4280 ± 70 BP; they suggested that the Burtle Beds might have been reworked in Recent times, and later research by Kidson and others (1981) afforded further evidence of Flandrian marine reworking at the margin of the Burtle Beds west of Westonzoyland.

Doubts remain. It seems, on grounds of nature and height, that Burtle Beds alongside the River Parrett may be equated with the (Ipswichian) raised beach and 1st Terrace, and that a glacial origin is less likely. But it is possible that not all such Burtle Beds have been differentiated from alluvium, and that to the east of the present district some Recent deposits may have wrongly been called Burtle Beds.

River terrace deposits that are too isolated, distant or ill defined to be correlated with the 1st or 2nd terraces are mapped as 'undifferentiated'. They commonly occur alongside the upper reaches of streams, or as near-featureless lowland spreads merging into Head.

The only Devensian sediments in the district occur within Head, a generally unsorted deposit comprising material soliflucted under periglacial conditions, together with the products of Recent weathering. Over most of the district, Head occurs as an ill-defined spread 0.5 to 2 m thick mantling flat or gently sloping ground at all altitudes; no attempt has been made to show this on the published 1:50 000 map. In the north-west, however, Head has accumulated as valley-fill in some of the short valleys draining north to the Bristol Channel; these deposits are fairly well defined and are delineated on the map.

Most of the Head comprises angular and subangular stones in a matrix of sands and clays, but in the north-west rounded pebbles are common. Except in the area west of the Quantock Hills few of these pebbles can have come ready-rounded from Permo-Triassic rocks; they are mainly of hard Devonian sandstone and, unless brought into the area by ice, they have probably not travelled far. It seems possible that the drift mapped in the north-west of the district ranges without sharp junctions from Head, through Head partially sorted and redistributed by water, to river deposits. The best exposures are of gravels at the coast near Doniford, some poorly sorted and some bedded with channel-fill structures. The form of the deposit at Williton suggests that it includes both alluvium and adjoining 1st Terrace, and in carrying out the one-inch survey in the 1864 H. W. Bristow mapped the whole as alluvium. A. N. Thomas (1940) mapped it as river gravels, and showed Head only as angular debris at the foot of steep slopes. Gilbertson and Mottershead (1975) envisaged a periglacial climate and a Devensian age, but interpreted the gravels, at least in part, as reworked river gravels, and considered that lenses of sand and fine-grained gravel in the cliffs at Doniford filled channels of small streams. Norman (1978) described two large flint blades found in gravels 50 m west of the Doniford stream [0903 4324] and reported a visit to the locality in 1977, when Professor C. Kidson and Dr D. N. Mottershead agreed that the lens of fine-grained well-sorted gravel that had yielded the larger blade was a fluvial deposit and that the whole gravel sequence was probably Devensian. He concluded that the flint artefacts were probably late Upper Palaeolithic, and referred to Mesolithic artifacts occasionally found in the 0.7 m of loam which capped the gravels. This suggests that the uppermost sediment is Flandrian, and although Norman equated his dating with late Devensian it could equally well be early Flandrian; furthermore, the time at which products of a late Upper Palaeolithic industry found their way into gravel deposits must remain unknown.

Recent

Modern beach deposits between Watchet and St Audrie's Bay comprise mud, sand and shingle. Within the estuary of the River Parrett estuarine alluvium grades into river alluvium. Alluvial deposits of clays, silts, sands and gravels, with which is associated peat, are extensive alongside the River Parrett, where they are up to 40 m or so thick, and bordering the River Tone above its junction with the Parrett. The River Tone upstream of Knap Bridge, and its tributary the Hillfarrance Brook, have produced alluvial flood plains locally over 0.5 km wide.

Whittaker and Green (1983) described a buried channel of the River Brue, running west-south-west to the north of Puriton and outside the present district, and sub-alluvium rises of Blue Lias to the north-north-east of Pawlett. Kidson and Heyworth (1973; 1976) concluded, on the evidence of radiocarbon dates, that sea-level in the Severn estuary had in general risen continuously since 9000 years BP. Rate of rise, and of consequent sedimentation, was a major factor in allowing the formation of peat.

Whittaker and Green (1983) noted thin peat at the base of the alluvium and a slightly thicker deposit (up to 2.13 m), known as the 'OD peat', immediately below the topmost clays and silty clays which are called the 'Roman Clay' and are up to 5.5 m thick. The 'OD peat' has yielded a radiocarbon date of over 5000 year BP.

Major peat deposits are known to be up to 5 m thick to the west and south-west of Glastonbury. Some of these spreads extend westwards into the present district. Godwin's (1948; 1975) work on them suggested that a number of climatic changes had occurred. The oldest peat, somewhat older than the 'OD peat' mentioned above, is composed largely of reeds and sedges. It is overlain by woody peat, with alder and willow which suggest slightly less damp growing conditions, and birch which points to drier times or localities. These lower peats, because of their depths, have been little worked. A return to wet ground and swamps is marked by peat rich in sphagnum moss and cotton grass, probably of Neolithic age (say 5500 to 3500 years BP) and formed at a time when men were first building brushwood trackways across the Somerset bogs. Towards the top of the peat there occur sphagnum and sedges (swampy growth), cotton grass (damp) and heather and woody remains (drier), possibly representing the passage from late Neolithic through the pleasanter living conditions of much of the Bronze Age to a cooler and wetter Iron Age. The oldest peat dated from artifacts (not the oldest peat present) is Neolithic, and the youngest is Roman, suggesting that peat formation continued until less than 2000 BP.

J. H. Blake and H. W. Bristow, while making geological surveys in the 19th century, noted evidence of coastal erosion near Watchet, and Woodward (*in* Ussher, 1908) reviewed historical evidence for retreat of the cliffs. Whittaker and Green (1983) noted that slight undercutting still occurred, and that resultant landslips from the cliffs took the form of sludged masses, rotational slips and collapse along fault lines; however, they considered that little change had taken place since Blake's record of 1871, mainly because waves now lose most of their energy in crossing the wide wave-cut platform.

Chronology

The probable Quaternary chronology may be summarised as follows. Over-large valleys in the Quantock and Brendon hills were traversed by glaciers descending from local ice caps in Anglian and Wolstonian times. Wolstonian ice blocked the Bristol Channel, impounding water at 85 to 90 m above OD which overflowed southwards at Chard (Figure 13). Pebbly drift at this altitude between Doniford and Weacombe may be a beach deposit related to this lake. Ice floes carrying small quantities of sediment drifted across the lake. Sediments of the 2nd Terrace are also Wolstonian, but somewhat later in age, when the ice front had begun to retreat, the lake level had fallen and drainage was again northerly. The 1st Terrace correlates with the Burtle Beds and the raised beach, all of Ipswichian age. Head was formed by periglacial (Devensian) and Recent weathering; in places it grades into river alluvium, which in turn passes into estuarine alluvium. The alluvial deposits are of Flandrian (Recent) age. Where conditions favoured the formation of peat, and it was not overwhelmed by accumulation of estuarine mud, considerable thicknesses built up; all the peat is of Flandrian age and its formation continued until Roman times.

EAE, BJW

DETAILS

2nd Terrace or ?Beach-deposits of 'Lake Maw'

Three patches of pebbly drift [100 410; 103 413; 103 407] to the west and north-west of Weacombe are characterised by well-rounded pebbles of Devonian sandstone and a few of (?Devonian) limestone. Some angular stones are present. The drift is thin, and the soil includes much silty clay derived from underlying mudstones of the Mercia Mudstone Group. The drift lies at 85 to 100 m above OD, somewhat higher than the 2nd Terrace deposits mapped elsewhere in the district.

2nd Terrace

Most of the 2nd Terrace deposits in the south of the district lie between Bishops Lydeard and Tone Vale Hospital. Traces of gravel are seen locally [1660 2913; 1663 2924] but most of the occurrences are evident only as patches of pebbly soil [165 294; 168 291; 171 287; 175 284; 165 279; 172 276], marking drift probably rarely more than 1 m thick at altitudes of between 60 m and 45 m above OD. A similar small patch [157 265] near Heathfield lies at 64 m above OD Woodward (*in* Ussher, 1908) recorded up to 1 m of gravel in the roadside east of Tithill [169 280]. The Iron Age fort [196 263] just north of Norton Fitzwarren was constructed on a hillock capped by 2nd Terrace gravels, where some flint and chert are present among pebbles of Devonian sandstone and slate with some quartz; Ussher (1908) recorded 0.76 m of gravel in a pit.

In the north of the district, two large patches of pebbly drift [212 395; 218 401] occur south of Fiddington, at 76 to 45 m above OD, and two smaller patches [222 400; 224 405] to the east are within the same height range. Pebbles of Devonian sandstone abound on the surface. About 1 m of gravel overlies red Mercia Mudstone in the bank of a pond [2219 3997], and 2.4 m of gravel in a roadside pit [2239 4052] south-west of Bonson comprise pebbles of Devonian sandstone in a matrix of red sandy loam.

1st Terrace

Flats adjoining but slightly higher than river alluvium to the west [145 243; 154 246] and east [176 245] of Hillfarrance are of silty clay with scattered stones and pebbles. Large patches of 1st Terrace remain between Kingston St Mary and Taunton. The biggest spreads occur around Taunton and range from 38 m above OD to occurrences alongside the River Tone at 15 m. Roadside exposures [2189 2964; 2214 2961; 2230 2904] in and near Kingston St Mary show gravel composed largely of rounded slaty fragments with lesser amounts of sandstone. Slightly clayey slate gravel [2173 2804] alongside the road near Dodhill was seen by Ussher (1908) to be current-bedded, and similar exposures [2131 2771] to the south-west show 2 m of poorly graded bedded slaty gravel.

Pebbly silt and sand have been dug [2121 2646] in the churchyard at Staplegrove, whereabouts Woodward (*in* Ussher, 1908) noted 4 m of fine gravel made up of slate, sandstone and quartz. Similar gravel, within a spread of 1st Terrace to the east of Staplegrove, was dug from a roadside trench [2151 2662]. Kingston Road shows traces of gravel in hedge banks [2230 2710; 2229 2697], and it was probably from these gravels in the neighbourhood of the school [223 262] immediately west of the road that remains of reindeer and bison, now in Taunton Museum, were recovered (Ussher, 1908). These terrace deposits extend eastward through Taunton, on the northern side of the railway, and adjoin the alluvium of the River Tone immediately east of the town; Ussher (1908) noted gravel of quartz and sandstone in loamy sand in a pit thereabouts. Gravels are seen to overlie red Mercia Mudstone [2271 2552] immediately north of the railway station. Woodward (*in* Ussher, 1908) recorded marl overlain by 2.7 m of gravel with seams of sand, capped by 1 m of 'brickearth', in a pit just north of the station. Similar deposits south of the railway, in North Town, contained pits that, in 1880, showed 1.5 m of gravel (Ussher, 1908). Pebbly soils extend over a wide area in the Pyrland district of Taunton [228 267]; three gravel pits are said to have been worked within the memories of older residents, but no trace remains.

1st Terrace deposits extend as broad flat areas alongside stream alluvium between Currypool Farm [226 384] and Blackmoor Farm [245 387]. Pebbles and subangular stones abound and the spreads pass up-slope into Head without any marked terrace back-feature. Similar sediments occur at Fiddington [217 406].

Terrace deposits, undifferentiated

Wide flat areas of drift sediments, comprising silts with local sands and clays, occupy valley heads at and north-east of Wiveliscombe, and between that town and Screedy to the south-east; their limits are commonly not well defined at the terrace backs. These deposits have been mapped as river terraces but they are too distant from 1st and 2nd terraces to permit correlation.

About 1 km south-west of Kingston St Mary, a low-lying area [215 287] north-west and south-west of Nailsbourne falls southwards from about 45 m above OD to 31 m. It is thus rather lower than the 1st Terrace alongside Kingston Road to the east, and only very slightly above the alluvium into which it merges. Although boundaries are poorly defined, roadside exposures [2167 2849] in Nailsbourne show up to 2 m of slaty gravel. No comparable spread of drift occurs near by, and the deposit is one which in the past might have been called 'older alluvium'.

Within the several patches of 'undifferentiated' terrace between Spaxton and Charlinch, east of the Quantock Hills, an excavation [2158 3670] at Absley Farm showed 0.5 m of well-sorted fine-grained gravel resting on Otter Sandstone, and a bank [2422 3739] west of Little Charlynch is in pebbly gravel.

Burtle Beds

The low relief of the outcrops of Burtle Beds and the nature of the deposits are not conducive to natural exposure. Kidson and others (1981, p. 39) recorded temporary exposures seen in 1973 at Penzoy Farm [337 348]. Their composite section of the Burtle Beds (overlain by made ground 1.1 m, on Flandrian silts 0.5 m, discontinuous detrital peat 0.2 m, and brown silty loams 0.05 m) was briefly as follows:

	Thickness m
Sands, cross-stratified, well sorted, with abundant *Macoma balthica* valves. A few pieces of drifted wood of Flandrian age at 0.07 m above the base	0.55
Intertidal/brackish water silts; blue-grey; rich in *Hydrobia* spp. The upper boundary interdigitates with the sands above	0.50
Sands, cross-stratified, well sorted; largely unseen below the water table	*more than* 1.50

Alluvium and peat

Alluvial surfaces generally have silty soils, which are locally clayey or sandy. Where streams have cut sharply into alluvium, the finer deposits near the surface are seen to be underlain by gravel, as in the minor stream [1123 3783] east of Kingswood. Farther up the stream of which that is a tributary, this gravel comprises pebbles of sandstone and slate [1149 3475]. Small streams farther south run in similar deposits [e.g. 1053 2820].

Larger streams converging on Taunton from the west are commonly slow moving and do not cut sharp sections. Material from a pipeline cutting [174 290] in alluvium south-east of Bishops Lydeard included pebbles of sandstone and quartzite up to 0.2 m across. The alluvial plain at Norton Fitzwarren is crossed by a number of small channels; gravel has been dug from one [1914 2567], and another shows 0.5 m of gravel overlain by 0.5 m of silt [1932 2584].

At Hillfarrance [167 247] the alluvial flat of the stream that approaches the village from the west divides to surround an 'island' of red Mercia Mudstone, beyond which it merges into the flood plain of the River Tone. Present flow is via the Hillfarrance Brook in the southern flat, with the northern flat containing only very small drainage channels but with 1.5 m of gravel exposed at a roadside [1662 2486]. Approximate altitudes are 32 m above OD at Hillfarrance and 27 and 24 m above OD at the two points of confluence with the River Tone. Between these two junctions a river-bank section in alluvium [1803 2429] shows 2.5 m of silt and sand. Both the wide alluvial plain on the north-west side of the river and the northern loop of alluvium at Hillfarrance relate to flooding which historical records suggest has been not infrequent during the last few thousand years. Two other exposures in this stretch of the River Tone, both in the north-western bank of the river [1799 2439; 1863 2477], show red marl up to 1.2 m thick apparently underlain by gravel. The marl is such as would normally be unhesitatingly accepted as an *in situ* exposure, and the most likely explanation is that the bank is deeply undercut, the River Tone having been confined within narrow lateral limits for a long time. A less probable explanation is that one or more rafts of red marl were transported and laid down, possibly by drifting ice floes or solifluction, either in a single move or in a succession of moves perhaps spanning a long period; large rafts of apparently undisturbed strata are known within glacial deposits in the Midlands, but it seems improbable that such incompetent rock as Mercia Mudstone would have survived the journey unless in a frozen state.

Alluvium north-west of Norton Fitzwarren also surrounds an 'island' of red Mercia Mudstone [189 264] and, as at Hillfarrance, this wide alluvial spread may be product of Flandrian flooding. The disposition of 1st Terrace and alluvium around the Mercia Mudstone of the Lambrook area [245 250] of Taunton suggests that similar flooding took place there in Ipswichian times. Ussher (1908) reported a discovery of the frontal bone and antlers of the Irish elk on the site of the gas works at Tangier [222 247], presumably from alluvium. Much of the alluvial flat immediately to the east of Taunton has been buried beneath refuse, the resultant made ground has been grassed, and the River Tone runs in a man-made channel.

The general alluvial sequence of silts overlying gravels, sporadically exposed alongside the River Tone as elsewhere, is much in evidence in the stream which flows east-north-eastward from Currypool Farm [226 384] to Cannington; up to 2 m of gravel and up to 1.5 m of silt, locally stony, are visible. EAE

The M5 motorway crosses the valley of the River Tone between Bathpool and Ruishton to the east of Taunton, and trial boreholes [2585 2525 to 2625 2581] proved the alluvial deposits to range in thickness from 5.17 m in the south to 2 m in the north. The red Mercia Mudstone is overlain by 0 to 2.44 m of gravel, with 1.2 to 3.8 m of brown silty and sandy clays and top soil above. Downstream along the River Tone grey to yellowish brown silty clay is exposed in the drainage ditches and bluish grey clay is occasionally seen. Soils are rather peaty on Curry Moor but no mappable deposit of peat was detected.

In the south-eastern extremity of the district an extensive peat deposit is found on West Sedge Moor. The boundary of the peat is not marked by a feature. Dredging near Huntham [3450 2570] revealed 0.35 m of topsoil, on 0.25 m of bleached peat, on 1.3 m of dark grey peat, on 0.5 m of dark grey to black peat. Deeper ditches show at least 2.5 m of peat. The alluvium in this valley is a greyish brown silty clay.

A narrow tract of alluvium consisting of pale grey silty clay runs eastwards off the Quantocks through King's Cliff Wood towards North Petherton, where it terminates in a degraded spread some way from the alluvium of the River Parrett and about 20 m above its general level. A small area of peat was mapped around Northmoor Corner [314 309] and up to 1.75 m of peat was recorded in drainage ditches; the peat outcrop is not feature bounded and may possibly extend eastwards into North Moor, where rather peat-rich soils were seen, in places associated with shelly loamy clay. Two large areas of peat extend into the district from the east at Andersea and at Lang Moor.

Trial boreholes for the M5 motorway gave a section across the Parrett valley along a curved line on the east side of Bridgwater. A borehole [3115 3504] 0.5 km north of Huntworth proved the following drift succession above the red Mercia Mudstone, the surface level being 6.17 m above OD:

	Thickness m	*Depth* m
Top soil	0.30	0.30
ALLUVIUM		
Clay, reddish brown, silty, stiff	1.38	1.68
Sand, reddish brown and grey, clayey, fine-grained, dense	3.20	4.88
Peat, black and brown, fibrous and compact; a sample gave a radiocarbon date of 4200 ± 100 BP	1.52	6.40
RED MERCIA MUDSTONE	10.36	16.76

Closely spaced boreholes across the Parrett [3125 3512 to 3162 3563] showed the thickness of the drift deposits to increase north-north-eastwards; clay consistently overlay sand, but the thick basal peat was not everywhere present, being split by layers of clay and sand. A borehole [3176 3582] 0.7 km west-south-west of Dunwear House (surface level 6.02 m above OD) gave the following section, with no basal peat:

	Thickness m	*Depth* m
Top soil	0.61	0.61
ALLUVIUM		
Clay, grey and brown mottled, silty with fine sand laminae, firm	1.68	2.29
Sand, grey and brown, fine- to medium-grained, silty and slightly clayey	1.44	3.73
Sand, grey, fine- to medium-grained, silty and loose	1.45	5.18
Peat, black and brown, fibrous and fairly compact	0.45	4.11
Clay, grey, silty, with traces of peat	5.57	9.68
Peat, black and brown, silty, with traces of peat and sand	2.89	12.95
Sand, grey, fine-grained, silty; yellowish brown and clayey towards the base	7.62	20.57
Clay, dark greyish brown, peaty	0.46	21.03
Peat, black and brown	0.15	21.18
Gravel, brown, coarse- to fine-grained, and coarse- to fine-grained sand	2.90	24.08
RED MERCIA MUDSTONE	5.94	30.02

Boreholes near Metford House [3229 3801] and up to 1.7 km to the north-north-west proved shallower sequences. One [3205 3866], starting at 6.55 m above OD, penetrated the following strata:

	Thickness m	*Depth* m
Top soil	0.30	0.30
ALLUIIUM		
Clay, grey and brown, silty, with fine white rootlets; peaty below 2.6 m	3.66	3.96
Peat, black and brown, fibrous	0.61	4.51
Clay, grey, silty, with peat traces	5.95	10.52
Sand, grey, silty, fine-grained, with a little clay and traces of peat	1.67	12.19
Clay, dark grey, silty, with peat traces	2.44	14.63
RED MERCIA MUDSTONE	6.32	20.95

The borehole [3166 3925] 1.7 km north-north-west of Metford House started from a surface level of 6.1 m above OD and found 2.29 m of peat, with its base at 12.65 m depth. A borehole [3145 4020] 0.75 km south-south-east of Dunball was in a thicker sequence, as follows, the surface level being 5.49 m above OD:

	Thickness m	*Depth* m
Top soil	0.46	0.46
ALLUVIUM		
Clay, grey and brown, laminated with some fine sand; traces of peat below 2.44 m	3.81	4.27
Sand, grey, fine- and medium-grained, loose, with a trace of silt and clay	1.37	5.64
Clay, black and brown, peaty	0.46	6.10
Sand, grey, fine- and medium-grained, with laminae of silty clay	11.58	17.68
Peat, black and brown, fibrous and compact	0.76	18.44
Gravel, reddish brown and grey, with clayey sand matrix	2.89	21.33
RED MERCIA MUDSTONE	1.07	22.40

Near the margin of the alluvium to the east of Dunball the drift found in a further borehole [3146 4098] was entirely sand, grey and fine- to medium-grained, with laminae of clay and silt; the surface of the red Mercia Mudstone was reached at a depth of 9.14 m (3.47 m below OD). BJW

Head

In the north-west, where Head has accumulated as locally well-defined valley-fill (p.50), Whittaker and Green (1983) recorded the following exposures: red pebbly loamy sand 1.22 m thick in a bank [1333 4310], 0.9 m thick in a pond [1346 4318] and 1.07 m thick in a ditch [1350 4327]; pebbly sands and loams seen for 1.22 m [1497 4316], 0.91 m [1500 4341 and 1501 4337], and 0.5 m [1540 4340].

Elsewhere Head forms a mantle over most ground away from steep slopes. On the top of the Quantock Hills sections show up to 1.5 m of sandy stony drift. To the west, exposed thicknesses generally range up to 3 m at Flaxpool [141 353], and to the east up to 2.5 m at Pightley [228 359]. The material is commonly stony, with a matrix reflecting the nature of the local rock. A small pit [2393 3880] south-west of Brymore, having the appearance of an old marlpit but of which little now remains, was noted by Ussher (1908) as a gravel pit; his record of over 1 m of mainly angular and subangular stones in sand may be of Head. EAE, BJW

CHAPTER 8

Geological Structure

GENERAL ACCOUNT

The structure of the district (Figure 14) can be summarised very briefly. Folds and most faults in the Palaeozoic rocks were produced during the Variscan orogeny by compressive forces acting from the south. Tensional fractures accompanied early uplift and also followed the waning of the main fold movements, and some faults were probably active at different times under both compression and tension. Permo-Triassic rocks were deposited on an uneven post-orogenic surface in two major basins whose development was governed in part by continued subsidence between old boundary fault lines.

The Variscan Front may be defined as the northern limit of a region of intensely folded and fractured rocks of east – west structural grain. North of the front, in Variscan (late Carboniferous to early Permian) times, lay a more stable foreland and a transition to simpler folding. So defined, the Variscan Front may be thought to lie north of the Mendip Hills, well beyond the present district. However, it seems likely that the southward change from a northern-type Carboniferous sequence, represented by Carboniferous Limestone and Rodway Siltstones at Cannington, to a southern Culm facies, reflects a 'hinge' in basement rocks which divided a shallow shelf sea to the north from a basin deepening to the south. Perhaps this 'hinge' determined the position of the Variscan Front, even though it was overridden for a short distance by Variscan folds. The 'front' in this area might, therefore, be regarded as a zone extending in width from south of Cannington Park to north of the Mendip Hills. The isolated occurrence of Carboniferous strata at Cannington suggests an alternative, if highly speculative, possibility. It may be that this mass of Carboniferous rocks, possibly with some underlying Devonian, slid an unknown

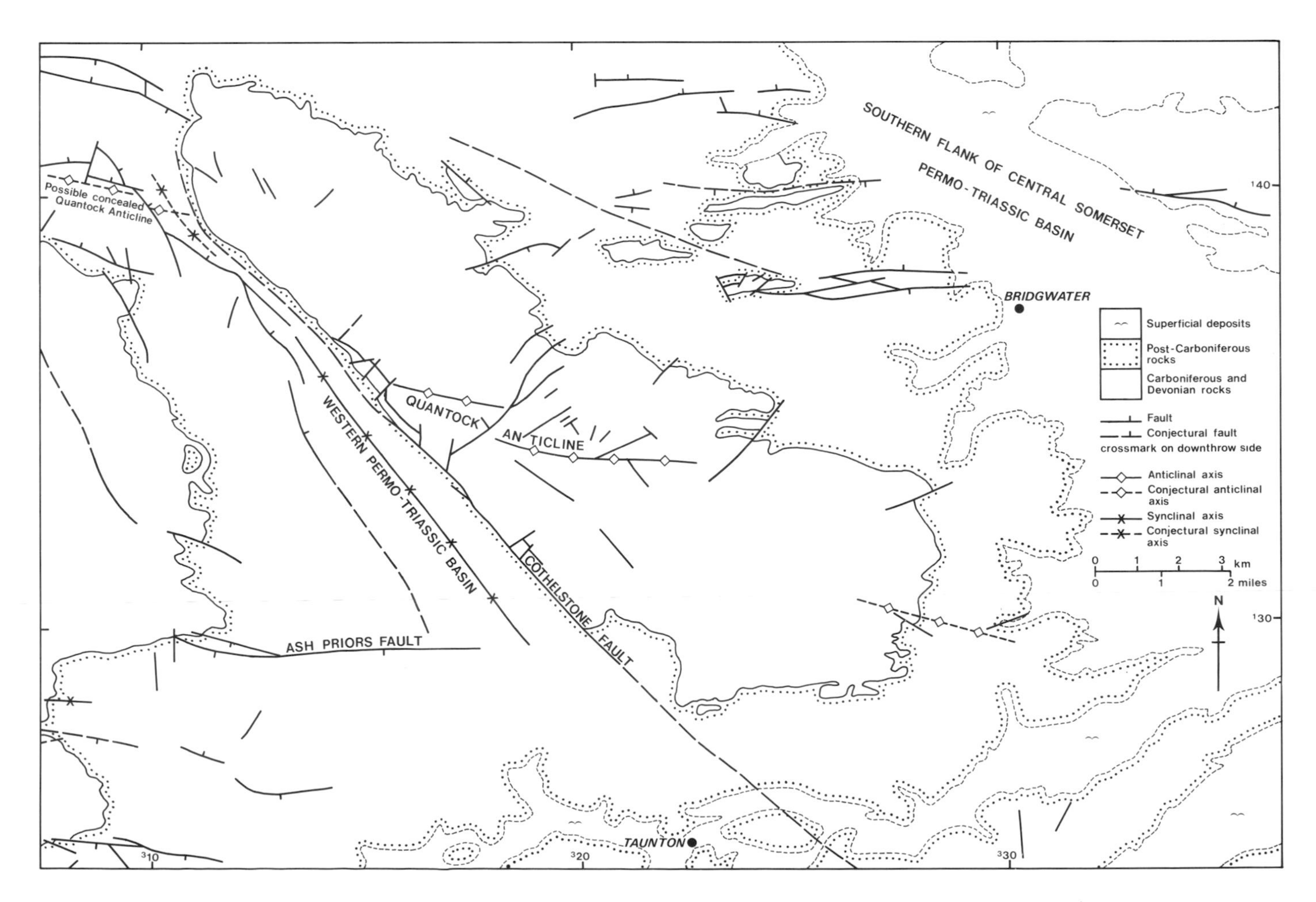

Figure 14 Main structural elements of Taunton and the Quantock Hills

distance southwards down the basinal slope in late Carboniferous times; if so the 'hinge' lies farther north, and is more nearly coincident with the change in fold style, than it now appears to be. Interpretation of the Cannington limestone as a local development on a rise of the sea floor would also accord with a more northerly position of the 'hinge'.

In a fairly rugged post-Variscan landscape, Permo-Triassic sediments accumulated in depressions, progressively younger deposits overlapping earlier strata so as gradually to coalesce from one depression to another. Two main sedimentary basins are present in the district. The smaller (western) basin trends north-westwards between the Devonian rocks of the Brendon and the Quantock hills. The larger, of which only the southern part lies within the present district, is the Central Somerset Basin which trends west-north-west between the Quantock and the Mendip Hills and may pass westwards into the Bristol Channel Syncline and eastwards into the Glastonbury Syncline (Whittaker, 1975a). It is likely that development of both basins was facilitated by normal fault movements in the tensional phase that followed the Variscan Orogeny, and that some, at least, of these movements occurred along existing fractures with a long history of activity which continued into Jurassic times and perhaps later. Lloyd and others (1973) suggested the presence of an east – west offshore fracture along the southern edge of the Bristol Channel Syncline, with a postulated downthrow of 450 m to the north. This fracture could be a normal fault, rather than the thrust suggested. Evans and Thompson (1979) however, considered that there is no major strike fault along the southern edge of the Bristol Channel Syncline, but that its northern margin is faulted in the west.

Given gradual subsidence into a trough, and final coalescing of the highest beds between one depositional area and the next, it may be presumed that within the major basins the Permo-Triassic rocks are synclinal, the formations being thicker towards the centres of the basins, and that the topmost beds are fairly flat lying except where affected by faults.

Quantock Hills and eastern Brendon Hills

The Quantock Anticline is a major open fold whose axis trends east-south-east through Triscombe [155 356] and east through Courtway [205 340], as the Courtway Anticline of Webby (1966a), roughly in line with the Lynton Anticline (Edmonds and others, 1985) 40 km to the west-north-west. It has a gentle easterly plunge. Dips are variable in amount, particularly within the more argillaceous sequences, and minor flexures are common locally, but the general dips of the limbs of the Quantock Anticline probably rarely exceed about 20°.

Webby (1965a) located several fold axes in the Devonian rocks which form the eastern end of the Brendon Hills, but none that could be traced into the present district. These rocks lie on the southern limb of the major anticline, having been moved dextrally by north-west – south-east faulting.

Cleavage planes in the Devonian rocks of the Quantock Hills, most evident in the slaty sequences, generally dip between south and south-south-east at various angles, perhaps on average more steeply in the south (about 50°) than in the north (about 40°) (Webby, 1966a). In the eastern Brendon Hills, too, the cleavage steepens from north to south. It may be presumed that these cleavage planes indicate the attitudes of the axial planes of minor folds, which are usually overturned to the north, and the southward steepening accords with evidence from the Bideford and Barnstaple districts (Edmonds and others, 1979; 1984). Scattered exposures of folded strata confirm the presumption.

Webby (1966a) considered that most of the displacement between the Devonian rocks of the Quantock Hills and those of the Brendons was accounted for by the Cothelstone Fault, which defines the Quantock Hills on their south-western side. He applied ratios of vertical to horizontal movement derived from a study of his Timberscombe fault system in the Brendon Hills, which trends north-westwards towards the Vale of Porlock Permo-Triassic basin, and suggested a dextral displacement of 5 km and a south-westerly downthrow of almost 2000 m. Steep-sided valleys trending south-south-east and north-north-west from Elworthy probably follow Webby's (1966a) Monksilver Fault, which he noted as showing a dextral displacement of about 360 m in the area to the west. The small Permo-Triassic outlier at Elworthy Cross lies on the divide between the two head-waters and is probably the remains of a larger deposit in a fault-controlled depression.

It seems possible that additional north-westerly faults are concealed beneath the Permo-Triassic rocks of the western sedimentary basin, perhaps along each side, and that the displacements of the adjoining Devonian rocks are cumulative. If we disregard the younger rocks and suppose the two areas of Devonian to be brought together, then upper Morte Slates abut against Lynton Slates and the downthrow is about 1400 m south-westerly; the base of the Morte Slates north of Stogumber shows an overall dextral displacement of about 8 km in relation to the same horizon near Cothelstone.

The Cothelstone Fault and related north-westerly fractures bounding or within or beneath the Permo-Triassic basin belong to the set of such wrench faults that cut across south-west England (Dearman, 1964). In many cases movement has been both horizontal and vertical, and activity has continued intermittently until Tertiary or even present-day times (Edmonds and others, 1968). Shearman (1967), basing his arguments on laboratory experiments, speculated that movement on north-westerly wrench faults in the basement could have produced east – west structures in the overlying blanket of Mesozoic rocks. Whittaker (1972) noted that the Liassic rocks of the west Somerset coast owed their position at the foot of the Quantocks massif to east – west faulting, but that renewed activity along the wrench faults in the basement might be expected to produce north-westerly structures in the younger rocks. He described a post-Liassic fault at the coast 1 km west of Watchet, and outside the present district, which is aligned with the Cothelstone Fault; it is a reverse fault downthrowing 55 m to the north-east and showing a dextral displacement of about 275 m. EAE, BJW

Palaeozoic rocks of the Cannington Park area

Geophysical data for north Devon and west Somerset have been interpreted as indicating the existence of an Exmoor-

Cannington Thrust (Falcon, *in* discussion of Cook and Thirlaway, 1952; Bott and others, 1958), with Devonian rocks thrust northwards over lower density Carboniferous strata. However, the evidence could equally well reflect facies or thickness variations within the Devonian (Bott and Scott, 1966; Cornwell, 1971; Donovan, 1971; Brooks and Thompson, 1973). Brooks and others (1977) envisaged that thick low-density Lower Palaeozoic or Precambrian rocks, whose upper surface dipped southwards beneath the Devonian, might be responsible for the observed anomaly.

Structural relationships of Palaeozoic rocks in the Cannington area are important to the possible interpretations of the geophysical evidence. One of the bounding faults of the Central Somerset Basin may be presumed to trend slightly north of west between the ?Namurian strata (Rodway Siltstones) of the Swang Farm inlier and the Ilfracombe Slates (Leighland Slates) little more than 300 m to the south. A possible vertical throw of a few thousand metres is indicated, but if the Carboniferous rocks slid into their present position (p. 55) this estimate loses much of its meaning. Swang Farm No. 1 Borehole [2295 3891] passed through red-stained faulted strata around the base of the Permo-Triassic rocks, and Swang Farm No. 2 Borehole [2296 3891] proved an unconformable base to the Permo-Triassic and a fault 4.55 m below (Whittaker, 1978). Probably the older rocks penetrated were the same as those of the Swang Farm inlier, the major fracture runs slightly to the south, and the fault proved is one of several (or many) of similar trend.

Withiel Farm No. 1 [2435 3981] and No. 2 [2452 3993] boreholes (p. 23) proved Rodway Siltstones of late Namurian age, locally overfolded and fractured, on Carboniferous Limestone, a stratigraphical break of at least several hundred metres, In both cases the contact was a normal fault and characterised by red staining. Whittaker (1975b) noted that the simplest structural explanation was high-angle normal faulting between Viséan rocks to the north and late Namurian rocks to the south, but went on to suggest that the low-angle (10°) contact in No. 2 Borehole might be a lag fault and that an association of lag faults with thrusts in the Mendip area (Green and Welch, 1965) might point to the presence of a major (northward) thrust below Cannington Park. However, the evidence is slender, and it is presumed here that both the major faults, between Carboniferous Limestone and Rodway Siltstone and between Rodway Siltstone and Leighland Slates, are east – west normal faults. EAE

Mesozoic basins

There is no direct evidence of the depth of the Permo-Triassic basin between the Quantock and the Brendon hills. Indications are of a gentle inward slope from the west and of a markedly steeper slope from the east, with most of the faulting towards the eastern side. Tentative estimates, little more than guesses, suggest a maximum depth of about 240 m to the base of the Permo-Triassic rocks in the area midway between Bishops Lydeard and Williton. The axis of the contined syncline runs roughly parallel to the edge of the Devonian rocks of the Quantock Hills and perhaps little more than 1 km from it.

The Cothelstone Fault cuts Otter Sandstone and Mercia Mudstone Group rocks at its south-eastern end. To the north-west of Triscombe it cannot be traced accurately within the red Mercia Mudstone, but it may pass close to Weacombe where fractured red Mercia Mudstone has been recorded. A roughly parallel fault bounds the red Mercia Mudstone on its south-western side for much of its outcrop from Rich's Holford to beyond Bicknoller. The vertical components of movement on these two faults are respectively down to the south-west and down to the north-east, and the axial region of the western Permo-Triassic syncline and trough lies between them. The basin is marked by east – west faulting near Sampford Brett towards the north-west and near Ash Priors and Bishops Lydeard towards the south-east. Northerly dips are associated with the faults near Sampford Brett.

The Central Somerset Basin (Whittaker, 1973; Whittaker and Green, 1983) has fairly steep sides and a flat bottom, and may have originated in a broad syncline in Palaeozoic rocks between the anticlines of the Quantock Hills and the Mendip Hills, a syncline which gradually developed into a fault-bounded trough or graben. Tectonic continuity westwards to the Bristol Channel and eastwards to Glastonbury was first suggested by Jones (1930). Mesozoic rocks within the trough are disposed in a syncline which follows a west-north-westerly trend. Many of the formations thicken into the basin, and it is possible that boundary faults were active in Mesozoic times. The Puriton Borehole, sunk to 631.64 m, failed to reach the floor of the basin, as did the Burton Row Borehole, sunk to 1105.17 m, north of the present district. Otter Sandstone crops out between Cannington and Wembdon, but lies beneath 388 m of Mercia Mudstone at Puriton and at 906 m depth at Burton Row, 11 km to the north. Penarth Group strata crop out at 60 m above O.D. near Puriton and were proved at 403 m below O.D. at Burton Row.

Dips in the Mercia Mudstone Group suggest a thickness of 150 m in the Cannington area, at the southern edge of the basin, although unknown faults may render this figure false, and the Group, including its contained saliferous strata and the Blue Anchor Formation, all thickens northwards into the basin (Whittaker, 1973).

It seems probable that downwarping of younger strata into the graben continued during Mesozoic times and perhaps later, and was accompanied by faulting, mainly near the margins of the basin, trending around west-north-west or west.

Whittaker and Green (1983) noted that on the coast, where the rocks of the upper parts of the two main Mesozoic basins coalesce, east-south-easterly normal faults with throws of up to 220 m are associated with minor folds of similar trend. Such flexures occur also in the Polden Hills, and presumably in Liassic strata beneath the adjacent alluvium. Minor normal faults of different trend are also present, together with small reverse faults and thrusts, indicating compressional and tensional movements in Jurassic or post-Jurassic times. EAE, BJW

DETAILS

Devonian

LYNTON SLATES

A quarry [1554 3543] near Triscombe shows cleavage planes inclined at 65°/180°. In another [1621 3452], near Rock Farm, the rocks are disposed in an east – west syncline whose limbs dip at 30° and 50° northwards and are cut by north – south faults.

HANGMAN GRITS

Trentishoe Grits

Shales, siltstones and sandstones in Halsway Quarry [1351 3808] are locally sheared, and a steep south-westerly dip [1343 3805] is associated with north-westerly fractures parallel to the Cothelstone Fault. A quarry [1444 3680] at the lower end of Crowcombe Combe is overgrown but appears to contain beds dipping at 20° north-westward, cut by joints inclined at 30° south-eastward. The trends do not accord with that of either the Quantock Anticline or the Cothelstone Fault and point to the probable presence of a north-east – south-west fault running up the combe.

On the opposite side of the Quantock Hills, in a quarry [1680 3764] in Rams Combe, strata at the top of the Trentishoe Grits appear to be cut by minor faults of various and uncertain trend. Exposures in a quarry [1699 3708] on the slopes of Quantock Combe are disturbed and cut by a vertical fault trending 350°. visible as a fault gouge 0.3 m wide.

The large quarry [161 356] east of Triscombe shows joints inclined to the south-west at moderate and steep angles of about 45° and 70° respectively; dips are 12° to 20° mainly between east-north-east and east-south-east. To the south, on Bagborough Hill [1618 3474], sandstones and slates are cut by a fault trending slightly west of north.

Rawn's Shales-and-Sandstones

The 'dog-leg' course of Weacombe Combe is attributable to a fault trending north-north-west, and siltstones and sandstones exposed near by [1197 4053] show traces of slickensides.

Red and cream shales in rubbly exposures [169 346] for 100 m alongside a track between Bagborough Hill and Middle Hill show dips to north-north-west and south-south-east. They lie on the southern limb of the Quantock Anticline, and their small-scale crumpling is indicative of the way in which argillaceous successions have accommodated much earth movement.

Little Hangman Sandstones

In the northern Quantock Hills, minor flexures aligned approximately with the Quantock Anticline are seen in a quarry [113 415] at West Quantoxhead (p. 14), irregular jointing is exposed on Stowborrow Hill [1200 4183], and joints dipping steeply south-south-west [1315 4129] and west-south-west [1403 4154] were noted in combes to the east. Strata near the top of the formation in a quarry [152 405] in Holford Combe are disposed in a near-recumbent minor anticline and syncline plunging at about 15° to just south of east; this is a rare example of intense folding in hard sandstones, and the rock is much fractured.

ILFRACOMBE SLATES

Avill Slates-and-Sandstones

Sandstones with tuff abut against Permo-Triassic conglomerates in Holford Glen; the junction [1553 4123] is a normal fault trending north-west – south-east (Figure 6). Strata near the top of the formation in a quarry [1782 3864] to the south-east are cut by joints dipping at 60° west-south-west.

In the southern part of the outcrop adjacent exposures [1735 3445] show dip and cleavage inclined at 15° to 30° between south-south-west and south-south-east.

Cutcombe Slates

Slates at the mouth of Keeper's Combe [1877 3720] show cleavage dipping at 30° southward. In a quarry [1898 3722] to the east, the Rodhuish Limestone is disposed in an overturned syncline (Figure 15) plunging east-south-eastward at about 17°. The axial plane of the fold is inclined at 20° to the south-east, and thin slaty calcareous rocks overlying and underlying the limestone show strong axial plane cleavage that, but for the folding of the limestone, could be mistaken for bedding. Slates immediately south-east of the quarry show cleavage dipping at 10° south-south-eastward [1902 3719].

Slates and calcareous slates in Hunt's Lane [1890 3530 to 1889 3478], east of Durborough Farm, show cleavage dipping south or south-south-west at up to 40° where not affected by superficial creep. Farther to the south-east, in the area around Courtway [204 340] through which runs the axis of the Quantock Anticline, cleavage in slates and silty slates dips at 20° to 45° mainly between south-south-east and south.

Figure 15 Overturned syncline in the Rodhuish Limestone at Pepper Hill

Leighland Slates: Roadwater Limestone

Massive limestone quarried [1723 4042] at Dodington dips at 80°/055° towards a fault trending north-west – south-east; calcareous slates above and below the limestone show cleavage planes dipping in the same direction as the limestone but less steeply. This suggests the possibility that overfolding has occurred, and strata to the south dipping at 65°/090° [1782 3964] and near horizontal [1793 3940] further indicate the presence of folds within the northern outcrop of the Roadwater Limestone.

South of Over Stowey, dips of 15° to east-north-east [1833 3827] and 45°/190° [1846 3820] indicate that the folding is less intense, and from north to south of Aisholt [1915 3619 to 1974 3514] dips of 10° to 20° to between east and north-east are apparently fairly uniform inclinations within the northern limb of the Quantock Anticline. The limestone outcrop in the Aisholt area is cut by a number of north-east – south-west sinistral faults, and by an east-north-east – west-south-west dextral fault west of Lower Aisholt. On the southern side of the last fault, to the south-west of Lower Aisholt, the outcrop is displaced by further small sinistral faults trending north-east – south-west, with which are associated an anomalous dip of 15°/140° [1967 3489] and traces of overfolds on east-north-east axes with axial planes inclined at 50° to the south-south-east [1981 3477].

A quarry [1998 3470] north-west of Lower Merridge shows limestone both horizontal and dipping at 25° to 30°/200° to 205°, and faulted against slates with calcareous lenses along a fracture aligned north-north-west – south-south-east. Close to the fault, slates are contorted and limestone shows traces of recumbent folds. Between Lower Merridge and Merridge the limestone is cut by three sinistral faults. In one quarry [2033 3457] massive limestone dipping gently north-north-eastward is overlain by slaty rocks with a strong cleavage inclined at 40° to the south. The outcrop in the Merridge area delineates the nose of the Quantock Anticline; dips swing from north-east, through east to south-east at 10° to 25°, but cleavage planes, in limestone and slates, are inclined southwards at 30° to 40°. Thus, in the quarry [2105 3400] that contains the entrance to Holwell Cave, the limestone dips at 10° eastward and cleavage at 35° south-south-eastward.

From Timbercombe to East Bagborough the Roadwater Limestone lies in the southern limb of the Quantock Anticline, and both bedding and cleavage dip south-south-east.

Leighland Slates: strata above the Roadwater Limestone

An old pit [1760 4027] in Otter Sandstone south-east of Dodington adjoins a north-west – south-east fault. The underlying Devonian slaty sandstone is exposed at one place in the pit and dips at 25°/200° towards the fault; a short distance to the north sandstones with slaty bands rise through red Mercia Mudstone and dip at 75°/050°.

Slates and sandstones west of Nether Stowey generally dip east or east-north-east, but in a small pit [1840 3931] near Bincombe sheared fractured sandstones strike north-west and dip vertically or steeply south-west, suggesting that north-west – south-east faulting may be present. In an inlier to the east, disturbed sandstone and Leigh Barton Limestone dip west-north-westward [2066 3882].

Manuscript records by Mr G. W. Green of site investigations for the dam [211 364] at Hawkridge reservoir suggest the presence of folding on north-west – south-east axes and at least one fault. A quarry [2013 3560] in Holwell Limestone on Hawkridge Common shows dips of 60°/190°; traces of cleavage inclined in a similar direction at lesser angle suggest the possibility of inversion, and the rocks have been disturbed by movement on bedding planes and by vertical strike faults.

The outcrop of the Holwell Limestone of Holwell Combe follows a gently sinuous course that indicates disposition in broad open folds of a few hundred metres wavelength on north-west – south-east axes. At the northern end of the crop dips of 15° and 20° around north-east and south-west point to the presence of small-scale folds of similar type and trend. At the southern end the limestone dips at 10° to 15° to the east, and cleavage planes at 35° to 45° south-eastward.

An old quarry [2468 3515] to the east of Enmore, at the easternmost limit of outcrop of the Ilfracombe Slates, shows folds whose axes trend just south of east and whose axial planes dip southward at 45° or more (Figure 16).

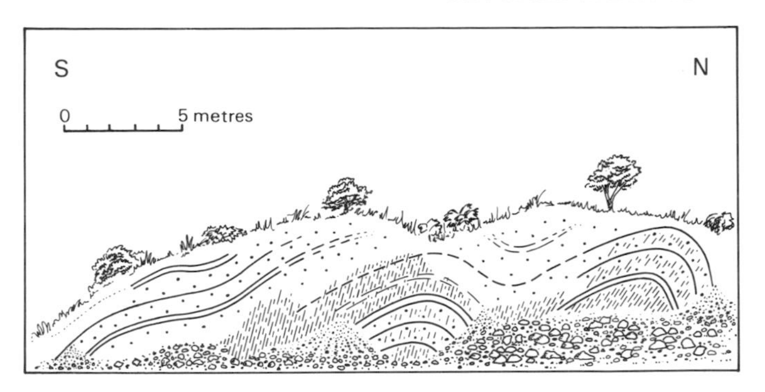

Figure 16 Folds in Leighland Slates at Enmore

Webby (1966a) noted a broad open syncline trending 110° in a quarry [2207 3401] in Wind Down. The Leigh Barton Limestone crops out to the east [231 337] in a form suggestive of folds trending east-north-east; Webby recognised some overturning thereabouts.

Quarries [1870 3191; 1884 3197; 1896 3184] in the Leigh Barton Limestone in Badger Copse show open flexures and also small-scale crumpling of about 0.3 m amplitude. Webby (1966a) noted the presence of overfolding. Axial planes dip at 15° to 45° northward.

Morte Slates

Throughout the western outcrop of Morte Slates, cleavage and bedding generally dip between south-east and south-west. On average, cleavage planes are less steep in the north than in the south; northerly inclinations, sporadic in the north, are commoner in the south. In a quarry [0776 3404] south-west of Elworthy, where relationships are clear, the bedding dips at 45°/150° and the cleavage at 60°/170°. In Oakhampton Quarries [085 301], cleavage is inclined at 60° to 80° between south-east and south-south-east; bedding, represented by silty streaks in the slates, dips at slightly lesser angles in similar directions.

In the eastern outcrop, slates to the east of Toulton and to the north of Cushuish show cleavage planes dipping steeply northerly or southerly, suggesting the presence of both north-facing and south-facing folds close to the Cothelstone Fault. Small folds in laneside exposures [195 309] north-west of Cushuish were recorded by Webby (1966a) as showing axial planes dipping at 25° south-east and a gentle plunge to east-north-east. A lane [1970 3067] in Cushuish exposes near-recumbent crumples on east – west axes. Slates in an old quarry [2035 3014] south-west of Tetton House show cleavage dipping at 60°/170°; some disturbance of the rocks may reflect proximity to the Cothelstone Fault.

Sandstones and slates in a quarry [2152 3095] north of Tanyard dip at about 35°/170°; in places cleavage planes dip steeply to the south at the top of the face, vertically midway down, and steeply to the north at the bottom, suggesting that the minor folds to which the cleavage is presumed to be axial planar have themselves suffered some distortion. Quartz veins following cleavage planes have been displaced by movements on bedding planes. Other quarries near by show cleavage dipping steeply to both north by east and south by east [2164 3081], and bedding and cleavage dipping respectively at 25° south-south-east and steeply south [2167 3060].

Slates in a quarry [2274 3235] north-east of Broomfield show cleavage dipping at 30°/175°; planes inclined southward at a slightly lesser angle may be joints or traces of bedding. In an exposure [2327 3150] 1 km south-east of the village, slates are cut by vertical joints trenting north-east – south-west. Contorted slates [2404 3079] at Oggshole Farm may indicate the presence of faults.

In the area south-east of Kingston St Mary, a small pit [2263 2928] shows bedding inclined at up to 25° southerly and cleavage at 45° to 50° southerly. A slightly larger pit [2318 2920], north of Upper Cheddon, shows slates with thin sandstones dipping at 40° to 50° southerly; cleavage is inclined at 65° to 75° southerly and two small normal faults coincident with cleavage planes have displaced sandstones by up to 0.5 m (Figure 8). Similar rocks in another quarry [2331 2911] near by show a clear distinction between bedding and cleavage, which respectively dip at 45°/180° and 55°/180°.

The quarry [2468 2915] north of Gotton, which lies roughly in line with the main dykes of Hestercombe, contains only slates with quartzites; the cleavage dips fairly steeply southward and the bedding mainly at about 20° south. The anticlinal undulation noted by Ussher (1908) trends east – west but is much obscured and overgrown.

In a wood [2545 3329] 0.4 km south of Halswell House, the strata dip at 20°/180°, and cleavage is inclined at 25°/160°; the dips of bedding and cleavage in a quarry [2610 3293] to the south-east are 15°/095° and 25°/155° respectively, and in the stream in Huntstile Bottom [2640 3385] they are 20°/200° and 60°/150°. In King's Cliff Quarry [277 326] bedding dip varies from 20° to 25°/100°, and cleavage is inclined at from 20° to 30°/155°. The strata seen in a roadside exposure [2753 3083] 250 m south of King's Farm dip at 15°/105°, the cleavage dip being 50°/172°. Laminated siltstones seen in an old quarry [2581 2919] east of Woodball Plantation and 700 m south of Quantock Farm dip at 50°/180°, with cleavage inclined at 55°/172°. In the quarries in Burlinch Plantation (p.19) the following dips were measured: bedding 40°/168° and cleavage 65°/175° [2630 2954]; cleavage 55°/168° [2632 2938]; and cleavage 70°/170° [2641 2940]. Just to the east of the plantation [2665 2948] inverted brownish grey slaty siltstone dips at 75°/188° with cleavage dipping at 55°/172°. At the northern end [2695 2913] of the quarry west of the road at Coombe, the beds dip at 65°/015° and cleavage dip is 75°/172°.

Pickwell Down Sandstones

Exposures within the small outcrop of Pickwell Down Sandstones occur mostly in the south, on the outskirts of Wiveliscombe. They show northerly dips of 50° to 60° [0739 2819; 0738 2774] with some faulting roughly coincident with bedding planes [0772 2790; 0769 2785]. No small folds were noted, but it seems possible that the whole outcrop is broadly synclinal on an east–west axis, with more sharply folded Morte Slates passing southward beneath it, and that the fairly steep northerly dips in the south may owe something to a conjectural east-west fracture concealed beneath the Permo-Triassic rocks whose narrow outcrop separates Pickwell Down Sandstones from Pilton Shales.

Pilton Shales

The Pilton Shales outcrop contains few large exposures. Observed dips are mainly steep, in one case 45° but usually 60° to 80°, in directions around north-north-west and south-south-east. This suggestion of the presence of upright close to tight folds is confirmed by exposures in the old railway cutting [066 251] west of Woodlands Farm and just outside the district.

Carboniferous

The Carboniferous Limestone of Cannington Park (Chapter 3) is much jointed and slickensided. As seen by Dr A. Whittaker during the recent survey it showed northerly dips of up to 15° in some places, and similar dips could be inferred in others. However, in the main quarry, Cannington Park Quarry [251 404], the dip is not clear. Broad stratigraphical sequences in the northern and southern faces suggest a gentle northward dip, but it was this quarry from which Ussher (1908) quoted records of the presence of an anticline in which he recognised traces of an undulating quaquaversal dip, and from the southern face of which he noted easterly and westerly dips of 50° to 55°. Wallis (1924), too, suggested a quaquaversal dip and a generally dome-shaped form. A dip of 35° to 40° was recorded in the Knap Farm Borehole (p. 23).

A fairly uniform northerly dip would accord with, although not confirm, emplacement by sliding southwards into a basin (p. 55) in the manner of an immense rotational landslip. Folding on north – south axes, as implied by Ussher's observations on the southern face, would follow a Malvernoid trend not readily explicable in the geographical position of Cannington Park.

Argillaceous strata near the base of the Carboniferous Limestone in the Knap Farm Borehole (p. 23) are locally overfolded and cleaved.

The junction between the Carboniferous Limestone and overlying Rodway Siltstones appears to be a normal fault in boreholes (p. 23), and locally the younger rocks are intensely folded and faulted (p. 23). Surface exposures of Rodway Siltstones show generally southerly dips at angles mostly up to 20°, but locally as steep as 50°. On the southern edge of the Swang Farm inlier [2317 3894; 2351 3910] the strata are cleaved and disturbed.

Permo-Triassic

Wiveliscombe Sandstones

Sandstones in and around Stogumber generally dip at 5° to 15° easterly, but at 15°/020° [0995 3778] near to a north-north-west-trending fault. In the quarry [104 369] between the village and the railway station the beds dip at 10° east-north-east. Between Coleford Water and Lydeard St Lawrence they dip at 5° to 10° eastward. Gentle dips to north-north-east at East Town may be related to the west-north-west-trending fault that passes beneath the village; farther south, the strata at Goulden Manor and West Leigh are horizontal. Sandrock immediately adjacent to a branch fault of the Ash Priors Fault at Hoccombe appears to be unaffected by the fracture, and dips at 3° eastward [1159 2981].

Extensive exposures in and near Langley, north of Wiveliscombe, show dips of 10° to 15° between east-south-east and north-east.

Vexford Breccias

Faults are common around Vellow [097 385], the larger ones trending slightly north of west, and the Vexford Breccias thereabouts commonly dip at 10° to 15° between north-north-east and north-east; in common with adjoining strata, they strike locally parallel to the faults. Farther south-east, in railway cuttings near Stogumber Station [110 372], the breccias and interbedded sandstones dip fairly uniformly at 5° eastward in the western limb of the major western Permo-Triassic syncline. Easterly dips continue to prevail to the south, steeper near Coleford Water (15°) and Westowe (10° to 12°) but 5° in and around Lydeard St Lawrence and near Chapel Leigh.

In the south-west of the district, between the roughly east – west Ash Prior Fault and a fault of similar trend passing near Spring Grove House [101 249], exposures showing reliable dips are rare. However, in the north of this tract basal breccias at Langley dip at 15° north-east, and in the south the formation east of Cobhay Farm [0928 2495] is inclined at 5°/150°. Exposures on the scarp face east of Bathealton Court [078 244] show dips of 5° to 10°/070° to 090°.

Littleham Mudstone

Exposures within the outcrop of the Littleham Mudstone are largely confined to small degraded marlpits. They afford no evidence of attitude, which must generally be presumed to accord with that of the formation below or above. Sandstones within the formation north-east of Pyleigh [129 308] seem to dip gently eastward. Marls with thin sandstones in the roadsides [105 269] between Slapemoor and Quaking House are nearly horizontal.

Budleigh Salterton Pebble Beds

The northernmost conglomerates of the Budleigh Salterton Pebble Beds in the district strike east or a little south of east, probably in line with the larger local faults. On Castle Hill [093 406], north-east of Sampford Brett, they lie within a triangle of faults and dip at 20° north-north-east. Similar rocks in Woolston Quarry [095 401], immediately south of the triangle, dip at 20° to 25° to just east of north. Within the large area of outcrop around and east of Capton [081 394] the beds are inclined at 8° to 15°/350° to 055°.

Farther south the conglomerates appear generally to dip eastward at no more than 5°, and in quarries at Combe Florey [153 312] they are horizontal. Extensive exposures around Denbury Farm [144 296], just north of the Ash Priors Fault, show strata either horizontal or inclined at 2° to 3° eastward, except for a slight south-south-westerly dip at the farm itself. In outcrops south of Chapel Leigh, isolated between the Ash Priors Fault and a branch fault on its northern side, and in a small inlier south of the faults, the formation dips at 3° to 10° to north-east or north-north-east. Similar dips prevail immediately south of the faults, near Barrow Hill Farm [111 295].

The beds of Holywell Quarries [127 270] are horizontal. The valley of the Hillfarrance Brook north of Milverton follows a north-west – south-east fault; conglomerates north of this fault in Haywood Quarry [1206 2655] dip at 20°/030°, and those south of the fault [1212 2633] dip at 15°/060°. Park Kiln Quarry [116 264] lies over 300 m from the fault and is in strata whose local deviation from horizontal is probably due to slip.

Laneside quarries [114 247] to the west of Burn Hill, and just north of a west-north-west-trending fault, show beds at the top of the formation dipping at 5°/025°. Towards the southern limit of the district, in a degraded quarry [092 246] south of Cobhay Farm, strata at a similar horizon dip at up to 10° south-eastward.

Otter Sandstone

Sandstones to the south-east of Williton generally dip at 10° to 12° between north and north-east; on the eastern side of the railway [0962 4010], adjoining the conglomerates of Woolston Quarry, they are inclined at 30° to just east of north.

Alongside and near the railway south-east of Crowcombe Station [137 343] strata dip very gently eastward or are nearly horizontal, and horizontal beds were worked [157 323] at Yarde Farm and crop out in roadsides at Shopnoller [163 325]. It is presumed that the axis of the major syncline in the Permo-Triassic rocks of the western basin runs north-west – south-east between Yarde Farm and Shopnoller. The Otter Sandstone of West Bagborough lies in the north-eastern limb of the fold. Ussher (1908, fig. 9) sketched a fault between Otter Sandstone and Devonian slates near West Bagborough church, but the exposure was not located during the recent survey.

From Combe Florey to East Combe and Bishops Lydeard the Otter Sandstone is nearly horizontal or dips at up to 5° eastward. On the outskirts of Combe Florey, alongside the road to Ash Priors, the basal beds of the formation in adjacent outcrops dip at 15° northward and are horizontal [149 309]. Scattered exposures to the south suggest a very gentle easterly inclination, and sandstones seen in separate sections in Ash Priors village, immediately on the north side of the Ash Priors Fault, are horizontal and dip at 5° north-east and at 5° east. H. B. Woodward (*in* Ussher, 1908) recorded that the Ash Priors Fault was exposed in the railway cutting west of Bishops Lydeard, where it was inclined southward at about 60°, separating Otter Sandstone from Mercia Mudstone.

Between Fitzhead and Halse, scattered exposures within a broad outcrop of Otter Sandstone indicate a gentle easterly dip. Within the area to the west, north and east of Preston Bowyer, the mapped base of the formation confirms this inclination, although individual exposures show strata horizontal [1318 2649; 1331 2644], dipping to the east [1327 2642] and, in part of the roadside section [1336 2640] in Preston Bowyer, dipping at 3° to the south. The last-mentioned dip is towards the valley and may reflect superficial movement, and on the southern side of the valley, in Mill Lane, Milverton [1227 2605], sandrock dips at 3° due north. Extensive roadside sections in Sand Street and Butts Way, Milverton, accord with a general formational dip of about 5° eastward, and the road up Burn Hill, 1 km to the south, passes by sandstones dipping at 5° to both east [1164 2481] and north-east [1166 2473].

The sandstones of Cushuish [196 304] adjoin the Cothelstone Fault. They form a slight rise above the marls which extend to the west and south, and dip gently south-westwards beneath the marls in the north-eastern limb of the major syncline. The Otter Sandstone is fairly flat-lying at Yarford, just north-east of the Cothelstone Fault, and dips at 4° east at Greenway [2140 2965], to the west of Kingston St Mary. In this vicinity it lies at the western edge of an area of Triassic rocks that forms a relatively thin mantle covering the Devonian basement between the two major Permo-Triassic basins. The general dip must be presumed to be gently southerly, carrying sandstones on higher ground beneath red Mercia Mudstone on lower. Sandstones just north of Taunton and west of Cheddon Fitzpaine occupy a comparable position; the only reliable recorded dip is 3°/210°, in the roadside [2355 2755] 350 m south-south-west of Rowford.

The faulted outcrop at Whitnell [214 399] probably lies just on the north-east side of one of the main boundary faults of the Central Somerset Basin; sandstones within it dip at 10° to the north [2143 3978].

Scattered outcrops of Otter Sandstone on the eastern side of the Quantock Hills, between Dodington and Enmore, probably lie within the gently shelving area south-west of the main boundary faults of the Central Somerset Basin. Variable fairly steep dips have been recorded to the south-west and south-east of Nether Stowey, where dips are 30°/120° [1780 3915] and 15°/360° [1964 3920] respectively, and at Plainsfield, where a dip of 10°/070° [1951 3676] was noted. North of Spaxton and around Charlinch the strata are nearly horizontal. The patch of Otter Sandstone west of Clayhill Farm [2653 3760] forms a narrow east – west ridge to the south of the Charlinch – Wembdon Fault, and is apparently bounded by a fault on its southern side also. Strata in an old quarry [2825 3788] at Wembdon (p. 38) dip at 10°/180°. Immediately south of Enmore the sandstones occupy two east – west strips and are horizontal or dip to the north at up to 5°.

In the Otter Sandstone outcrop between Goathurst, North Newton and West Monkton, bedding is horizontal in a quarry [2836 3348] north-west of North Petherton, but sandstone exposed 220 m to the south of this quarry, only 20 m from the boundary with the underlying Morte Slates, dips at 8°/040°. A large old sandpit [281 326] west of North Petherton is very close to the boundary with the Morte Slates, but the beds dip at only 3° to 4°/080°. Sandstones at Shearston [2824 3065] dip at 2°/098°. Honeycomb-weathered sandstones at the roadside [294 309] west of North Newton dip at up to 5°/005°, and south-west of the village the dip is 2°/090° [2922 3051]. In the centre of North Newton [2989 3105], in the roadside at Tuckerton [2974 3005] and north of West Newton [2886 2967] the beds are horizontal, but in other exposures near West Newton dips of 2°/005° [2886 2948] and 5°/170° [2864 2885] were measured. At West Monkton [2627 2820], 100 m from the Morte Slates contact, the sandstone dips at 2°/172°. These dips indicate gentle undulation in the central area of the outcrops, with northerly and southerly dips in the north and south respectively, and shallow dips away from the Morte Slates outcrop.

Mercia Mudstone Group and Lias

Coastal exposures

The following brief account is based on Whittaker and Green (1983).

A curved normal fault, the Doniford Bay Fault, trends east and south-east from Watchet to pass beneath the Doniford holiday camp. It throws Lias strata of the *semicostatum* Zone down to the south against Mercia Mudstone Group, Penarth Group and exposed Lias beds of the *planorbis* and *liasicus* zones. Where it cuts the cliff [0786 4336] the fault throws about 210 m, and a similar throw persists eastwards for 1 km, beyond which the fault is obscured by drift.

North of the Doniford Bay Fault a syncline trends 095°; it appears to close at both ends and is cut by small normal faults trending 075°. Strike faults are common in the Westbury Formation. Shales and limestones of the *planorbis* Zone dip vertically [0784 4363] in a structure that may be tectonic or superficial in origin. The southern limb of the syncline carries small flexures that are truncated by the Doniford Bay Fault.

Strata in the cliff and foreshore of St Audrie's Bay [1025 4326] lie in the northern limb of the syncline mentioned above. At the western end of the bay, beds dip at about 13° to south-west or west-south-west, and rocks of the Lias are cut by several small faults parallel to strike or dip. A small low-angle thrust in the cliff [1029 4319] affects *planorbis* Zone strata. Small steep reverse faults occur in the Mercia Mudstone Group [1053 4310]. The incompetent Westbury Formation commonly contains strike faults, and its contact with the overlying Lilstock Formation is a fault [1033 4317]. Minor faults in red Mercia Mudstone trend at about 110° [1050 4348] and between 125° and 145° [1082 4351]; the red Mercia Mudstone shows minor flexures near the latter locality and around a slightly larger basin [1125 4350] to the east of it, and these small folds may reflect the form of the surface of the Devonian rocks at shallow depth.

Inland sections

As with the Littleham Mudstone, inland exposures affording structural detail are few. At about 350 m south-east of Weacombe, a temporary excavation [1125 4041] in red and greyish green silty marls showed a dip of 15° westward. The pit is about 30 m west of the Trentishoe Grits of the Quantock Hills and the strata lie in the eastern limb of the major western Permo-Triassic synlcine. Steep fractures run parallel to the strike, suggesting the presence of normal faults along the boundary of the sedimentary basin. Green-spotted red marls at Shopnoller [1644 3289], near the axis of the syncline, are flat-lying or locally with a slight northerly dip.

Marls with sandy bands in a stream at Pickney are horizontal [1928 2914]. Farther south, alongside on old railway cutting [1697 2570], marls dip southward into the cutting but may have slipped. Farther still, just beyond the River Tone and near the southern limit of the district, sandstones within the red Mercia Mudstone south of Hele Manor are horizontal [1877 2434]. Similar sandstones on the eastern side of Taunton, possibly overlying the concealed south-eastern extension of the Quantock massif, dip at 5° southwards [2373 2529].

The red Mercia Mudstone beds in old brick pits [307 283] at Durston Station are near the horizontal, but in the south-eastern extremity of the district the North Curry Sandstone provides evidence of southerly dips. A sandstone 4.57 m thick penetrated in a borehole [3058 2431] near Borough Post is taken to be the North Curry Sandstone, indicating a gentle south-south-easterly dip from the outcrop at Lower Knapp, and at Churley Farm [3569 2814] the sandstone dips at 3°/170°. Sandstones within the red Mercia Mudstone near Knoll Green, east of the Quantock Hills, are horizontal [2307 3971]. Opposed dips at Kilve [1492 4365] suggest the presence of east – west-trending structures, and faults in the southerly-facing Penarth Group scarp trend 100° [1447 4324]. Farther east, beyond Stogursey, strata of the Blue Anchor Formation and Penarth Group strike east – west within outcrops largely delineated by a complex system of mainly east – west-trending faults. Beds of the Lower Lias yielding *P. planorbis* commonly dip at 7° to 12° northerly, and the Lias is faulted against red Mercia Mudstone.

Strata of the *planorbis* Zone form a northerly dip slope at Puriton. At the foot of this slope a clay feature rises to 15 m O.D., and a borehole [3156 4161] sited on this ridge yielded a schlotheimiid ammonite of either the *liasicus* or the *angulata* Zone. Motorway excavations [3161 4183] showed basal *angulata* Zone shales and limestones with *Schlotheimia* sp. resting on shales with *Waehneroceras* sp. of the *liasicus* Zone. A borehole [3192 4313] to the north yielded a coroniceratid at 8 m depth, suggesting an eastward continuation of the *bucklandi* Zone have been recorded northof Eddington (Kidson and Haynes, 1972) and of the *raricostatum* Zone near by at Calcott Burtle [399 430] (Kidson and others, 1974). Whittaker and Green (1983) concluded that these identifications pointed to the presence of a fault, probably trending east – west and throwing down about 220 m to the north. They also suggest that a record of *angulata* Zone strata in a borehole [3231 4436] north-east of Pawlett indicated that an east – west fault throwing down about 30 m to the south probably lay between that borehole and the one [3192 4313] mentioned above.

For further information concerning structures in the Blue Anchor Formation and younger rocks the reader is referred to Whittaker and Green (1983). EAE, BJW

Chapter 9

Economic geology

Traces remain in and around the Quantock Hills of several small trials for metalliferous ores. The oldest known records are dated 1714 and relate to Perry Hill, in the north of the district, but probably some operations took place in earlier times. Buckingham Mine, at Dodington north-west of Nether Stowey, was worked for copper from 1786 to 1801 and from 1817 to 1822. Three tons of copper ore were produced in Somerset in the year ended June 1820 and 28 tons in the following year, probably all from Buckingham Mine.

Baryte has been worked on a small scale from veins in Carboniferous Limestone at Cannington Park, and gypsum and alabaster spasmodically from Mercia Mudstone Group cliffs at Watchet. The only substantial reserve of evaporite minerals beneath the district is rock salt, contained in 30 to 40 m of strata within the red Mercia Mudstone and worked at Puriton by brine-pumping between 1911 and 1922.

All the rock formations of the district, except those of clay, marl and mudstone, have been quarried for building stone at some time, commonly from small pits for immediate local use. None is now so exploited. The same rocks have been even more widely dug for roadstone, although the only quarries active in recent years have been Triscombe Quarry in Trentishoe Grits and quarries at Cannington Park in Carboniferous Limestone. The latter rock was also at one time burnt for lime, and scattered disused limekilns show where the same treatment has been accorded to calcareous sandstones of the Permo-Triassic and to limestone pebbles taken from the Budleigh Salterton Pebble Beds. Limestone has also been quarried from the middle and upper Ilfracombe Slates and from the Blue Lias.

Interbedded clays and limestones of the Blue Lias have been used in the production of cement. Bricks have been manufactured from marls of the Mercia Mudstone Group and from superficial deposits, notably at Bridgwater. Peat is cut just east of the district, from deposits which extend westwards to the north and south of Westonzoyland and to the south of Stoke St Gregory. A little is still sold as fuel, and another source of energy, never exploited successfully, is the Liassic oil shale of Kilve.

Soils of the district range from deep sandy loams on Permo-Triassic sandstones, and calcareous clayey loams on the Mercia Mudstone Group, to thin poor soils covering much of the Devonian rock, sandy peaty podzols on the top of the Quantock Hills, and the silty peaty flats of the Somerset Levels (Figure 17).

Surface water supplies are available, and may be stored, on most of the pre-Permian rocks. The Permo-Triassic includes one important aquifer, the combined Budleigh Salterton Pebble Beds and Otter Sandstone, and one yielding less, the combined Wiveliscombe Sandstones and Vexford Breccias.

METALLIFEROUS MINERALS

Hamilton and Lawrence (1970) have written a detailed history of copper mining at Dodington. The first workings were in Otter Sandstone, possibly as early as 1720, and up to late 1790 or early 1791, five years after the opening of Buckingham Mine, it was believed that these rocks contained all the copper ore. References to iron ore are obscure. Workings entered Devonian slates late in 1790, and Devonian limestone (Roadwater Limestone) in January 1791. Solution cavities were discovered, at least one cave, ore-bearing vughs were common, and it became apparent that the main concentrations of copper were in the limestone. Mention was made of an abrasive product ('emery') and graphite. Working was stopped in 1801 and resumed in 1817. Hamilton and Lawrence (1970) inferred, from the type of pumping engine used, that during the second period of working (1817 to 1822) Buckingham Mine may have been developed to 30 m below the drainage adit, but only to a very small lateral extent. This second attempt to operate the mine cost over £20 000 and recovered only £2500 from sales of ore.

Copper minerals at Dodington were carbonate in the Otter Sandstone and sulphides in the Devonian. The mine plan (Mining Records Office number A.M. R 27 E) shows two lines of workings, perhaps on two lodes, which trend south-eastwards and are clearly aligned with the strike of the Roadwater Limestone (Figure 18). The most north-westerly relic of Buckingham Mine is Beech Grove engine house [1732 4032], and progressively south-eastwards from there are the sites of Roskrow's Shaft [1741 4026], Barret's Shaft [1745 4014], Holman's Shaft [1749 4009], Glebe Shaft [1753 4004], Glebe Middle Shaft [1757 4000] and Hill's Shaft [1765 3983]. Of the two lines of workings the more northern was entered via an adit [1739 4027] 27 m west-north-west of Roskrow's Shaft and extended 91 m south-eastward. The more southern was entered [1740 4018] 91 m north-west of Barret's Shaft and driven about 460 m to 36 m south-east of Hill's Shaft. A drainage adit, with portal [1752 4045] 220 m north-north-east of Roskrow's Shaft, runs east of south and west of south to join the southern drive about 10 m south-east of Barret's Shaft. Derbyshire Miners' Adit, a crosscut adit, runs 80 m south-westward from its mouth [1771 3998]. Four crosscourses are shown on the mine plan intersecting the southern drive.

Hamilton and Lawrence (1970) identified the approximate positions of Dodington Mine [1739 3990], Garden Mine [1741 3997] and Timberyard Mine [1730 3999], all on Otter Sandstone and probably representing some of the earliest workings. New Hall Adit runs west of south and south from its portal [1712 4020], crossing from Permo-Triassic rocks into Devonian slates 50 m west of the Castle of

Comfort. Hamilton and Lawrence suggested that quarries [1753 3943] east of Walford's Gibbet mark the site of High Park Mine, a trial for copper; the direction of entry of an adit [about 1735 3938] in Five Lords appears to be east-north-easterly towards these pits. They also recorded a similar trial, Bincombe Mine, at the site of an old quarry in Roadwater Limestone [179 394], and three prospecting pits [1775 4037; 1789 4037; 1787 4026] of which few traces remain.

Occurrences of metalliferous minerals, noted and reputed, elsewhere in the district include: Jacob's Pond Mine [?077 382], in Leighland Slates, no trace of reputed copper; Jacob's Pond Quarry [0812 3906], in Otter Sandstone, malachite traces; Bicknoller, quarry [1153 3990], in Trentishoe Grits, malachite films and iron-manganese staining; Perry Hill (West Hill), overgrown pit [126 419], in Little Hangman Sandstones, no trace of reputed copper; Smith's Combe, quarry [1314 4226], in Little Hangman Sandstones, malachite films; Crowcombe Court [139 369] and Crowcombe churchyard [141 367], in red Mercia Mudstone, reputed malachite in dug sandstone, but red marl seen to 1.5 m in churchyard; Cothelstone Park, possibly refers to a fenced depression [1796 3235] (shaft?) in Otter Sandstone, but more likely to pits in Roadwater Limestone [1801 3268; 1821 3275], no trace of reputed copper; Over Stowey [?185 387], thin red Mercia Mudstone on Otter Sandstone on Devonian (possibly Roadwater Limestone) at shallow depth, no trace of reputed copper; Pepper Hill, quarry [1905 3719], in Rodhuish Limestone, no trace of reputed copper; Lower Aisholt, quarry [2018 3494], in Aisholt Limestone, no trace of reputed native copper; Merridge, said to be between Merridge and Courtway (Cutcombe Slates) [207 341] but possibly one of the nearby quarries in Roadwater Limestone or Rodhuish Limestone, reputed source of malachite specimens in Taunton Museum and of iron ore (Dines, 1956) but no trace noted; Great Holwell, quarry [?2180 3427], in Holwell Limestone, no trace of reputed malachite; Raswell Farm, old

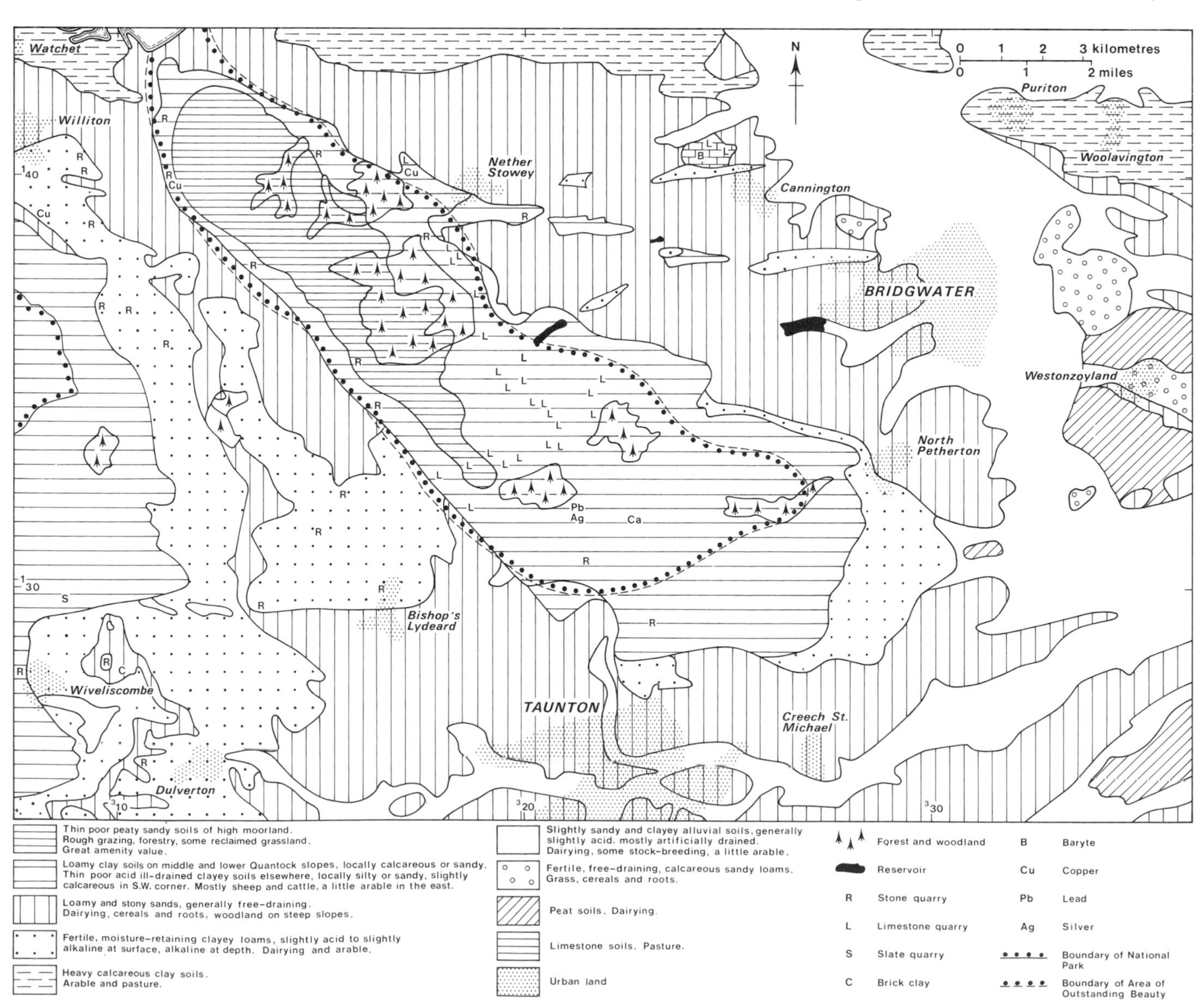

Figure 17 Soils, land use and economic geology

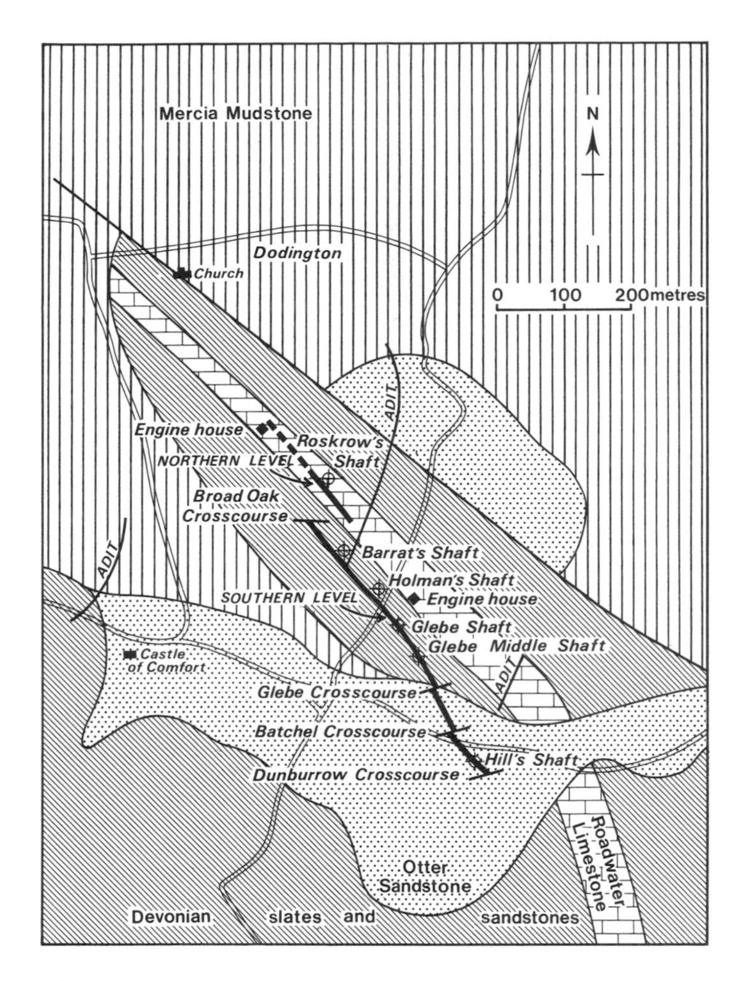

Figure 18 Buckingham Mine, Dodington

Plate 7 Beech Grove engine house, Buckingham Mine, Dodington. (A 13849)

The engine house is of a 19th century copper mine

shaft and dump [2128 3167] and another dump [2129 3159], possibly a north-trending adit from the latter dump to the shaft, in basal Morte Slates, no trace of reputed copper, silver or lead; Wort Wood, old shaft [2277 3164] with collapsed adit [2273 3167] trending south-east, no trace of ore minerals; Lord's Lane, Kingston St Mary [?222 303], in Morte Slates, no trace of reputed copper; Kingston St Mary [?222 299], in Morte Slates, no trace of reputed copper.

Dines (1956) recorded that a shaft was said to have been sunk on the hill between Kingston St Mary and Cothelstone, for lead ore carrying silver and gold; he also referred to a trial of a vein of quartz and chalcopyrite at Broomfield. Hamilton and Lawrence (1970) used papers of Mr E. J. Waddon to compile a historic account of Broomfield Mine in which workings on lodes, from a single adit, are referred to as Wheal Penelope, Wheal Halswell and Wheal Cornelia. It seems possible that Broomfield Mine, and the references to lead, silver and gold, relate to Raswell Farm, and that Dines's mention of chalcopyrite relates to Wort Wood.

The old mineral assemblages of the district, mainly copper with a little iron, lead and silver, are generally indicative of moderate or low-temperature origin, and are so distant from the Cornubian batholith that a direct relationship seems unlikely. Scrivener and Bennett (1980), writing of the ores of north Devon, envisaged that exhalative volcanic fluids distributed base metals which were subsequently mobilised and concentrated by and during the Variscan orogeny. In the Quantock Hills a tuff in the Avill Slates-and-Sandstones indicates volcanicity at a time before the formation of the present host rocks of most of the ore minerals. The only evident stratigraphic control is that of the limestones in the Ilfracombe Slates. Copper carbonates in Permo-Triassic rocks have probably been derived from the underlying Devonian.

BARYTE

The Carboniferous Limestone of Cannington Park is cut by steeply inclined or vertical veins of baryte which have been noted up to 0.6 m wide and contain cavities lined with crystals of the mineral. Dines (1956) recorded that, where the veins were narrow or contained fragments of host rock, the baryte gave way to quartz and calcite with specks of chalcopyrite and malachite. The material has been worked by digging out the veins from the quarry face and hand-sorting into pink and white varieties, and by trenching on veins in the south-western part of Cannington Park. Before 1920, between 15 and 20 tonnes per month were extracted for a time (Dines, 1956).

Hallam (1934) saw a baryte vein in a quarry [1454 4141] west of Alfoxton Park, probably at the junction of the Hangman Grits and the Ilfracombe Slates. Dines (1956) noted an impregnation of baryte in sandstones at the head of the combe south of Aisholt Common [about 180 349], and H. H. Thomas (*in* Ussher, 1908) recorded the occurrence of baryte as a cement in Permo-Triassic sandstones east of Langley and east of Plainsfield (pp.31 and 38).

EVAPORITE MINERALS

Gypsum occurs as veins and pods in the Triassic marls of the Watchet coast; its working was mentioned by De la Beche (1839), and ceased about 1923. Whittaker and Green (1984) described how gypsum was dug from the cliffs and taken to Watchet harbour by cart or small boat. The massive form, known as alabaster, has been used locally for carvings.

In 1910 rock salt was discovered accidentally in the Mercia Mudstone Group in the course of an unsuccessful attempt to find coal beneath Puriton. A borehole [3191 3088], sited just below the top of the red Mercia Mudstone, proved a little gypsum below 30 m, and saliferous strata from a depth of 183 m to 219.5 m (McMurtrie, 1912). Commercial extraction (Whittaker, 1970; 1972) was mainly from a second hole a few metres from the first; brine was pumped into a storage reservoir and thence run into shallow pans where industrial salt was produced by slow evaporation for about two weeks. Table salt was obtained by boiling the brine, and drying and grinding the salt. Three additional boreholes were sunk. The main (second) boring was abandoned in 1914 and the works closed in 1922. Puriton lies near the southern edge of the Somerset saltfield, which may contain 13 000 million tonnes or more of rock salt.

STONE, CONSTRUCTION AGGREGATES AND LIME

The only quarry currently active in the district is in the Carboniferous Limestone of Cannington Park, utilised mainly for roadstone and as an aggregate for concrete. Triscombe Quarry, in Trentishoe Grits, continues to supply small quantities of unscreened rubble from screes at the foot of the rock faces. Only the larger disused quarries in the district are mentioned below.

Lynton Slates have been dug [162 345] near Rock Farm but, as elsewhere, are too fractured and slaty to be of use except for surfacing rough roads and tracks.

Trentishoe Grits have been quarried in Bicknoller Combe [115 399], Halsway Combe [135 381], and from several smaller pits within Quantock Forest for Forestry Commission roads. They are predominantly hard quartzitic sandstones and have been used as building stone, wall stone and roadstone. Such rocks contain the largest quarry in the district, Triscombe Quarry [162 355], active in recent years but whose future is uncertain; about 80 m of strata are exposed in the main face. Plentiful reserves exist, but the size and depth of the quarry constitute a problem in such a small range of hills as the Quantocks.

Little Hangman Sandstones have been extensively worked [113 415] at West Quantoxhead, principally for roadstone, but none is now dug and much ground in and around the quarries has been levelled as 'made ground'. A smaller disused pit, whence stone has been taken for local buildings and walls, occurs in Holford Combe [152 405].

The basal Ilfracombe Slates, the Avill Slates-and-Sandstones, contain hard sandstones which have been used locally for buildings and roads, as near Holford [157 407] and north of Friarn [178 387]. Tuff within this formation was previously worked in a single quarry [183 371] in Keeper's Combe and is reported to have been shaped as ornamental stone for both exterior and interior work.

All the limestones of the Ilfracombe Slates have been extensively quarried. The larger pits are: Rodhuish Limestone [183 379; 190 372]; Roadwater Limestone [172 404; 179 394; 183 383; 186 380; 193 370; 192 361; 198 348; 208 344; 211 340; 208 336]; Aisholt Limestone [202 349; 212 336]; Holwell Limestone [199 357; 218 347]; Leigh Barton Limestone [230 337]. Many of the quarries retain no sign of a limekiln, and it seems probable that most of the stone was used for building, with smaller quantities being burnt for lime.

Quarries in Cutcombe Slates and Leighland Slates, other than limestone workings, commonly mark the positions of interbedded sandstones and siltstones [183 396; 247 351; 221 340].

Morte Slates of the western outcrop have been dug for local building stone, as at Willett [106 337] and Tolland [102 323], but the only large workings were Oakhampton Quarries [085 301]. The rocks at that locality are mostly sufficiently well cleaved to have been used as roofing slates, and have been worked to a depth of about 76 m. Where silty interbeds have prevented the development of closely spaced cleavage planes, the rock has provided rough building stone and walling stone. Ussher (1908) recorded that such thicker slabs had been shaped for ornamental use.

No large quarries exist in the Morte Slates of the eastern outcrop, but pits [215 309; 217 308; 220 308] north of Kingston St Mary show many interbedded sandstones and siltstones, suggesting that no slate suitable for roofing was available in this area. The stone has been used for buildings and roads. Many smaller pits, in slates and silty slates, have been dug for walling stone and roadstone. Quarry Lane, north of Upper Cheddon, leads to several stone quarries in slates with distinct sandstones [232 292; 233 291], and another quarry [247 292], north of Gotton, shows slates with thin quartzitic sandstones. Hestercombe contains pits [241 292; 242 292] in similar slates with silty bands and sandstones. Intrusive into the Morte Slates, and worked in a single quarry comprising two bays [243 293], is a lamprophyre dyke known at various times as pottle stone, Hestercombe Syenite or Hestercombe Diorite. Used locally as a building stone, the rock was seldom worked even at the time of Ussher's survey in the 1870s and the quarry looks now as though it has not been used for many years.

Thickly bedded sandstones of the Pickwell Down Sandstones have been quarried [077 279] at Wiveliscombe and used as building stone and roadstone. Pits in the Pilton Shales south of the town have yielded rubbly stone for rough roads.

Carboniferous Limestone is still quarried in Cannington Park, for use as concrete aggregate and roadstone. In the past it has been used as a building stone and also burnt for lime at the quarries.

Wiveliscombe Sandstones, cemented by calcite, were quarried [0965 3685] on site for building Stogumber brewery, and probably provided some stone for other buildings in the village. As with other Permo-Triassic sandstone, and much of the breccia, the rock was capable of being cut into square-hewn stones or ashlar. Similar rock with some interbedded breccia, worked [104 369] midway between Stogumber and its railway station, yielded building stone, sandstone calcareous enough to be burnt for lime on site, and sandrock friable enough to use as sand; quarries [114 339; 114 336] at Coleford Water were operated in the same way. In the neighbourhood of Langley and Wiveliscombe, and in the area to the south-east and south, the sandstones are extensively exposed but friable and poorly cemented.

Vexford Breccias from Carslake Quarry [113 360], a large overgrown and long-disused working north-west of Lower Vexford, have been used as building stone. In a smaller pit [1202 3335] near Dean's Cross, now almost obliterated, the stone was calcareous and burnt for lime. West Leigh was built of breccia blocks from a pit [122 306] on the scarp above the farm. Farther south, small pits opened for local use lie mainly near the base of the formation and contain interbedded breccias and sandstones.

The Budleigh Salterton Pebble Beds have been used for building where the pebbles were small and the cement strong, but the extensive working of these rocks has been mostly for use as roadstone. Larger pebbles of limestone have afforded a useful byproduct locally, being picked out by hand and burnt for lime in kilns on the spot. Many pits were opened in pebble beds around Williton and Sampford Brett, the two largest being Woolston Quarry [094 401] and on Castle Hill [093 406]. Large quarries [096 390; 097 388] at Vellow provided both stone and lime, as did another [155 384] in Upcott Wood, east of Newton. Southwards to Crowcombe Station much of the formation is poorly cemented, but a quarry [142 330] at Coursley is in stronger beds, and another [148 325] at Nethercot yielded pebble beds for roadstone, interbedded sandstone for building, and limestone pebbles for lime. Quarries [150 316; 152 311; 155 311] at Combe Florey, near the top of the formation, contain interbedded sandstones; widespread presence of calcareous cement suggests the possibility that the local limekilns were fed whole rock loads rather than selected pebbles. The same was probably true of several large old workings [143 304; 135 296; 136 295] around Ash Priors, although in one, Denbury Quarry [146 295], limestone pebbles are especially plentiful. Disused limekilns are characteristic of most of the larger pebble beds quarries farther west and south [128 294; 1104 2945; 105 294; 111 276; 125 270; 127 270; 125 263; 121 265; 116 264; 104 258; 114 247]; one of the quarry faces [104 258] shows extensive calcareous films, collapse due to undermining in search of limestone pebbles, and fissures enlarged by solution. Big quarries [098 292; 096 284] in outliers of pebble beds north-east of Wiveliscombe have yielded large quantities of roadstone, but contain five old limekilns and rock faces masked by calcareous films.

One of the most widely used building stones in the district is Otter Sandstone, which has proved easy to cut and is characteristic of many churches and large houses. As with so much other local Permo-Triassic stone, it is variably cemented by calcite and has been burnt for lime at some quarries. Where soft and friable, the formation has been dug for sand.

Much of the sandstone near Williton is poorly cemented and rather soft, but Ussher (1908) noted that in quarries [079 406; 084 407] south of the town some of the lower stone had been worked for use in buildings and walls. Stronger calcareous sandstone at Lawford has been burnt for lime [135 363]. Building stone and sand have been worked [157 323] at Yarde Farm. A large quarry [166 300] near Bishops Lydeard provided stone for restoring the church tower and was used in constructing the asylum, now Tone Vale Hospital, and other local buildings; Ussher (1908) was told that some facing stone had been sent to Bath.

Building stone has been dug [196 302] at Cushuish, but the rock exposed in the old quarry is friable and has been pitted by 'masonry' bees. Sandstone, locally decalcified, has been worked [203 299] at Yarford.

East of the Quantock Hills, friable sand has been dug [246 346] south of Enmore, and calcareous sandstone [226 372] at Spaxton. Good building stone was obtained from Stowey Rocks [203 390], south-east of Nether Stowey. Farther west, at 440 m south of the church, a quarry [196 392] in Otter Sandstone shows strata, at a similar position near the top of the formation, that include more friable beds. And farther west still, the formation has been dug for sand [190 390].

The North Curry Sandstone, quarried at Knapp, provided an excellent freestone (Ussher, 1908), and the villages hereabouts are largely built with it. Similar rocks west of Taunton have been worked [187 244] at Hele and are much in evidence in walls and buildings in the immediate neighbourhood.

Limestones of the Blue Lias commonly occur in beds up to 0.3 m thick, so jointed that they break naturally into rectangular blocks. They have been worked in a number of small pits, mostly in the lower beds; some individual beds were given names suggesting uses, such as 'paviours' (paving stones), 'building stone' and 'hearth stone'. The pale grey limestone is common in buildings in the north of the district, and has been used as roadstone. It has also been burnt for lime, and used together with the interbedded clays in the manufacture of cement at Puriton.

Shelly sands of the Burtle Beds were once spread on arable land as a source of lime.

CLAY AND MARL

Littleham Mudstone has been worked for brickmaking near Croford, probably at a site now occupied by farm buildings [1004 2805]; old marl pits to west [0998 2784] and east [1012 2817] may have supplied clay. Red marls of the Mercia Mudstone Group were used for bricks on the south-western outskirts of Taunton, just outside the present district; the pit [209 241] is now filled and developed as a light industrial estate. Ussher (1908) recorded a brickpit about 800 m west of Taunton Station, but no trace remains, unless it was the small pit [2174 2552] in the nearby allotments. He also noted pits north of Taunton Station on the south side of the turning to Staplegrove [? about 225 258], by the canal near Durston Station [about 305 283], and midway between Durleigh and Goathurst.

Red marls of the Mercia Mudstone Group have also been used in the past at the well-known Bridgwater brickworks, but only occasionally and as an accessory. The main material used there over many years has been alluvial clay. Indeed bricks and tiles were important in the history of Bridgwater until the local products were superseded by cement tiles and by mass manufacturing.

Bath bricks, named after their inventor, were unique to Bridgwater and were used for cleaning knives and for other scouring jobs in Victorian kitchens. They were made alongside the River Parrett from alluvial silt. Production began in the 1820s and is said to have reached 24 million 'bricks' a year. Platforms ('slime-batches') were cut in the river bank within the tidal range, and the silt which was deposited on them, totalling over 3 m in thickness in a year, was regularly collected. Ussher (1908) described how this 'slime' was passed through a pug mill and moulded by hand into 'bricks', which were dried in the sun; he quoted analyses and examinations of the slime that showed it to be predominantly a fine sand, about 60 per cent SiO_2. When newer scouring powders captured the market, the slime continued to be used for a time to seal the entrances of local brick-kilns.

The outcrops of the Littleham Mudstone and the red Mercia Mudstone are pock-marked by small pits, some shallow and now grassed over, others deeper and overgrown by scrub, filled with rubbish or flooded. They are marlpits, relics of the widespread 19th-century practice of 'sweetening' arable land by dressings of limy clay. The Mercia Mudstone Group has been recorded as containing up to 16 per cent $CaCO_3$.

OIL SHALES

A brick-built retort, close to an old limekiln near the end of the track from Kilve to the coast and just north of the district, is the most substantial relic of a short-lived attempt to extract oil from bituminous Liassic shales that were first noted in 1916 in the cliffs north of Kilve. A borehole at Kilve entered bituminous shales at 91 m depth and was still in Lias when abandoned at 168 m. Analyses showed 156 litres of oil to 1 m^3 of shale, and several hundred barrels of oil were produced from retorts at Kilve.

PEAT

Commercial working of peat, for horticultural use and for fuel in the case of some of the deeper peat, began about 1870. It takes place mainly on the heaths west-north-west of Glastonbury to the east of the present district, where the peat is up to 5 m thick; these deposits do not extend into the present district, but a more southerly accumulation, underlying King's Sedge Moor, continues westwards as Lang Moor, north of Westonzoyland, and Weston Level and South Moor, south of that village. Few sections have been seen on King's Sedge Moor, but Avery (1955) noted that the peat ranged from 0.6 m thick to over 3 m. It is presumed that the peat around Westonzoyland is not more than 2 m thick; beneath West Sedge Moor, in the south-eastern corner of the district, it is probably thinner still. Workings are therefore unlikely to extend into the present district in the near future. Nevertheless, annual production was 63 000 tonnes in 1966 and is now more, and the first half of the 21st century could present the choice of cessation of operations, or of deep drainage and working of peat currently below the water table, together with exploitation of thinner deposits. There has been no attempt to extract oil from Somerset peat.

SOILS

Hangman Grits of the highest ground, the central and northern parts of the Quantock Hills, yield thin poor peaty sandy soils (Figure 17). Before the arrival of commercial forestry in 1920, cash returns were derived largely from very rough moorland grazing, perhaps seven sheep to a square kilometre, and from whortleberries. Now, some grassland has been established around Quantock Farm [159 370], and Quantock Forest covers about 1000 hectares. The trees, mainly spruce, fir, hemlock, pine and larch, come to maturity in about 50 years and the felling and replanting of about 26 hectares a year more or less keeps pace with annual growth. Plantations extend on to the Ilfracombe Slates, upon which the soils are variable; loamy clays are common, locally limy and with sandy patches. Unforested areas thereon include the high moorland of Lydeard Hill, pasture of the middle slopes and mixed grass and arable in the east.

Where appreciably silty and sandy, the Morte Slates yield stony acid brown-earth soils, but much of the formation is covered by thin poor acid soils beneath which drainage is commonly bad with extensive iron pan; most is given over to sheep and cattle.

In the Permo-Triassic country, loamy sands of the Wiveliscombe Sandstones merge eastwards into free-draining stony soils on the Vexford Breccias, all typified by mixed dairy and arable farming. Soils on the Littleham Mudstone differ from those on the Mercia Mudstone Group only in that the narrow outcrop of the older rocks has facilitated the admixture of stony sandy wash and Head from adjoining formations. Clayey loams may be slightly acid near the surface, but the range of wild shrubby plants attests the presence of lime at moderate depth. Rich grassland predominates with some arable.

The Budleigh Salterton Pebble Beds commonly form a scarp bearing woodland or scrub and permanent pasture. Free-draining stony sands on the dip slope grade eastwards into the light sandy soils of the Otter Sandstone, which support much cereal farming, together with root crops including potatoes.

The red Mercia Mudstone is the most widespread rock unit of the district. It weathers to a fertile moisture-retaining clayey loam and gives rise to a mixed dairying and arable countryside typified by Taunton Deane. Surface soils range from slightly limy to slightly acid, but the underlying rock is calcareous. Ussher (1908) quoted Dr W. Buckland as saying, in 1851, 'Let gentlemen buy their estates . . . on the red marl.'

The Blue Anchor Formation mudstones and Penarth Group shales with thin limestones weather to grey calcareous clays and silty clays, but their area of outcrop is small. Blue Lias soils are heavy calcareous clays, locally with angular limestone fragments. They support both arable farming and permanent pasture.

Burtle Beds are overlain by fairly free-draining calcareous sandy loams, fertile soils that have borne rich crops of grass, cereals and roots. The surrounding alluvial surface comprises silts and clays, generally slightly acid although locally, where derived from limestone-rich rock, calcareous at shallow depth. Drainage is artificial and soils are commonly waterlogged within 1 m of surface. With the control of drainage have come more attempts at arable farming, but the levels remain traditionally dairy country. Local cheese is still made, although less commonly since rapid systematic milk collection began. Stock-breeding too has declined. Specialised crops of the past included woad, hemp and flax. Today teazles are grown in and near the south-eastern extremity of the district. Most of the English crop of withies (willow), for basket-makers, fishermen and thatchers, comes from this same locality. The first sizable commercial plantings in Britain were on West Sedge Moor, south-east of Stoke St Gregory, and that village and North Curry were once centres of the withy trade.

WATER SUPPLY

Groundwater resources are available in two principal aquifers, the combined Wiveliscombe Sandstones and Vexford Breccias and the combined Budleigh Salterton Pebble Beds and Otter Sandstone. Small local supplies may be obtained from fissures in Palaeozoic rocks, sandstones in the red Mercia Mudstone and drift deposits, but most of the district relies on surface water. Public supplies are controlled by the Wessex Water Authority.

Only two records are available of groundwater yields from the Hangman Grits. A 42.7-m borehole [1599 3690] in Trentishoe Grits at Quantock Farm was tested at 6.314 litres/second (l/s), and a 65-m combined well and borehole [1490 4093] in Little Hangman Sandstones west of Holford at 0.530 l/s. The former is presumed to have intersected a system of fissures; the latter is more typical of what might be expected from most of the Palaeozoic rocks. Yields from ten shallow boreholes (27 m to 39 m deep) in Morte Slates range up to only 0.568 l/s. A 16.8-m borehole [0770 2654] in Pilton Shales yielded 0.316 l/s; another [0885 2660], 35 m deep, which yielded 0.947 l/s, passed through thin Wiveliscombe Sandstones into Pilton Shales. A 34-m borehole [2566 4021] at Rodway Farm, which probably penetrated about 3.7 m of Head and Otter Sandstone on Rodway Siltstones, is recorded as yielding 3.030 l/s. Recovery of water from the Carboniferous Limestone would depend on intersecting water-bearing fissures; the rock may 'feed' water into adjoining strata.

The physical properties of aquifer rocks in the Permo-Triassic are listed in Table 5 (p. 71), which was prepared by Dr J. D. Cornwell with the assistance of Miss. S. Pease. These properties are variable, but in the Otter Sandstone density is generally low and porosity high; in the Wiveliscombe Sandstones density is high and porosity low.

Yields from the combined Wiveliscombe Sandstones – Vexford Breccias aquifer range from 0.455 l/s from a 69-m borehole [1308 3133] at the Friendship Inn and 0.505 l/s from a 15-m well [090 249] at Cobhay Farm to 5.682 l/s from a 40-m borehole [1133 3700] south-east of Stogumber Station. This last borehole is mainly (32.3 m) in breccias. A public supply borehole [0816 2781] at Wiveliscombe, completed to 87 m in 1907, yielded 7.925 l/s, later reduced to 4.546 l/s; the boring passed through Wiveliscombe Sandstones (? about 35 m) into Pickwell Down Sandstones.

The higher aquifer, of Budleigh Salterton Pebble Beds and overlying Otter Sandstone, is the main source of groundwater in the district, and most current abstraction is from the sandstones. A borehole [2559 3750] at Gothelney Hall, sunk to 87 m, yielded 0.884 l/s from strata below 3.7 m of red Mercia Mudstone; probably most of the yield came from thin Otter Sandstone overlying Devonian rocks. Elsewhere, boreholes 26 to 29 m deep yielded more than 1.263 l/s. Two boreholes in Otter Sandstone at the Somerset Farm Institute gave 3.536 l/s from 21 m of strata [2571 3974] and 3.030 l/s from 20 m of strata [2571 3955]. Larger yields have been obtained as follows: 3.16 l/s from 46 m of Otter Sandstone [1648 3269] at Shopnoller Farm; 5.556 l/s from 55 m of combined Otter Sandstone and Budleigh Salterton Pebble Beds on 6 m of Littleham Mudstone [1257 2897] near Halse; 6.95 l/s from 57 m of Otter Sandstone with thin overlying red Mercia Mudstone [1401 2639] at Preston Bowyer; 9.57 l/s from a borehole [2889 3714] at Bridgwater that passed through 34.7 m of red Mercia Mudstone on 26.2 m of Otter Sandstone; 11.364 l/s from a 92-m borehole [1559 2963] west of Bishops Lydeard that passed from Otter Sandstone into Budleigh Salterton Pebble Beds at 26.5 m and probably entered Littleham Mudstone.

The Mercia Mudstone Group appears to be the least permeable rock unit in the district. Nevertheless, shallow boreholes (up to 30 m deep) have commonly yielded around 0.5 l/s, some up to 1.263 l/s. Of the latter, several have probably tapped small supplies in interbedded sandstones [3240 2535; 2974 2439], and a yield of 3.788 l/s from a 46-m borehole [1953 2570] at the cider works, Norton Fitzwarren, was obtained from marls with sandstones. Altogether exceptional is the yield of 4.546 l/s recorded from a 30-m borehole [2551 3637] in red Mercia Mudstone at Rexworthy Farm. A borehole [3116 3824] sunk at Bridgwater proved 25.6 m of alluvial deposits on 50.5 m of red Mercia Mudstone; it yielded 13.372 l/s of water too saline for use, but it is uncertain how much came from the alluvium and whether the salinity was attributable to estuarine water or salt in the red Mercia Mudstone or both.

Little information is available about groundwater in the Littleham Mudstone, which may be presumed to be similar to the red Mercia Mudstone. Of four boreholes sunk at Culverhays [110 381], only one, near the base of the Budleigh Salterton Pebble Beds, and perhaps passing through a little arenaceous material before entering Littleham Mudstone, yielded a supply.

A borehole [0938 4211] at Rydon, north-east of Williton, penetrated 15.5 m of Blue Anchor Formation on 28.7 m of red Mercia Mudstone and gave 0.821 l/s. Corresponding figures for a boring [2551 4283] north of Combwich were 7.6 m, 4.6 m and 0.884 l/s. A yield of 0.253 l/s from a 26.8-m borehole [2978 4269] in Blue Lias at Pawlett was probably mainly from bands of jointed limestone within the shales.

Groundwater within the alluvial deposits is in hydraulic continuity with river water and commonly polluted. Supplies have, however, been drawn from Burtle Beds, as at Chedzoy (0.909 l/s from 12.8 m of strata and 0.884 l/s from 7.6 m of Burtle Beds on 7.6 m of red Mercia Mudstone) and at Westonzoyland (2.525 l/s from 4 m of Burtle Beds).

Surface water supplies predominate on the Palaeozoic rocks, and also east of the Quantock Hills where most of the younger rocks are of low permeability. Clatworthy Reservoir, on Morte Slates about 3 km west of the district, yields 20 250 m³/day. Hawkridge Reservoir, on the Leighland Slates of the eastern Quantocks, and the smaller Ashford Reservoir, on red Mercia Mudstone midway between Hawkridge Reservoir and Cannington, have a combined yield of 10 125 m³/day. Durleigh Reservoir, on red Mercia Mudstone on the western outskirts of Bridgwater, yields 6300 m³/day.

Much of the area of Quantock Forest is used as a gathering ground for surface water, collected by means of several stream intakes, for domestic use. In the northern part of the Quantock Hills, a spring [1330 4241] on the flanks of Smith's Combe supplied 113.65 m³/day to East Quantoxhead. Another [1382 4106] at the head of Dens Combe, yielded 31.822 m³/day. EAE

CHAPTER 10
Geophysical investigations

Geophysical investigations that have been carried out in the Taunton district consist mainly of regional gravity and aeromagnetic surveys, with additional detailed gravity measurements over some significant features. The Bouguer gravity anomaly data provide evidence concerning the geological structure but there are few magnetic anomalies that can be related to the surface geology, confirming the paucity of igneous or other magnetic rocks.

PHYSICAL PROPERTIES

The physical properties of some of the main rock types are known from laboratory measurements on samples and from geophysical borehole logs. The properties can be estimated from published values (Table 5) but information is also available for 13 sites, mostly in the Permo-Triassic, within the Taunton district (Table 6).

The densities of the Devonian sediments are variable but overall there is a difference of 0.12 to 0.17 g/cm^3 between the lower-density arenaceous members of the sequence and the higher-density argillaceous members (Table 5). Sonic velocities probably show similar differences, but insufficient data are available to demonstrate this. A mean value of 5.30 km/s was obtained for a 25-km-long north to south refraction line across many of the main horizons in the Devonian sequence of Exmoor at about the Grid line 272 east just east of Challacombe.

The densities and sonic velocities of the Permo-Triassic sediments in the Burton Row Borehole (Figure 19) were found to be unusually high for rocks of this age (Cornwell *in* Whittaker and Green, 1983). The density of the Wiveliscombe Sandstones (2.59 g/cm^3) west of the Quantock Hills is lower than the mean of 2.69 g/cm^3 for rocks of the same age at Burton Row but is very similar to the value for the arenaceous Devonian formations (Tables 5 and 6). The density for the Otter Sandstone is variable, with an abnormaly low value of 2.11 g/cm^3 at one site. Geological information from outcrops (p.35), however, indicates that the Otter Sandstone can vary considerably in its degree of cementation and this will be reflected by the density values, the higher values being associated with a greater degree of cementation. Similar comments have been made about the Wiveliscombe Sandstones (pp.29–30), although all the sites providing density samples apparently contained only the well-cemented sandstones. This evidence suggests that a considerable lateral variation in density can occur and this uncertainty restricts the successful application of geophysical methods in estimating the depths of Permo-Triassic basins in the northern part of the Taunton district.

Table 5 Average densities and sonic velocities of the main geological formations in the Taunton district

	Saturated density g/cm^3)	Sonic velocity (km/s)
JURASSIC		4.28 [5]
Lias	2.55 [1]	3.2 [1]
PERMO-TRIASSIC	2.65 [1]	4.46 [1]
	2.50 [3]	3.92 [5]
	2.41 [6]	
CARBONIFEROUS		
Culm	2.61 [3]	
	2.69 [6]	
Viséan limestone	2.67 [1]	5.80 [1]
	2.72 [2]	5.68 [2]
		5.1–5.3 [5]
DEVONIAN	2.71 [2]	5.18 [2]
	2.62 [3]	
Pilton Shales	2.72 [4]	
Pickwell Down Sandstones	2.60 [4]	
Morte Slates	2.72 [4]	
Ilfracombe Slates	2.72 [4]	5.27 [5]
Hangman Grits	2.55 [4]	
Lynton Slates	2.65 [4]	5.35 [5]

Sources
1 BGS data, including Knap Farm Borehole (2)
3 Bott and others, 1958
4 Reported by Al-Sadi, 1967
5 Brooks and Al-Saadi, 1977
6 Edmonds and others, 1968

GEOPHYSICAL SURVEYS IN THE KNAP FARM BOREHOLE

Geophysical logging surveys were carried out in Knap Farm Borehole by Schlumberger Inland Services (UK) Incorporated for the depth interval 161 m to 1153 m. The following log suites were recorded on 21 July, 1976:

1 Dual Laterolog, consisting of a deep and a shallow sounding configuration, and a spontaneous potential (SP) electrode.
2 Sidewall neutron porosity, caliper and gamma-ray logs.
3 Compensated formation density, gamma-ray and caliper logs.
4 Borehole compensated sonic log.

All these geophysical logs were recorded at scales of 1:200 and 1:1000 and the results have been referred to by Whittaker and Scrivener, 1982.

In addition to the above logs, the density and porosity of core samples were measured in the laboratory (Mr A. Forster, IGS internal report). The six samples, of limestone,

Table 6 Densities and sonic velocities of rock samples from sites in the Taunton district

	Locality Grid reference	Number of specimens	Density (g/m³) Saturated	Grain	Porosity per cent	Sonic velocity (km/s) Dry	Saturated
PERMO-TRIASSIC							
Otter Sandstone	119 257	3	2.51±0.04	2.70±0.01	10.9±1.7		
	135 363	6	2.11±0.05	2.61±0.06	31.2±3.6	1.64±0.20	
	166 299	3	2.36±0.02	2.64±0.01	17.1±1.7		
Mean			2.33±0.20	2.65±0.05	19.7±10.4		
Budleigh Salterton Pebble Beds	121 371	3	2.48±0.02	2.60±0.03	8.0±2.7	4.03±0.42	
Vexford Breccias	117 367	3	2.52±0.03	2.67±0.01	8.9±1.8	2.88±0.38	
	120 362	4	2.53±0.03	2.67±0.08	8.1±1.4	2.78±0.57	
	129 327	3	2.56±0.03	2.72±0.02	9.4±1.0	2.65±0.50	3.8
Mean			2.54±0.02	2.68±0.03	8.8±0.7	2.77±0.12	
Wiveliscombe Sandstones	083 288	3	2.60±0.01	2.69±0.01	5.2±0.5		
	100 374	3	2.59±0.02	2.67±0.02	4.7±1.5		
	104 369	3	2.58±0.01	2.65±0.01	4.4±0.6		
	109 350	4	2.59±0.01	2.68±0.00	5.7±0.4	4.49±0.19	
Mean			2.59±0.01	2.67±0.02	5.0±0.6		
CARBONIFEROUS							
Carboniferous Limestone	251 404	6	2.67±0.01	2.68±0.01	0.5±0.1	6.43±0.09	6.47±0.10
DEVONIAN							
Trentishoe Grits	161 356	6	2.61±0.04	2.64±0.04	1.7±1.0	5.29±0.22	5.50±0.13

gave a mean density (2.70±0.05 g/cm³), typical for this rock type but slightly lower than that obtained from the logs (2.73 ±0.05 g/cm³), and also indicated, with one exception, low effective porosities of less than 0.7 per cent.

The uppermost 450 m of massive limestones in the borehole (Figure 19) produced undisturbed geophysical logs with typically high velocities (about 6.2 km/s) and resistivities (more than 3000 Ω m). The gamma-ray values increased gradually from 10 to 20 API in this range and the SP values became more positive and irregular below about 351 m where chert bands were present in the limestones. A more pronounced change in the character of the geophysical logs occurred within the Cynwir Cherty Limestones below about 455 m, where the resistivities tended to decrease to about 2000 Ω m, probably owing to connate water filling fractures in the brittle chert and to the presence of some argillaceous rocks. The SP values were also deflected towards the positive and the gamma-ray values were large.

The Cannington Reef Limestones between 558 m and 778 m were distinguished by some of the highest densities (reflecting the presence of dolomite, which has a density of 2.87 g/cm³) and velocities in the borehole, and the resistivities were also high (3000 to 4000 Ω m). Argillaceous partings in the limestones between 778 m and 900 m were probably responsible for the lower resistivities (less than 1000 Ω m), densities and velocities in this interval, and there was also a pronounced positive SP deflection, reaching a maximum at about 850 m.

The limestone beds between 900 m and 966 m (equivalent to the lower part of the Black Rock Limestone of the Mendip Hills) were characterised by abnormally low densities, velocities and resistivities (less than 100Ω m in places). The geophysical logs were probably affected between 920 m and

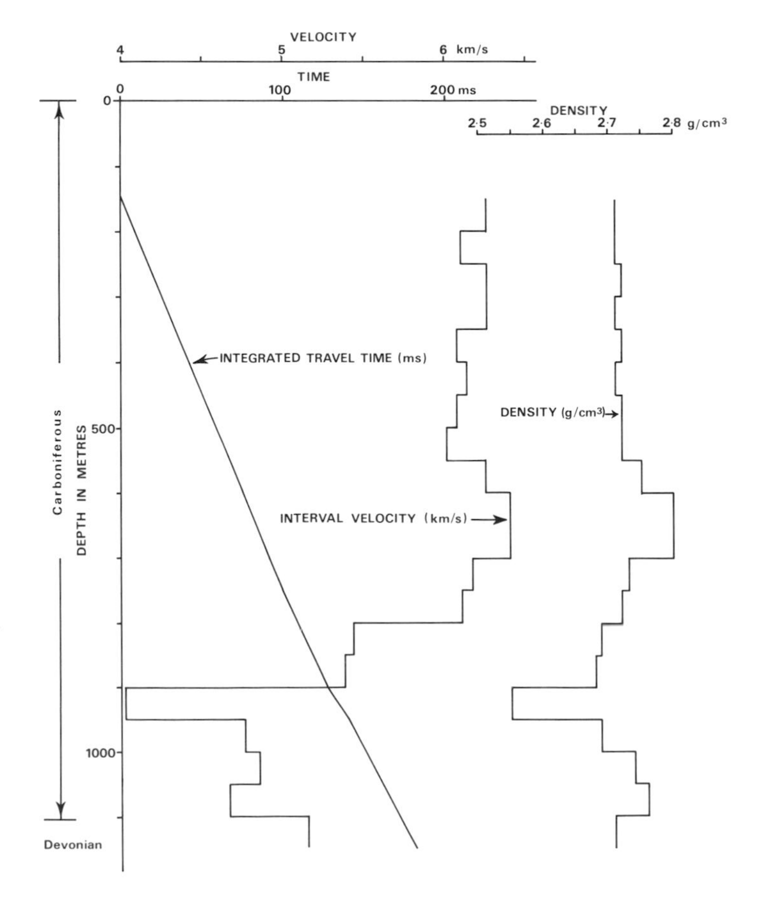

Figure 19 Densities and sonic velocities averaged over 50-m intervals and integrated travel time for the Knap Farm Borehole

945 m by the increase in borehole diameter owing to caving, but one sample of a muddy limestone from 943 m exhibited a low density (2.57 g/cm^3) and high effective porosity (7.3 per cent), suggesting that these limestone beds had distinctive physical properties.

The predominantly argillaceous nature of the strata between 966 m and 1106 m (Lower Limestone Shale) resulted in low resistivity (about 250 Ω m) and velocity values and high density and gamma-ray values, the latter increasing with depth from 40 API to 70 API.

The Devonian – Carboniferous boundary was placed at 1104 m on the evidence of conodonts and spores (Mitchell and others, 1982), and the nearly coincident lithological change from argillaceous measures to underlying sandstones was reflected on several logs, including neutron porosity and resistivity. The average density of the Devonian sandstones (2.71 g/cm^3) did not differ significantly from the value of 2.72 g/cm^3 for the Carboniferous rocks. The velocity (5.18 km/s) for the Devonian was lower than the means for all the Carboniferous sequence (5.68 km/s), and considerably lower than the mean of 6.21 km/s for the massive limestone in the top 800 m of the borehole.

GRAVITY SURVEYS

The Bouguer gravity anomaly map of the Taunton district (Figure 20) is based on data collected by BGS surveys, and the terrain-corrected values have been reduced using the 1967 International Gravity Formula (IGF 67). The Taunton district is included in the 1:250 000-scale Bouguer anomaly map for the Bristol Channel (British Geological Survey, *in preparation*), but the map shown in Figure 20 differs in that some additional survey results have been included (mainly near Cannington Park and in the Quantock Hills) and the Bouguer correction was calculated using a variable density. A density of 2.6 g/cm^3 was used for stations on Devonian rocks and 2.4 g/cm^3 for areas of Triassic and younger sediments (boundaries shown in Figure 20).

The Bouguer anomaly map (Figure 20) is dominated by a regional southward increase in values from the low (7) over the Central Somerset Basin of Mesozoic sediments to the high orientated east – west over the eastern part of Exmoor (2) and south of the Quantock Hills (2A). The gradient zone 1 and 1A is interrupted in the Quantock Hills area by a weak Bouguer anomaly low (3), bordered on the south-west side by a zone of particularly steep gradients (4). In the southern part of the area a trough of low Bouguer anomaly values (5) expands southwards into a broad low (6) extending beyond the boundaries of the area. Some of these features, such as the lower values over the Mesozoic sediments and higher values over the usually higher-density Devonian rocks, appear to indicate a simple relationship between Bouguer anomaly values and the known geology, but a closer examination of the data suggests that a more complicated interpretation is necessary.

The Bouguer anomaly gradient 1 and 1A across the Devonian sediments of Exmoor and the Quantock Hills has no obvious explanation in the surface geology, although the east-south-east trend of the contours parallels the strike of the Devonian sediments. It was suggested originally by Falcon (*in* Cook and Thirlaway, 1952) that in the Quantock Hills the gradient could represent the effect of the deep-seated thrust postulated on geological evidence to exist near Cannington Park. On the basis of gravity evidence from Exmoor, Bott and others (1958) suggested that the Devonian sediments there had been thrust over a wedge, thinning southwards, of lower density rocks, possibly of Carboniferous or Devonian age. Brooks and Thompson (1973) subsequently slightly modified the thrust model on the basis of marine gravity data from the Bristol Channel. An alternative interpretation has been proposed by Brooks and others (1977), in which the Bouguer anomaly gradient is explained by concealed low-density Lower Palaeozoic or late Precambrian rocks in the core of the west-north-west-trending Lynton Anticline.

Superimposed on the regional southward increase of Bouguer anomaly values in the zone 1 and its westward extension across Exmoor are less-well defined changes of gradient which can be related to changes in the lithology of the Devonian sequence and which appear to be relevant to the geological interpretation of the gradient. The Hangman Grits are characterised over most of their outcrop in Exmoor by low gradients which increase abruptly southwards near the boundary of these lower-density arenaceous sediments with the overlying higher-density Ilfracombe Slates (Figure 21A). The gradient then decreases slightly south of the boundary but continues across the Morte Slate until it decreases abruptly at the top of these southward-dipping argillaceous sediments. The Pickwell Down Sandstones are marked by low gradients or even Bouguer anomaly minima (Figures 21 and 22A), although in Figure 21A the syncline in the rocks produces no gravity response. The minima become better defined westwards and, in the area north of Barnstaple [about Grid line 250 east], Al-Saadi (1967) described a residual Bouguer anomaly low of −7 mGal over these low-density sediments. In the overlying Carboniferous sequence the top of the Pilton Shales is marked by a small east to west Bouguer anomaly high [050 225] (Figure 20) which can be followed eastwards into the area where these rocks are covered by Triassic sediments. Burley (*in* Edmonds and others, 1979) and Tombs (*in* Edmonds and others, 1985) have described a similar correlation of Bouguer anomaly features with stratigraphic horizons in the Devonian and Carboniferous sequences in north Devon.

The main features of the observed Bouguer anomaly profile AA′ (figure 21A) can be reproduced by a model in which the main density boundaries occur at the margins of the Pickwell Down Sandstones and the Hangman Grits. The model differs slightly from that proposed by Brooks and others (1977) but is generally similar in that it ascribes the main cause of the gradient to the southward dip and consequently to the increasing thickness of the Devonian argillaceous measures and the northward rise of low-density pre-Devonian rocks. It is also possible that the density boundaries, particularly within the Devonian sequence, might coincide with the planes of strike faults as well as with bedding planes. The observed profile AA′ (Figure 21A) could also include a long-wavelength regional variation in the gravity field due to deep crustal variations which might be expected in the vicinity of the Variscan Front in the Bristol Channel area.

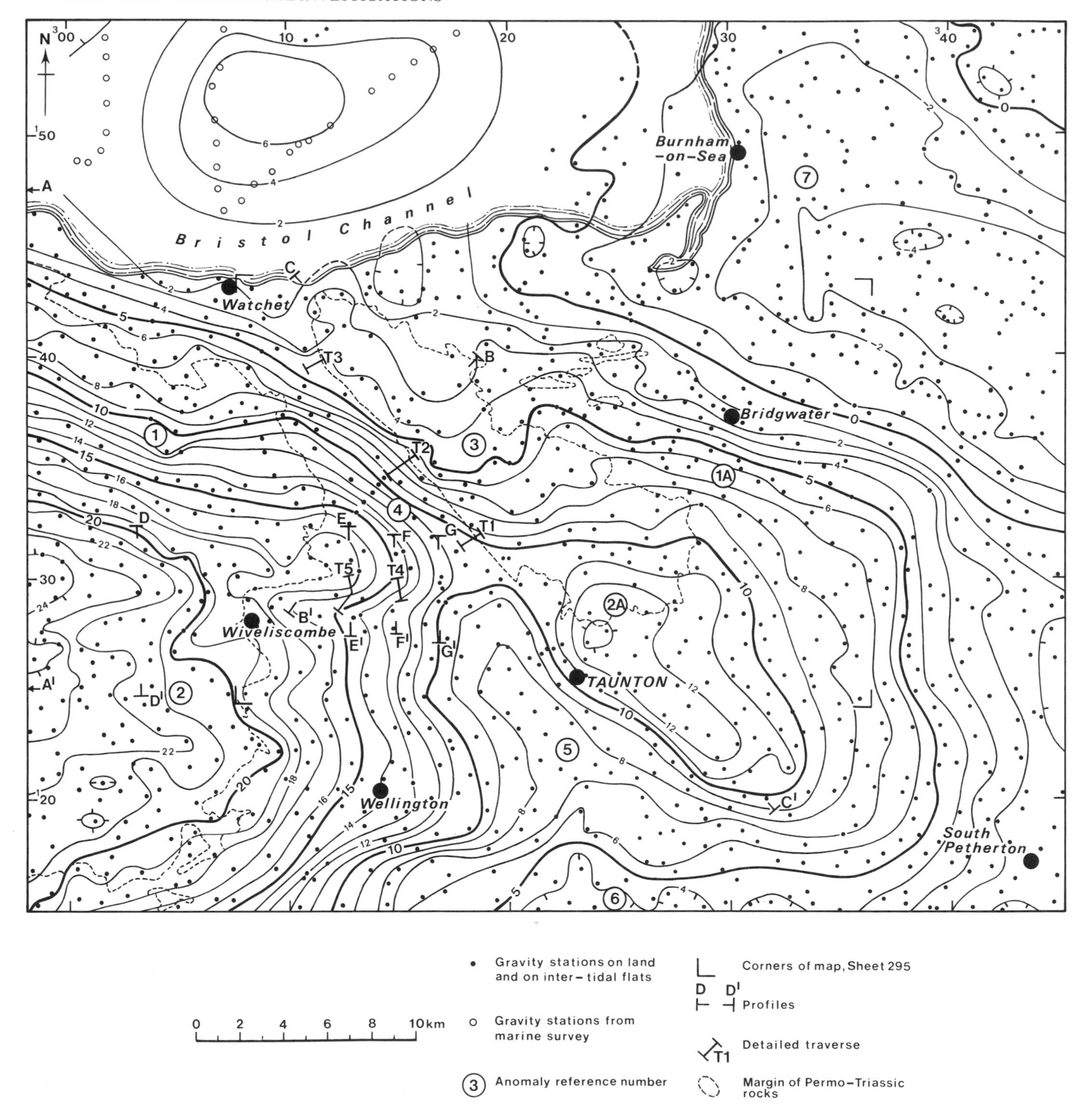

Figure 20 Bouguer anomaly map of the Taunton district.

Contours are at 1 mGal intervals and locations of detailed traverses T1 to T5 and profiles are shown. The gravity features 1 to 7 are referred to in the text. Marine data are based on Brooks and Thompson (1973)

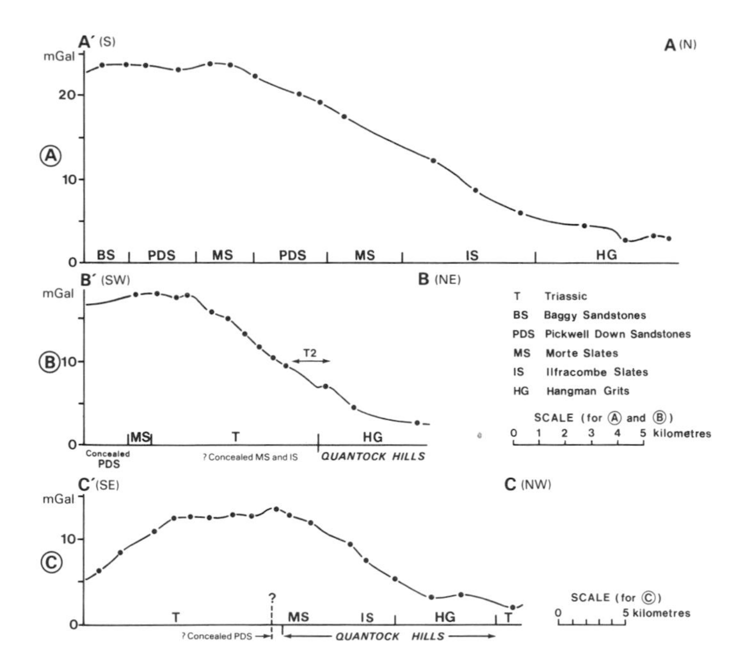

Figure 21 Observed Bouguer anomaly profiles AA′, BB′ and CC′ (locations in Figure 20) across the gradient zone.

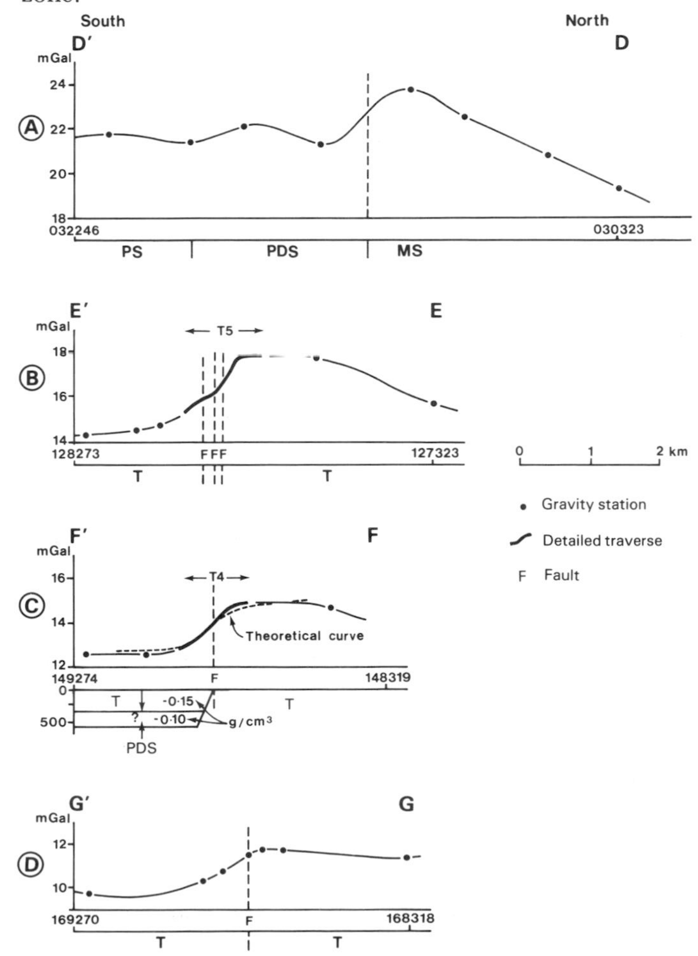

Figure 22 Observed Bouguer anomaly profiles DD′ to GG′ (Figure 20) with model and theoretical curve for profile FF′. Key as for Figure 21

The Bouguer anomaly profile (Figure 21C) along the length of the Quantock Hills (CC′ in Figure 20, with the horizontal scale changed to correct for the 40° angle of intersection between the profile and the contours) appears to show the same features as Figure 21A, the main difference being that the change of gradient characterising the top of the Morte Slates appears just south of the exposed Devonian sediments in the Quantock Hills. The possibility that the change of gradient is due to the thickening of the Permo-Triassic sediments cannot be ignored, but there is no evidence of such an anomaly from surveys elsewhere at this boundary (Figure 21B). It is suggested, therefore, that the Pickwell Down Sandstones sub-crop beneath a thin cover of Triassic beds in the Taunton area (Figure 23) and are probably succeeded to the south-east by the same stratigraphical units as on Exmoor.

The form of the anomaly 2A in Figure 20 suggestes that this proposed extension of the Palaeozoic rocks of the Quantock Hills is bounded on its south-west side by a prolongation of the Cothelstone Fault beneath the Permo-Triassic. Whittaker (1972) has postulated from geological evidence the existence of a fault in the same position, extending south-eastwards to the Hatch Fault (Figure 23). The amplitude of the Bouguer anomaly step-like feature along this south-west margin is about 6 mGal; it must be due to a density boundary within 1 km of the surface, but there is no other evidence for the depth to this concealed platform of Devonian and probably Carboniferous rocks.

The gravity effect of the Cothelstone Fault itself is small along the detailed traverses T1 to T3 (Figure 20), which reveal a local increase of less than 1 mGal over the Devonian sediments of the Quantock Hills (Figure 21B). This change could be accounted for by a thickness west of the fault of only 70 m of Otter Sandstone (Table 6), with a density contrast of -0.25 g/cm^3 against the Devonian.

East of the Quantock Hills the interpretation of the gradient zone 1A is complicated by the cover of Mesozoic sediments. Cornwell (*in* Whittaker and Green, 1983) has produced alternative interpretations for the gradient zone in the Bridgwater area, pointing out that, although it follows the southern margin of the Central Somerset Basin and extends eastwards to coincide with the Polden Hills Fault (Figure 23) in Mesozoic sediments, there is evidence that it also reflects variations in the concealed basement rocks. Two explanations of such variations are possible; either the gradient reflects the large fault which probably exists south of Cannington Park, accounting for the observed stratigraphical break of several kilometres between Devonian and Namurian sediments, or alternatively the gradient zone 1A could be simply a continuation of the zone 1.

The results of the Knap Farm Borehole, sited near the minimum of the Bouguer anomaly gradient 1A, are relevant to the interpretation. Beneath the thick inclined sequence of the high-density (2.72 g/cm^3) Carboniferous Limestone in this borehole, the Upper Devonian sediments are arenaceous in character but also have a high density compared with other rocks with this lithology (Table 5). However, by analogy with profiles across Exmoor (e.g. Figure 21A), Lower or Middle Devonian (Hangman Grits) rocks would be expected to coincide with the low Bouguer anomaly values around Cannington Park. If the interpretation that relates the gradient to lithology is correct, then another explanation (perhaps the major fault mentioned above) must exist for the gradient zone 1A, despite its apparent continuity with the zone 1 over Exmoor. Subsequent movements along such a fault would explain the apparent correlation of the gravity feature with Mesozoic structures.

The Knap Farm Borehole, therefore, indicates a more complicated structural situation than that existing farther to the west and uncertainties continue to exist in the interpretation of the geophysical data.

The lower-density Hangman Grits in the core of the Quantock Anticline (Figure 23) are considered to be the cause of the deflection in the Bouguer anomaly contours (3 in Figure 20) over the Quantock Hills. On the west side, the zone 4 is marked by higher gradients than exist farther west and by a change in the direction of the trend of the contours towards the north-west. The rather abrupt termination of this trend seems to indicate a shallow origin for the anomalous body and a maximum depth of less than 2 km has been estimated along the profile BB′ (Figures 20 and 21B). This supports the idea that the high-density argillaceous members of the Devonian sequence contribute a large part of the Exmoor gradient and also indicates that these sediments have been displaced on the north-west side of the Quantock Hills from the east-south-east trend typical for much of Exmoor. The observed gradient on profile BB′ implies a steeper boundary to the base of the Ilfracombe Slates than that existing to the west (Figure 21A) and could possibly indicate that a fault plane forms the south-western margin of the Hangman Grits core of the Quantock Anticline. The north-westerly trend of this boundary is parallel with the Watchet Fault (Figure 23), described by Whittaker (1972) as being associated with the Cothelstone Fault system. The gradient zone extends so far to the north-west that it is difficult to relate the Quantock Anticline to the Croydon and Withycombe Anticlines (Webby, 1965a) at the eastern end of Exmoor (Figure 23) without recourse to the transcurrent component of faulting between the two structures indicated by the geological evidence.

In the south-western corner of Figure 20 the Bouguer

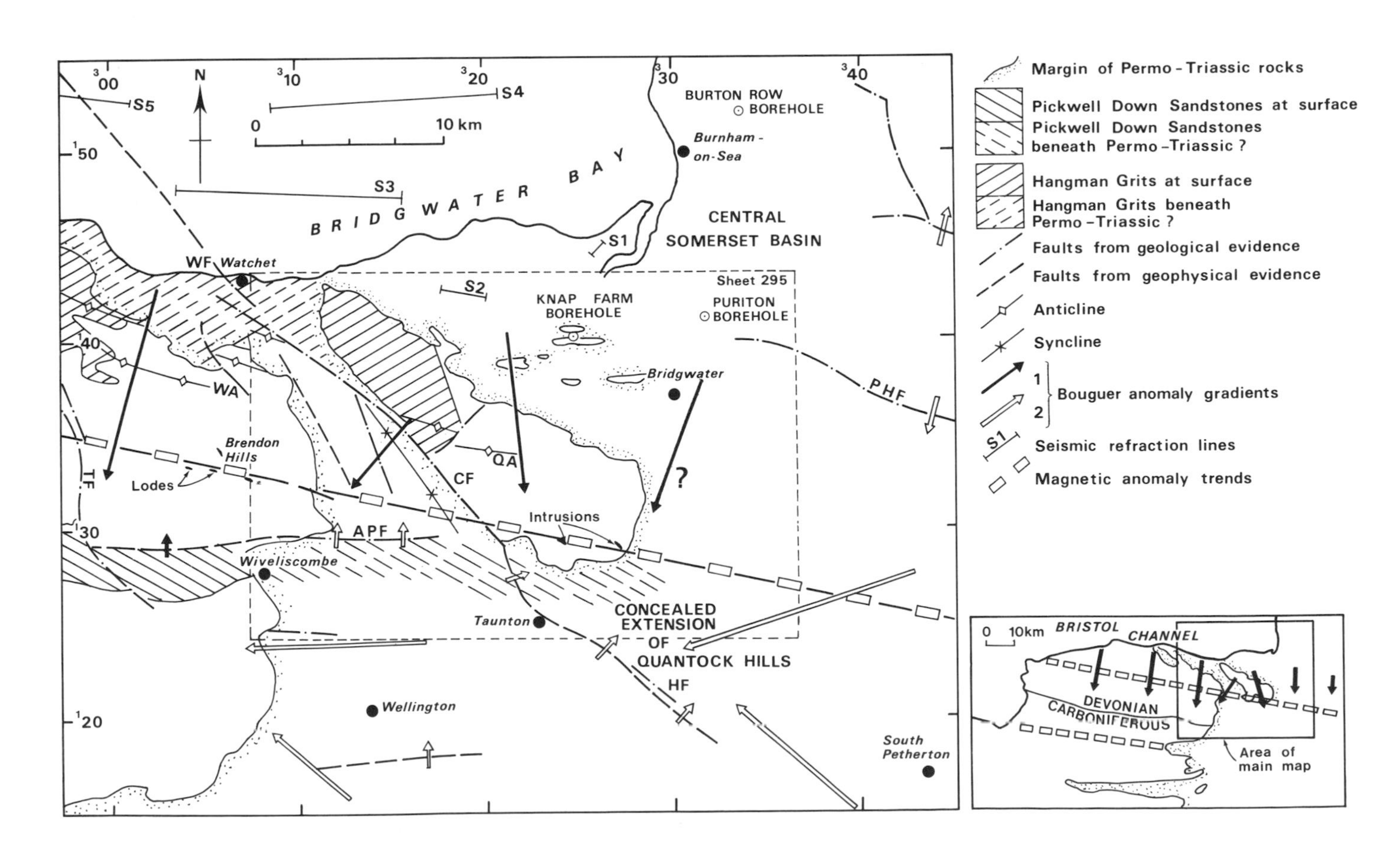

Figure 23 Schematic interpretation of geophysical results and some major geological features for the Taunton district.

The Bouguer anomaly gradients are divided into (1) a group probably due to density variations within the Devonian sequence (the arrows are then perpendicular to the geological strike) and (2) a group which could be due to Mesozoic thickness variations. Gradient arrows point in direction of increasing values.
Key to abbreviations: APF Ash Priors Fault CF Cothelstone Fault HF Hatch Fault PHF Polden Hills Fault TF Timberscombe Fault WF Watchet Fault CA Croydon Anticline QA Quantock Anticline WA Withycombe Anticline. Small map shows location of area covered.

anomaly values fall rapidly eastwards away from the Devonian and Carboniferous rocks forming the eastern end of Exmoor, and gradients of this nature have been interpreted above in terms of changes in the lithology of Devonian sediments. Such an explanation could also be valid for this area, although it implies a strike direction for the structures normal to those described earlier, and it is, therefore, suggested that the thickening Permo-Triassic sediments are largely responsible for this particular gradient.

Although thick Permo-Triassic and Jurassic sediments are present north of the Taunton district—more than 1100 m were recorded in the Burton Row Borehole (Whittaker and Green, 1983)—their comparatively high densities result in poorly defined Bouguer anomaly lows (Cornwell *in* Whittaker and Green, 1983). In the area of Permo-Triassic sediments north-west of Taunton the Wiveliscombe Sandstones in particular also have comparatively high densities (Table 6) but the Otter Sandstone can have a density as low as 2.11 g/cm^3 (Table 6). In the Okehampton district, the Permian sequence, with 50 per cent sandstone and 50 per cent breccia, has been given an average density of 2.41 g/cm^3 (Table 5), and Permian sediments in a trough in the Culm give rise to a well-defined Bouguer anomaly low (Edmonds and others, 1968). There is some evidence, therefore, that the existence of higher-density Permo-Triassic sediments may be restricted largely to the Central Somerset Basin and adjacent areas. Other gradients (Figure 23), notably those surrounding the Bouguer anomaly high over the extension of the Quantock Hills structure (2A in Figure 20), also probably reflect the effect of large-scale variations in the thickness of low-density Mesozoic sediments.

Within the area covered by Mesozoic sediments there are a few indications on the Bouguer anomaly map of anomalies related to smaller-scale thickness variations. In the Cannington Park area, a detailed gravity survey was carried out to determine the near-surface structure of the Devonian and Carboniferous inliers. A residual Bouguer anomaly map of the area shows an east to west-elongated high of about 2 mGal across the Cannington Park inlier, which is thought to represent the effect of the buried topographic high formed by the limestone. The extension of this high beneath the Rodway inlier [25 40], which is composed of lower-density rocks originally regarded as being of Devonian age but subsequently shown to be Namurian (Whittaker, 1975b), provided part of the evidence suggesting that Lower Carboniferous strata must exist here at depth, an interpretation subsequently confirmed by the drilling. The pronounced east to west elongation of the residual Bouguer anomaly contours and their linear character south of the Rodway and Padnoller House inliers indicate that this area is probably bounded by a fault which would be analogous to those mapped around the Charlinch inlier [215 388] and could possibly be the near-surface continuatin of the fault, described earlier, throwing the Carboniferous rocks of Cannington Park against the Devonian rocks to the south. A local area of low Bouguer anomaly values extending in an east to west direction north of Cannington Park coincides with a syncline in Mesozoic sediments.

North-west of Taunton, the Bouguer anomaly maps shows a linear step-like feature coincident with the Ash Priors Fault (Figure 23) extending westwards from Bishops Lydeard [169 295]. The step-like feature was examined by two detailed traverses (T4 and T5 in Figure 20) which revealed an anomaly of 2 to 4 mGal (Figure 22) and maximum gradients of up to 3.8 mGal/km, both decreasing eastwards. Maximum depths to the top of the body causing the anomaly must be about 0.2 to 0.3 km to produce these values, and the most obvious explanation is that the anomaly is due to the increased thickness of low-density Triassic sediments south of the fault. The model shown in Figure 22 for profile FF′ is one of a large number of possible ones, and indicates a thickening mainly of the Otter Sandstone. The reasons for suspecting this are that on profile EE′ (Figure 22) the Mercia Mudstone Group overlying the Otter Sandstone is absent, but the anomaly is even larger than on profile FF′, and for strata older than the Otter Sandstone the geological evidence does not support an increased thickness south of the fault.

If the Ash Priors Fault is traced westwards it coincides approximately with the boundary between the Morte Slates and the Pickwell Down Sandstones. This boundary corresponds with a Bouguer anomaly feature due to the density contrast between these two Devonian formations and in places, such as profile DD′ (Figure 22A) which is 10 km west of profile EE′ and 9 km east of profile AA′ (Figure 21A), the presence of a step-like anomaly suggests the boundary could be faulted. The density contrast within the Devonian at depth could add a small contribution to the observed anomaly on the profiles EE′ to GG′ and the lower part of the low-density model in Figure 22C could include Pickwell Down Sandstones.

The zone of steep gradients (Figure 20) south-east of Wellington [15 18] suggests the presence of another important east to west fault with an increased thickness of Permo-Triassic rocks to the south. This fault is close to the northern limit of the Upper Greensand and Gault outcrop of south Devon and Dorset and, if it is projected westwards (Figure 23), it coincides with the northern margin of the trough of Permian sediments around Tiverton [SS 96 12]. suggesting that the latter east to west elongated structure is fault-controlled.

AEROMAGNETIC SURVEYS

The aeromagnetic data for the Taunton district form part of a survey flown on contract in 1957. The total magnetic field recordings were made at a constant barometric height of 1800 feet (549 m) along north – south flight lines 2 km apart and east – west tie lines 10 km apart. The aeromagnetic map for the Taunton district (Figure 24) forms part of the 1:250 000 map of the Bristol Channel (Institute of Geological Sciences, 1980). The generally widely spaced contours suggest deeply buried magnetic bodies, some of which occur within the Weston-super-Mare district (Whittaker and Green, 1983). Shallower sources are indicated at the western edge of the map; the −20 nT closure [01 34] coincides with the Brendon Hills mining district (although individual lodes do not appear to give rise to magnetic anomalies), and is the eastern continuation of a belt of strong anomalies associated with mineralisation in north Devon

(Tombs *in* Edmonds and others, 1985). The northern part of the Quantock Hills is associated with local northward deflections of the contours between Taunton and Watchet; the magnetic low indicated by these deflections can be seen again as a trough of low values running north-westwards from Watchet and provides evidence for the seaward extension of the Cothelstone Fault system (Figure 23).

One weak magnetic anomaly crossing the southern part of the Quantock Hills is indicated on the aeromagnetic map by the east-south-east-elongated −50 nT contour north-east of Taunton (Figure 24). This anomaly occurs over the Morte Slates and also crosses the only known igneous intrusions in the Taunton district—the quartz-diorite sills and dykes at Coombe [271 290] and the lamprophyre dykes at Hestercombe [243 291]. Although detailed ground surveys would be needed to prove the near-surface continuity of these intrusions the aeromagnetic evidence tends to support the suggestion of Evens and Wallis (1930) that they are underlain by a larger igneous mass (p.47).

This east-south-east-trending anomaly near Taunton also lies directly in line (Figure 24) with a pronounced linear belt of magnetic anomalies extending for about 40 km across Exmoor. These Exmoor anomalies run parallel with the linear geological strike but decrease in amplitude where the sediments are folded to form the Croydon Anticline. Detailed investigations, including drilling, of the Exmoor anomalies indicate that they are due to pyrrhotite mineralisation in the Ilfracombe Slates and Morte Slates (Edmonds and others, 1985). This linear feature coincides with lodes worked in the Brendon Hills iron mines, suggesting that it could represent a major fault (Figure 23) which provided a channel for the passage and deposition of ore-bearing and igneous material. The linearity of the feature also suggests that it post-dates the folding of the Devonian sediments and most of the transcurrent component of movement along the Cothelstone Fault, since there is no evidence of a displacement as large as the 4.8 km proposed by Webby (1966a). Other evidence for the age of the feature comes from the observation by Evens and Wallis (1930) that the Coombe intrusions were formed after the cleavage in the Devonian rocks and before the deposition of the Permo-Triassic strata. A late Carboniferous to early Permian age seems to be indicated, perhaps close to that of the Dartmoor Granite.

East of the Quantock Hills, the linear feature extends through the −50 nT contour closure [37 27] and can be traced eastwards for a further 35 km beyond the area shown in Figure 24. This feature is closely paralleled by the Exmoor Bouguer anomaly gradient zone and, in central Devon, by a step-like magnetic anomaly (insert map in Figure 23) which can be interpreted as being due to the northern edge of a deep-seated magnetic block. The great lateral and vertical extent of features trending to the east or east-south-east suggests that they represent an extensive set of strike faults. Both faults and folds with this trend are common within the Taunton district and, on a larger scale, the same trend is repeated by the main Culm synclinorium of Devon and the Mesozoic basins of the Bristol Channel and Central Somerset.

The contour interval in Figure 24 is too wide to reveal several anomalies of less than 10 nT amplitude that cross the

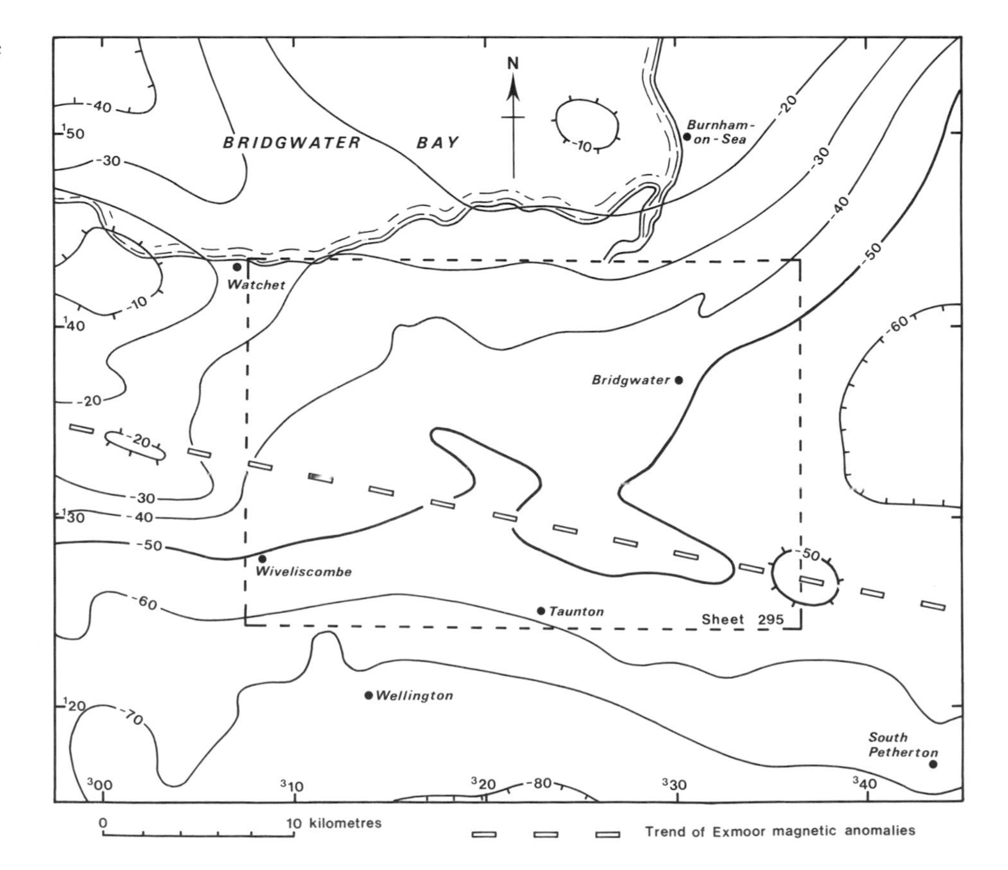

Figure 24 Aeromagnetic map of the Taunton district with total field magnetic intensity contours at 10 nT intervals

western part of the district. Depths to the corresponding magnetic sources appear to be small and the bodies probably occur near the surface, and are perhaps similar in origin to that responsible for the −20 nT closure described above.

SEISMIC SURVEYS

Seismic investigations on land in the Taunton district consist of refraction surveys carried out to investigate the shallow structure of the Cannington Park inliers and the adjacent area. These surveys traced a high-velocity layer (Carboniferous Limestone?) for 0.5 km away from the inlier in an easterly direction and confirmed the shallow extension of limestone to the small inlier 0.3 km west of the main outcrop on Cannington Park. Seismic records obtained on the Rodway inlier gave a velocity of about 3.5 km/s for the Rodway Siltstones and also revealed a high-velocity layer at depth which was originally interpreted as Carboniferous Limestone and subsequently confirmed as such by drilling (Whittaker, 1975b). Farther away from the inliers, the overlap in the velocities of the Permo-Triassic sequence and some of the Palaeozoic basement rocks (Table 6 and Cornwell *in* Whittaker and Green, 1983) makes the geological interpretation of refraction results difficult.

Two examples of this uncertainty in the interpretation are for the refraction lines S1 and S2 (Figure 23) at Stockland Bristol [26 45] and Stogursey [20 42] respectively. At site S1, a layer with a velocity of 4.6 km/s occurs at a depth of 140 m beneath Triassic sediments (3.4 km/s) and 20 m of recent deposits (0.8 km/s). At site S2, Professor M. Brooks (personal communication) reports that a high-velocity layer (5.0 km/s) occurs at an average depth of 412 m beneath Jurassic and Triassic sediments (3.4 km/s). The velocities of both deep refractors are high but it is still not established that they represent the pre-Mesozoic basement.

Seismic refraction surveys have been carried out in marine areas to investigate the geology of the sea-floor of the Bristol Channel, and Brooks and Al-Saadi (1977) have described results for the area north of the Taunton district (lines S3 to S5 in Figure 23). JDC

REFERENCES

AL-SAADI, H. M. 1967. A gravity investigation of the Pickwell Down Sandstone, north Devon. *Geol. Mag.*, Vol. 104, 63–72.

AVERY, B. W. 1955. The soils of the Glastonbury district of Somerset (Sheet 296). *Mem. Soil. Surv. G.B.*

BAKER, W. 1851. Geology of Somersetshire. *Proc. Somerset Archaeol. Nat. Hist. Soc.*, Vol. 1, 127–139..

— 1852. The Cannington Park Limestone. *Proc. Somerset Archaeol. Nat. Hist. Soc.*, Vol. 3, 125–131.

BOTT, M. H. P., DAY, A. A. and MASSON SMITH, D. 1958. The geological interpretation of gravity and magnetic surveys in Devon and Cornwall. *Philos. Trans. R. Soc. London*, Ser. A, Vol. 251, 161–191.

— and SCOTT, P. 1966. Recent geophysical studies in south-west England. *In* Present views of some aspects of the geology of Cornwall and Devon. *R. Geol. Soc. Cornwall*, Commem. Vol. (for 1964), 25–44.

BRISTOW, H. W. and ETHERIDGE, R. 1873. Vertical sections of the Lower Lias and Rhaetic or Penarth Beds of Glamorgan, Somerset and Gloucestershire. *Vert. Sect. Geol. Surv. G.B.* 47

BROOKS, M. and AL-SAADI, R. H., 1977. Seismic refraction studies of geological structure in the inner part of the Bristol Channel. *J. Geol. Soc. London*, Vol. 133, 433–445.

— BAYERLY, M. and LLEWELLYN, D. J. 1977. A new geological model to explain the gravity gradient across Exmoor, north Devon. *J. Geol. Soc. London*, Vol. 133, 385–393.

— and THOMPSON, M. S. 1973. The geological interpretation of a gravity survey of the Bristol Channel. *J. Geol. Soc. London*, Vol. 129, 245–274.

BULLEID, A. and JACKSON, J. W. 1937. The Burtle sand beds of Somerset. *Proc. Somerset Archaeol. Nat. Hist. Soc.*, Vol. 83, 171–195.

— — 1941. Further notes on the Burtle Beds of Somerset. *Proc. Somerset Archaeol. Nat. Hist. Soc.*, Vol. 87, 111–114.

CHAMPERNOWNE, A. and USSHER, W. A. E. 1879. Notes on the structure of the Palaeozoic districts of west Somerset. *Q. J. Geol. Soc. London*, Vol. 25, 532–548.

CLARK, J. A. 1854. On the Bridgwater and other Levels of Somersetshire. *J. Bath & West of England Soc.* Vol. 2, No. 5, 99–128

COOK, A. H. and THIRLAWAY, H. I. S. 1952. A gravimeter survey in the Bristol and Somerset coalfields. *Q. J. Geol. Soc. London*, Vol. 107, 255–286, 302–306.

COPE, J. C. W., GETTY, T. A., HOWARTH, M. K., MORTON, N. and TORRENS, H. S. 1980. A correlation of Jurassic rocks in the British Isles. Part 1, Introduction and Lower Jurassic. *Spec. Rep. Geol. Soc. London* No. 14.

CORNWELL, J. D. 1971. Geophysics of the Bristol Channel area. *Proc. Geol. Soc. London*, No. 1664, 286–289.

CROSSE, A. 1851. Holwell Cavern. *Proc. Somerset Archaeol. Nat. Hist. Soc.*, Vol. 2, 14–32, 123, 124.

DAWKINS, W. B. 1864. On the Rhaetic Beds and White Lias of western and central Somerset; and on the discovery of a new fossil mammal in the Grey Marlstones beneath the Bone-bed. *Q. J. Geol. Soc. London*, Vol. 20, 396–412.

— 1865. Note on the palaeontology of the Rhaetic (Penarth) Beds in western and central Somerset. *Geol. Mag.*, Vol. 2, 481–484.

DEARMAN, W. R. 1964. Wrench-faulting in Cornwall and south Devon. *Proc. Geol. Assoc.*, Vol. 74, 265–287.

DE LA BECHE, H. T. 1839. Report on the geology of Cornwall, Devon and west Somerset. *Mem. Geol. Surv. G.B.*

DINES, H. G. 1956. The metalliferous mining region of south-west England. *Mem. Geol. Surv. G.B.*

DONOVAN, D. T. 1971. In discussion of a symposium on the Bristol Channel. *Proc. Geol. Soc. London*, No. 1664, 305–306.

EDMONDS, E. A., MCKEOWN, M. C. and WILLIAMS, M. 1975. *British regional geology: south-west England* (4th Edition). (London: HMSO for Institute of Geological Sciences.)

— WILLIAMS, B. J. and TAYLOR, R. T. 1979. Geology of Bideford and Lundy Island. *Mem. Geol. Surv. G.B.* 143 pp.

— WHITTAKER, A. and WILLIAMS, B. J. 1985. Geology of the country around Ilfracombe and Barnstaple. *Mem. Geol. Surv. G.B.* 97 pp.

— WRIGHT, J. E., BEER, K. E., HAWKES, J. R., WILLIAMS, M., FRESHNEY, E. C. and FENNING, P. J. 1968. Geology of the country around Okehampton. *Mem. Geol. Surv. G.B.* 256 pp.

ETHERIDGE, R. 1867. On the physical structure of west Somerset and north Devon and on the palaeontological value of the Devonian fossils. *Q. J. Geol. Soc. London*, Vol. 23, 568–698.

— 1873. Notes on the physical structure of the Watchet area, and the relation of the Secondary rocks to the Devonian series of west Somerset. *Proc. Cotteswold Nat. Field Club*, Vol. 6, 35.

EVANS, D. J. and THOMPSON, M. S. 1979. The geology of the central Bristol Channel and the Lundy area, South Western Approaches, British Isles. *Proc. Geol. Assoc.*, Vol. 90, 1–20.

EVANS, J. W. 1922. The geological structure of the country around Combe Martin. *Proc. Geol. Assoc.*, Vol. 33, 201–228.

— RICHARDSON, L. and MARTIN, E. C. 1914. Report of an excursion to west Somerset. *Proc. Geol. Assoc.*, Vol. 25, 97–105.

— and STUBBLEFIELD, C. J. 1929. *Handbook of the geology of Great Britain.* (London: Thomas Murby & Co.)

EVENS, E. D. and WALLIS, F. S. 1930. The igneous rock at Hestercombe, Somerset. *Geol. Mag.*, Vol. 67, 193–199.

FRESHNEY, E. C., EDMONDS, E. A., TAYLOR, R. T. and WILLIAMS, B. J. 1979. Geology of the country around Bude and Bradworthy. *Mem. Geol. Surv. G.B.* 62 pp.

GEORGE, T. N., JOHNSON, G. A. L., MITCHELL, M., PRENTICE, J. E., RAMSBOTTOM, W. H.C., SEVASTOPULO, G. D. and WILSON, R. B. 1976. A correlation of Dinantian rocks in the British Isles. *Spec. Rep. Geol. Soc. London.* No. 7, 87 pp.

GILBERTSON, D. D. and MOTTERSHEAD, D. N. 1975. The Quaternary deposits at Doniford, west Somerset. *Field Studies*, Vol. 4, 117–129.

GODWIN, H. 1948. Studies of the post-glacial history of British vegetation. 10. Correlation between climate, forest composition, prehistoric agriculture and peat stratigraphy in Sub-Boreal and Sub-Atlantic peats of the Somerset levels. *Philos. Trans. R. Soc. London*, Ser. B, Vol. 233, 275–286.

— 1975. *The history of the British flora* (2nd edition). (Cambridge University Press.)

— SUGGATE, R. P. and WILLIS, E. H. 1958. Radiocarbon dating of the eustatic rise in ocean-level. *Nature, London*, Vol. 181, 1518–1519.

GOLDRING, R. 1955. The Upper Devonian and Lower Carboniferous trilobites of the Pilton Beds in N. Devon with an appendix on goniatites of the Pilton Beds. *Senckenb, Lethaea*, Vol. 36, 27–48.

— 1957. The last toothed Productellinae in Europe (Brachiopoda, Upper Devonian). *Palaeontol. Z.*, Vol. 31, 207–228.

GREEN, G. W. and WELCH, F. B. A. 1965. Geology of the country around Wells and Cheddar. *Mem. Geol. Surv. G.B.* 225 pp.

HALLAM, A. D. 1934. The geology of the Hangman Grits of the Quantock Hills. *Geol. Mag.*, Vol. 71, 433–446.

HAMILTON, J. R. and LAWRENCE, J. F. 1970. *Men and mining on the Quantocks.* (Bracknell: Town and Country Press Ltd.)

HICKS, H. 1896. On the Morte Slates and associated beds in north Devon and west Somerset, Part 1. *Q. J. Geol. Soc. London*, Vol. 52, 254–272.

— 1897. On the Morte Slates and associated beds in north Devon and west Somerset, Part 2. *Q. J. Geol. Soc. London*, Vol. 53, 438–462.

HOLWILL, F. J. W. 1963. The succession of limestones within the Ilfracombe Beds (Devonian) of north Devon. *Proc. Geol. Assoc.* Vol. 73, 281–293.

— HOUSE, M. R., LANE, R., GAUSS, G. A., HENDRIKS, E. M. L. and DEARMAN, W. R. 1969. Summer (1966) field meeting in Devon and Cornwall. *Proc. Geol. Assoc.*, Vol. 80, 43–62.

HORNER, L. 1816. Sketch of the geology of the south-western part of Somersetshire. *Trans. Geol. Soc. London.*, Ser. 1, Vol. 3, 338.

HOUSE, M. R. and SELWOOD, E. B. 1966. Palaeozoic palaeontology in Devon and Cornwall. *In* Present views of some aspects of the geology of Cornwall and Devon. *R. Geol. Soc. Cornwall,* Commem. Vol. (for 1964), 45–86.

INSTITUTE OF GEOLOGICAL SCIENCES. 1980. 1:250 000 Series. Aeromagnetic Anomaly map (Provisional Edition), Bristol Channel sheet, 51°N–4°W. (London: Institute of Geological Sciences.)

JONES, O. T. 1930. Some episodes in the geological history of the Bristol Channel region. *Rep. Br. Assoc.* (Bristol), 57–82.

KELLAWAY, G. A. 1971. Glaciation and the stones of Stonehenge. *Nature, London*, Vol. 232, 30–35.

KIDSON, C. 1970. The Burtle Beds of Somerset. *Proc. Ussher Soc.*, Vol. 2, 189–191.

— 1971. The Quaternary history of the coasts of south-west England, with special reference to the Bristol Channel coast. *In Exeter essays in geography.* GREGORY, K. J. and RAVENHILL, W. L. D. (editors). (Exeter.)

— BECK, R. B. and GILBERTSON, D. D. 1981. The Burtle Beds of Somerset: temporary sections at Penzoy Farm, near Bridgwater. *Proc. Geol. Assoc.*, Vol. 92, 39–45.

— and HAYNES, J. R. 1972. Glaciation in the Somerset levels; the evidence of the Burtle Beds. *Nature, London*, Vol. 239. 390–392.

— — and HEYWORTH, A. The Burtle Beds of Somerset—glacial or marine? *Nature, London*, Vol. 251, 211–213.

— and HEYWORTH, A. 1973.The Flandrian sea-level rise in the Bristol Channel. *Proc. Ussher Soc.*, Vol. 2, 565–584.

— — 1976. The Quaternary deposits of the Somerset Levels. *Q. J. Eng. Geol.*, Vol. 9, 217–235.

LAMING, D. J. C. 1968. New Red Sandstone stratigraphy in Devon and west Somerset. *Proc. Ussher Soc.*, Vol. 2, 23–25.

LANE, R. 1965. The Hangman Grits—an introduction and stratigraphy. *Proc. Ussher Soc.*, Vol. 1, 166–167.

LEES, A. and HENNEBERT, M. 1982. Carbonate rocks of the Knap Farm Borehole at Cannington Park, Somerset. *Rep. Inst. Geol. Sci.*, No. 82/5, 19–36.

LEWIS, C. A. (Editor.) 1970. *The glaciations of Wales and adjoining regions.* (London: Longmans.)

LLOYD, A. J., SAVAGE, R. J. G., STRIDE, A. H. and DONOVAN, D. T. 1973. The geology of the Bristol Channel floor. *Philos. Trans. R. Soc. London.*, Ser. A, Vol. 274, 595–626.

MCMURTRIE, J. 1912. On a boring at Puriton, near Bridgwater, in search of coal south of the Mendip Hills. *Proc. Somerset Archaeol. Nat. Hist. Soc.*, Vol. 57, 25–53.

MARTIN. E. C. 1909. The probable source of the limestone pebbles in the Bunter Conglomerate of west Somerset. *Geol. Mag.*, Vol. 46, 160–165.

MAW, G. 1864. On a supposed boulder clay in north Devon. *Q. J. Geol. Soc. London*, Vol. 20, 445–451.

MAYALL, M. J. 1979. The clay mineralogy of the Rhaetic transgression in Devon and Somerset—environmental and stratigraphic implications. *Proc. Ussher Soc.*, Vol. 4, 303–311.

— 1981. The late Triassic Blue Anchor Formation and the initial Rhaetian marine transgression in south-west Britain. *Geol. Mag.*, Vol. 118, No. 4, 377–384.

MITCHELL, G. F. 1960. The Pleistocene history of the Irish Sea. *Adv. Sci., London*, Vol. 17, 313–325.

— 1972. The Pleistocene history of the Irish Sea; second approximation. *Sci. Proc. R. Dublin Soc.*, Ser. A, Vol. 4, 181–199.

MITCHELL, M., REYNOLDS, M. J., LALOUX, M. and OWENS, B. 1982. Biostratigraphy of the Knap Farm Borehole at Cannington Park, Somerset. *Rep. Inst. Geol. Sci.*, No. 82/5, 9–17.

NORMAN, C. 1978. Two flint artifacts from the gravel cliffs at Doniford, west Somerset. *Proc. Somerset Archaeol, Nat. Hist. Soc.*, Vol. 122, 157–159.

ORBELL, G. 1973. Palynology of the British Rhaeto-Liassic. *Bull. Geol. Surv. G.B.*, No. 44, 1–44.

ORCHARD, M. J. 1979. On a *varcus* Zone conodont fauna from the Ilfracombe Slates (Devonian, north Devon). *Geol. Mag.*, Vol. 116, 129–134.

OWENS, B. 1972. A derived Lower Tournaisian miospore assemblage from the Permo-Triassic deposits of south Devon, England. *C.R. 7e Congr. Inst. Stratigr. Carb., Krefeld 1971*, Vol. 1, 359–365.

PAUL, H. 1937. The relationship of the Pilton Beds in north Devon to their equivalents on the continent. *Geol. Mag.*, Vol. 74, 433–442.

PAYNE, J. H. 1854. On the geology of the Quantocks. *Proc. Somerset Archaeol. Nat. Hist. Soc.*, Vol. 5, 95–106.

PERCEVAL, S. G. 1872. On the limestone at Cannington Park, near Bridgwater. *Geol. Mag.*, Vol. 9, 94–95.

PETTIJOHN, F. J. 1957. *Sedimentary rocks.* 718 pp. (New York: Harper.)

POLLARD, J. E. 1976. A problematic trace fossil from the Tor Bay Breccias of south Devon. *Proc. Geol. Assoc.*, Vol. 87, 105–108.

RICHARDSON, L. 1911. The Rhaetic and contiguous deposits of west, mid and part of east Somerset. *Q. J. Geol. Soc. London*, Vol. 67, 1–74.

RIDGWAY, J. M. 1974. A problematic trace fossil from the New Red Sandstone of south Devon. *Proc. Geol. Assoc.*, Vol. 85, 511–517.

SCRIVENER, R. C. and BENNETT, M. J. 1980. Ore genesis and control of mineralisation in the Upper Palaeozoic rocks of north Devon. *Proc. Ussher Soc.*, Vol. 5, 54–58.

SCRUTTON, C. T. 1975. Preliminary observations on the distribution of Devonian rugose coral faunas in south-west England. In *Drevnie Cnidaria*, Vol. 2. 131–140. SOKOLOV, B. S. (Editor). (Novosibirsk.)

SHEARMAN, D. J. 1967. On Tertiary fault movements in north Devonshire. *Proc. Geol. Assoc.*, Vol. 78, 555–566.

SIMPSON, S. 1964. The Lynton Beds of north Devon. *Proc. Ussher Soc.*, Vol. 1, 121–122.

SMITH, D. B. The palaeogeography of the British Zechstein. *In* DELLWIG, L. F., and RAU, J. L. (editors). Third symposium on salt. *N. Ohio Geol. Soc., Cleveland.* 20–23.

— BRUNSTROM, R. G. W., MANNING, P. I., SIMPSON, S. and SHOTTON, F. W. 1974. A correlation of Permian rocks in the British Isles. *Spec. Rep. Geol. Soc. London*, No. 5, 54 pp.

STEPHENS, N. 1970. The west country and southern Ireland. *In The glaciations of Wales and adjoining regions*, LEWIS, C. A. (editor). (London: Longmans).

STEVENSON, C. R. and WARRINGTON, G. 1971. Jurassic and Cretaceous rocks of Wessex: highest Keuper deposits; discussion to report of field meeting. *Proc. Geol. Assoc.*, Vol. 82, 297–300.

THOMAS, A. N. 1940. The Triassic rocks of north-west Somerset. *Proc. Geol. Assoc.*, Vol. 51, 1–43.

TIDMARSH, W. G. 1932. Permian lavas of Devon. *Q. J. Geol. Soc. London*, Vol. 138, 712–773.

TOMBS, J. M. C, BEER, K. E. and JONES, R. C. (*In preparation*) Investigation of an aeromagnetic anomaly at Exmoor, north Devon. *Miner. Reconnaissance Programme Rep. Br. Geol. Surv.*

TUNBRIDGE, I. P. 1978. *In* A field guide to selected areas of the Devonian of south-west England. International symposium on the Devonian system (P.A.D.S. 78). *Palaeont. Assoc.*, 11–13.

USSHER, W. A. E. 1875. On the subdivisions of the Triassic rocks between the coast of west Somerset and the south coast of Devon. *Geol. Mag.*, Vol. 12, 163–168.

— 1876. On the Triassic rocks of Somerset and Devon. *Q. J. Geol. Soc. London*, Vol. 32, 367–394.

— 1879. On the geology of parts of Devon and west Somerset, north of South Molton and Dulverton. *Proc. Somerset Archaeol. Nat. Hist. Soc.*, Vol. 25, 1–20.

— 1881. On the Palaeozoic rocks of north Devon and west Somerset. *Geol. Mag.*, Vol. 18, 441–448.

— 1889. The Triassic rocks of west Somerset and the Devonian rocks on their borders. *Proc. Somerset Archaeol. Nat. Hist. Soc.*, Vol. 35, 1–36.

— 1900. The Devonian, Carboniferous and New Red Rocks of west Somerset, Devon and Cornwall. *Proc. Somerset Archaeol. Nat. Hist. Soc.*, Vol. 46, 1–64.

— 1906. Geology of the country between Wellington and Chard. *Mem. Geol. Surv. G.B.* 68 pp.

— 1908. Geology of the Quantock Hills and of Taunton and Bridgwater. *Mem. Geol. Surv. G.B.* 109 pp.

WALKER, A. D. 1969. The reptile fauna of the 'Lower Keuper Sandstone'. *Geol. Mag.*, Vol. 106, 470–476.

WALLIS, F. S. 1924. The Avonian of Cannington Park, near Bridgwater, Somerset. *Geol. Mag.*, Vol. 61, 218–225.

WARRINGTON, G. 1971. Palynology of the New Red Sandstone of the south Devon coast. *Proc. Ussher Soc.*, Vol. 2, 307–314.

— 1974. Studies in the palynological biostratigraphy of the British Trias. 1. Reference sections in west Lancashire and north Somerset. *Rev. Palaeobot. and Palynol.*, Vol. 17, 133–147.

— 1978. Palynological features of the late Triassic – early Jurassic sequence in west Somerset (Abstract). *Proc. Ussher Soc.*, Vol. 4, 157.

— 1979. A derived late Permian palynomorph assemblage from the Keuper Marl (late Triassic) of west Somerset. *Proc. Ussher Soc.*, Vol. 4, 299–302.

— 1980. Palynological studies of Triassic rocks in central Somerset (Abstract). *Proc. Ussher Soc.*, Vol. 5, 90.

— 1981a. The indigenous micropalaeontology of British Triassic shelf sea deposits. In *Microfossils from Recent and fossil shelf seas*, 61–70. NEALE, J. W. and BRASIER, M. D. (editors). (Chichester: Horwood.)

— AUDLEY-CHARLES, M. G., ELLIOTT, R. E., EVANS, W. B., IVIMEY-COOK, H. C., KENT, P., ROBINSON, P. L., SHOTTON, F. W. and TAYLOR, F. M. 1980. A correlation of Triassic rocks in the British Isles. *Spec. Rep. Geol. Soc. London*, No. 13, 78 pp.

WEBBY, B. D. 1964. Devonian corals and brachiopods from the Brendon Hills, west Somerset. *Palaeontology*, Vol. 7, 1–22.

— 1965a. The stratigraphy and structure of the Devonian rocks in the Brendon Hills, west Somerset. *Proc. Geol. Assoc.*, Vol. 76, 39–60.

— 1965b. *Quantoxocrinus*, a new Devonian inadunate crinoid from west Somerset, England. *Palaeontology*, Vol. 8, 11–15.

— 1966a. The stratigraphy and structure of the Devonian rocks in the Quantock Hills, west Somerset. *Proc. Geol. Assoc.*, Vol. 76, 321–343.

— 1966b. Middle – Upper Devonian palaeogeography of north Devon and west Somerset, England. *Palaeogeogr., Palaeoclimatol, Palaeoecol.*, Vol. 2, 27–46.

— and THOMAS, J. M. 1965. Whitsun field meeting: Devonian of west Somerset and the Carboniferous of north-east Devon. *Proc. Geol. Assoc.*, Vol. 76, 179–194.

WHITTAKER, A. 1970. The salt industry at Puriton, Somerset. *Proc. Somerset Archaeol. Nat. Hist. Soc.*, Vol. 114, 96–99.

— 1972. The Watchet Fault—a post-Liassic transcurrent reverse fault. *Bull Geol. Surv. G.B.*, No. 41, 75–80.

— 1973. The Central Somerset Basin. *Proc. Ussher Soc.*, Vol. 2, pp. 585–592.

— 1975a. A postulated post-Hercynian rift valley system in southern Britain. *Geol. Mag.*, Vol. 112, 137–149.

— 1975b. Namurian strata near Cannington Park, Somerset. *Geol. Mag.*, Vol. 112, 325–326 [Correspondence].

— 1978. Swang Farm No. 1 Borehole and Swang Farm No. 2 Borehole. *In* IGS boreholes 1976. *Rep. Inst. Geol. Sci.*, No. 77/10, 11–12.

— and GREEN, G. W. 1983. Geology of the Country around Weston-super-Mare. *Mem. Geol. Surv. G.B.*, 147.

— and SCRIVENER, R. C. 1978. Knap Farm Borehole, Cannington Park. *In* IGS boreholes 1976. *Rep. Inst. Geol. Sci.*, No. 77/10, 12–13.

— — 1982. The Knap Farm Borehole at Cannington Park, Somerset. *Rep. Inst. Geol. Sci.*, No. 82/5, 1–7.

APPENDIX 1

Palynology of the Permo-Triassic and lower Jurassic succession

G. Warrington

The Littleham Mudstone to Lower Lias (*planorbis* Zone) succession in the Taunton district has been examined for palynological evidence of age. Samples from the sequence from the Littleham Mudstone to the higher part of the Mercia Mudstone Group below the Blue Anchor Formation, were obtained from inland exposures and, by kind permission of the authorities at the Bristol and Taunton museums, from cores from the Puriton Borehole. The upper part of the Mercia Mudstone Group was sampled in a major coastal section in the north-western part of the district together with the Penarth Group and beds to the top of the *planorbis* Zone in the Lias sequence.

Although reworked late Permian palynomorphs were recovered from late Triassic Mercia Mudstone deposits, there is no palynological evidence for the existence of Permian rocks *in situ* in the district. The oldest beds in the Permo-Triassic sequence which are dated palynologically are the Carnian (late Triassic) Somerset Halite Formation, North Curry Sandstone and contiguous beds in the Mercia Mudstone Group. Higher beds in that group, including the Blue Anchor Formation, are, with the Penarth Group and the basal beds of the Lias (below the incoming of *Psiloceras*), of Rhaetian (late Triassic) age.

LITTLEHAM MUDSTONE

Three samples from this unit at sites at Bicknoller [1064 3890] and north-west of Milverton [1050 2680 and 1060 2650] were devoid of stratigraphically significant palynomorphs (p. 32).

SHERWOOD SANDSTONE GROUP: OTTER SANDSTONE

Core material from the lower part of this unit at depths of 437.21 and 443.59 m in the Puriton Borehole [320 408] was examined but contained no stratigraphically useful palynomorphs.

MERCIA MUDSTONE GROUP

Seven samples from this unit at five localities west and south-west of the Quantock Hills [1116 3883, 1448 3403, 1462 2844, 1793 2993, and 1682 2573 to 1690 2572] proved barren, as did six from beds underlying the North Curry Sandstone in a section [3245 2626; p.41] north of Moredon House in the South-eastern part of the district.

The North Curry Sandstone and overlying beds in the Mercia Mudstone Group were examined in sections (p. 41) south of Moredon House [3253 2586 to 3255 2580], near Dyke's Farm [3512 2770], in Gainsload Drove [3570 2812] near Churley Farm, and in a railway cutting [3640 2820] near Stathe Court. Fourteen of the seventeen samples from these sites yielded generally profuse and moderately diverse associations of rather poorly preserved miospores. These assemblages are dominated by disacciatrilete taxa which, though commonly indeterminate because of poor preservation, include representatives of *Alisporites* and, in lesser numbers, genera including *Cuneatisporites*, *Platysaccus*, *Rimaesporites* and *Vesicaspora*. Taeniate bisaccates (*Lunatisporites*, *Striatoabieites*) and disaccitriletes (*Triadispora*) are present only sporadically, and trilete spores (*Microreticulatisporites* and *Verrucosisporites*) occur in low relative abundance. The assemblages are further characterised by generally consistent occurrences of *Camerosporites secatus*, *Duplicisporites granulatus*, *D. verrucosus*, *Ellipsovelatisporites plicatus*, *Ovalipollis pseudoalatus* and *Vallasporites ignacii*, and by sporadic occurrences of *Aratrisporites spp.*, *Brodispora striata* and *Patinasporites densus*. The composition of these assemblages and features such as the presence of *P. densus*, the scarcity of *Triadispora* and the absence of *Echinitosporites iliacoides*, are, by comparison with records from other European Triassic sequences (Scheuring 1970, 1978; Visscher and Brugman 1981), indicative of a late Triassic (Carnian) age. The North Curry Sandstone assemblages are comparable with those documented from the analogous Arden Sandstone and Weston Mouth Sandstone units of central England and south Devon respectively (Clarke 1965; Warrington 1970. 1971; Fisher 1972, *in* Jeans 1978).

The Mercia Mudstone sequence from the Puriton Borehole was sampled at eighteen levels between depths of 15.24 m and 342.29 m (inclusive). Two samples, from 199.39 m and 217.02 m, represented the main halite-bearing sequence proved in that borehole; four samples represented lower levels, and the remainder higher levels in the section. Miospores were recovered from thirteen horizons but determinable indigenous material was obtained from only eight of these (15.24 m, 114.86 m, 176.02 m, 181.66 m, 186.54 m, 191.44 m, 235.31 m and 287.83 m). Assemblages from 176.02 m to 287.83 m (inclusive) are characterised by poorly preserved disacciatriletes, including *Alisporites spp.*, associated with *Camerosporites secatus* (common to abundant), *Duplicisporites granulatus*, *Ellipsovelatisporites plicatus* and *Ovalipollis pseudoalatus* with, less consistently, *Duplicisporites scurrilis*, *D. verrucosus*, *Enzonalasporites vigens*, *Porcellispora longdonensis* and *Vallasporites ignacii*, and sporadic occurrences of *Aratrisporites sp.*, *Triadispora sp.*, *Verrucosisporites contactus* and *V. morulae*. These assemblages are broadly comparable with, but slightly older than, those recorded from the North Curry Sandstone in the south-eastern part of the district, and beds from 176.02 m to 287.83 m at Puriton, including the halite-bearing unit (Warrington 1980), are assigned a Carnian age.

Miospores recovered from material reputedly from depths of 15.24 m and 114.86 m in the Puriton Borehole throw doubt on the depths attributed to those samples. The former yielded an assemblage comparable with those recorded at and below 176.02 m, and the latter yielded a very sparse association of miospores including *Rhaetipollis germanicus*, a form indicative of a Rhaetian age. This sample may have originated from a higher level in the borehole but, though possibly displaced, the presence of *R. germanicus* in material from Puriton supports the view (McMurtrie 1912, p. 49) that the borehole commenced as little as 23 m below the Penarth Group; *R. germanicus* occurs within the highest 45 m of the Mercia Mudstone Group at St. Audrie's Bay in the north-western part of the district (Warrington 1974; see also below) and within the uppermost 53 m of that Group in the Burton Row Borehole in the adjacent Weston-super-Mare district (Warrington *in* Whittaker and Green 1983).

At St Audrie's Bay an almost uninterrupted coastal section [110 431 to 103 433] was sampled at eighty-seven levels through a 118-m sequence which spans the Triassic – Jurassic boundary and comprises beds between an horizon in the Mercia Mudstone some 92 m below the base of the Penarth Group and the top of the *planorbis* Zone in the Lias. Forty-two samples, comprising fourteen from the Lias, twelve from the Penarth Group and sixteen from the uppermost 45.04 m of the Mercia Mudstone, including the Blue Anchor Formation, were productive. Beds lower in the Mercia Mudstone section proved barren except for reworked late Permian palynomorphs recovered 48.09 m below the top of that group (Warrington 1979). In this section, therefore, indigenous palynomorphs have been recovered through a 73-m sequence, from 45.04 m below the Penarth Group to the top of the *planorbis* Zone (Warrington 1974, 1978, 1981a, *in* Whittaker and Green 1983).

The palynomorph occurrences in the upper beds of the Mercia Mudstone Group at St Audrie's Bay and in the neighbouring Weston-super-Mare district (Whittaker and Green 1983) are currently the most extensive known from those beds in Britain. The lowest indigenous Triassic miospores from the St Audrie's section (Warrington 1974), from some 45 m below the top of the Mercia Mudstone Group, include *Rhaetipollis germanicus* which is indicative of a Rhaetian age; beds between that level and the base of the Hettangian Stage, as defined (Cope and others 1980; Warrington and others 1980) by the appearance, within the Lias, of *Psiloceras*, are therefore assigned to that age.

Except within the topmost metre of the Blue Anchor Formation, where organic-walled microplankton occur sporadically, palynomorph assemblages from the Mercia Mudstone Group comprise only miospores (Warrington 1974, 1978, 1981a). Miospore associations from the Mercia Mudstone sequence below the Blue Anchor Formation, and from the lower part of that formation, are of limited diversity but have affinity with those from the overlying Penarth Group rather than with older associations from the Mercia Mudstone (e.g. those recorded from the Puriton Borehole and the North Curry Sandstone). This affinity increases within the uppermost 10 m of the Blue Anchor Formation and is enhanced by the appearance of the dinoflagellate cyst *Rhaetogonyaulax rhaetica* at the top of that unit. The diversity of the palynomorph assemblages increases progressively through the same interval and upwards into the Penarth Group.

Palynomorph assemblages from the Penarth Group at St Audrie's Bay are comparable with those documented from that unit elsewhere in Britain (Orbell 1973; Morbey 1975; Warrington *in* Poole 1977, 1978). The diversification initiated in the Blue Anchor Formation continues within the Westbury Formation and the Cotham Member of the Lilstock Formation. The majority of the taxa present in assemblages from the Mercia Mudstone Group persist in those from the Penarth Group, but are joined there by additional miospore and organic-walled microplankton taxa (Warrington 1974, 1981a) dinoflagellate cysts, principally *Rhaetogonyaulax rhaetica*, occur in profusion in several Westbury Formation and Cotham Member assemblages, and scolecodonts and test linings of foraminifera are also present in Penarth Group preparations (Warrington 1974, 1978, 1981a).

A marked change in the character of the palynomorph assemblages occurs at or near the top of the Langport Member, the highest unit in the Penarth Group. Associations from the succeeding basal (pre-*planorbis*) Lias beds and from the *planorbis* Zone are of very limited diversity and are dominated by miospores, principally *Classopollis* and related forms. The organic-walled microplankton component of these assemblages is dominated by acanthomorph acritarchs; dinoflagellate cysts are comparatively scarce (Warrington 1981a).

The basal beds of the Lias are assigned to the Triassic (Cope and others 1980; Warrington and others 1980) and palynomorph assemblages from them are considered, with those from the Penarth Group and the highest beds of the Mercia Mudstone Group, to be of Rhaetian age. No change in the assemblages occurs at the level in the Lias defined by the appearance of *Psiloceras* as the base of the Jurassic. The changes observed in palynomorph associations within this highest Triassic succession result at least partly from environmental changes associated with the onset and progress of the marine transgression which, entering the region during Rhaetian times, resulted in the establishment of an open marine environment throughout much of the British Isles by Hettangian times (Warrington 1978, 1981a).

Palynological features of the remainder of the lower Jurassic sequence of this region, based mainly upon sections in the adjacent Weston-super-Mare district, are summarised elsewhere (Warrington 1981b, *in* Whittaker and Green 1983).

REFERENCES

The following items are cited in this Appendix but are not included in the main bibliography of this memoir.

Clarke, R. F. A. 1965. Keuper miospores from Worcestershire, England. *Palaeontology*, Vol. 8, 294–321.

Fisher, M. J. 1972. The Triassic palynofloral succession in England. *Geoscience & Man*, Vol. 4, 101–109.

Jeans, C. V. 1978. The origin of the Triassic clay assemblages of Europe with special reference to the Keuper Marl and Rhaetic of parts of England. *Phil. Trans. R. Soc.*, Ser. A, Vol. 289, 549–639.

Morbey, S. J. 1975. The palynostratigraphy of the Rhaetian Stage, Upper Triassic in the Kendelbachgraben, Austria. *Palaeontographica*, Ser. B., Vol. 152, 1–75.

Poole, E. G. 1977. Stratigraphy of the Steeple Aston Borehole, Oxfordshire. *Bull. Geol. Surv. G.B.*, No. 57.

— 1978. Stratigraphy of the Withycombe Farm Borehole, near Banbury, Oxfordshire. *Bull. Geol. Surv. G.B.*, No. 68.

Scheuring, B. W. 1970. Palynologische und palynostratigraphische Untersuchungen des Keupers im Bölchentunnel (Solothurner Jura). *Schweiz. Palaöntol. Abh.*, Vol. 88, 1–119.

— 1978, Mikrofloren aus den Meridekalken des Mte. San Giorgio (Kanton Tessin). *Schweiz. Paläontol. Abh.*, Vol. 100, 1–100.

Visscher, H. and Brugman, W. A. 1981. Ranges of selected palynomorphs in the Alpine Triassic of Europe. *Rev. Palaeobot. Palynol.*, Vol. 34, 115–128.

Warrington, G. 1970. The stratigraphy and palaeontology of the 'Keuper' Series in the central Midlands of England. *Q. J. Geol. Soc. London*, Vol. 126, 183–223.

— 1981b. Palynology of the Lias, Brent Knoll, Somerset (Abstract). *Proc. Ussher Soc.*, Vol. 5, 241.

APPENDIX 2

List of Geological Survey photographs

Copies of these photographs may be seen in the Library of the british Geological Survey, Exhibition Road, South Kensington, London SW7 2DE. Prints and lantern slides may be purchased. The photographs were taken by Mr C. J. Jeffery and are available in colour and black and white. The photographs belong to Series A.

DEVONIAN

12823 Quarry in Trentishoe Grits, Halsway Combe [134 380].
13822 Quarry in Trentishoe Grits, Bicknoller Combe [1154 3990].
13824 Quarry in Trentishoe Grits, Halsway Combe [134 380.]
13825 Quarry in Trentishoe Grits, Rams Combe [1681 3766].
13826 Quarry in Trentishoe Grits, Rams Combe [1681 3766].
13827 Triscombe Quarry [161 356] (Plate 2).
13828 Quarry in Rodhuish Limestone (Ilfracombe Slates) [1898 3724].
13829 Leigh Barton Limestone (Ilfracombe Slates) [1896 3184].
13830 Oakhampton Quarries, Morte Slates [086 300].
13831 Quarry in Morte Slates, Willett [1061 3366].
13849 Buckingham Mine, Dodington [1733 4032] (Plate 7).

PERMO-TRIASSIC

11702 Basal junction of Blue Anchor Formation, St Audrie's Bay [1050 4315].
11703 Blue Anchor Formation and Penarth Group, St Audrie's Bay [1040 4326].
11718 Shrinkage cracks in the Cotham Member, St Audrie's Bay [1033 4316] (Plate 6).
13832 Quarry in Wiveliscombe Sandstones, Stogumber [0965 3681].
13833 Quarry in Wiveliscombe Sandstones, Stogumber [1045 3690].
13834 Junction between Wiveliscombe Sandstones and Vexford Breccias, Wiveliscombe [0830 2883].
13835 Quarry in Vexford Breccias, Castlake Farm [1116 3671].
13836 Quarry in Budleigh Salterton Pebble Beds, Fitzhead [1103 2946].
13837 Quarry in Budleigh Salterton Pebble Beds, Milverton [127 270] (Plate 4).
13838 Quarry in Budleigh Salterton Pebble Beds, Castle Hill, Wiveliscombe [096 284].
13839 Quarry in Budleigh Salterton Pebble Beds, Castle Hill, Wiveliscombe [096 284].
13840 Vellow Quarry, Bicknoller [097 388].
13841 Quarry in Budleigh Salterton Pebble Beds, Coursley [142 330].
13842 Road cutting in Otter Sandstone, Preston Bowyer [134 264].
13843 Quarry in Otter Sandstone, Bishop's Lydeard [166 300] (Plate 5).
13844 Quarry in Otter Sandstone, Bishop's Lydeard [166 300].
13845 Quarry in Otter Sandstone, Crowcombe [135 363].
13846 North Curry Sandstone, Moredon House [3252 2585]
13847 North Curry Sandstone, Moredon House [3252 2585].
13848 North Curry Sandstone, Moredon House [3253 2588].

JURASSIC

11704 Landslipped Penarth Group and Lower Lias strata, St Audrie's Bay [1034 4322].
11705 Cliffs in Lower Lias strata, St Audrie's Bay [0991 4336].
11706 Large-scale faulting, Helwell Bay [0786 4335].
11716 Small-scale low-angle thrusting, St Audrie's Bay [1031 4319].
11717 Triassic – Jurassic boundary, St Audrie's Bay [1032 4328].

PLEISTOCENE AND RECENT

11707 Frost-heaved Head Gravels, Helwell Bay [0787 4332].

TOPOGRAPHY

11701 Inlier of Devonian rocks, West Quantoxhead [1165 4333].
13850 Quantock Hills topography, Flaxpool [140 355].
13851 Quantock Hills scenery, Hurley Beacon [142 381].
13852 Quantock Hills scenery, Robin Upright's Hill [155 384] (Plate 1).
13853 Quantock Hills scenery, Triscombe Stone [164 358].
13854 Quantock Hills scenery, Triscombe Stone [164 358].
13855 Quantock Hills scenery, Triscombe Stone [167 358].
13856 Quantock Hills scenery, Bicknoller [101 399].
13857 Topography, general, Stogumber [105 369].
13858 Topography, general, Crowcombe [138 362].
13859 Topography, general, Halsway [127 382].
13860 Topography, general, Preston [103 359].
13861 Scarp formed by Vexford Breccias, Lydeard St Lawrence [120 305] (Plate 3).
13862 Feature formed by Vexford Breccias, Lydeard St Lawrence [120 305].
13863 Permo-Triassic topography, Bicknoller [115 386].
13864 North Curry Sandstone escarpment [318 263].
13865 Pendon Hill [352 377].
13866 Burrow Mount [352 300].

INDEX OF FOSSILS

In compiling the following, signs which qualify identification (e.g. aff., cf., ?) have been disregarded.

GENERAL INDEX

Cothelstone Fault 16, **56**, 57, 58, 59, 61, 75, 76, 78

HER MAJESTY'S STATIONERY OFFICE

Government Bookshops
49 High Holborn, London WC1V 6HB
13a Castle Street, Edinburgh EH2 3AR
Brazennose Street, Manchester M60 8AS
Southey House, Wine Street, Bristol BS1 2BQ
258 Broad Street, Birmingham B1 2HE
IDB House, Chichester Street, Belfast BT1 4JY

Government publications are also available through booksellers

BRITISH GEOLOGICAL SURVEY

Keyworth, Nottingham NG12 5GG

Murchison House, West Mains Road,
Edinburgh EH9 3LA

The full range of Survey publications is available through the Sales Desks at Keyworth and Murchison House. Selected items are stocked by the Geological Museum Bookshop, Exhibition Road, London SW7 2DE; all other items may be ordered through the BGS Information Desk adjacent to the Geology Library in the Geological Museum. All the books are listed in HMSO's Sectional List 45. Maps are listed in the BGS Map Catalogue and Ordnance Survey's Trade Catalogue. They can be bought from Ordnance Survey Agents as well as from BGS.

On 1 January 1984 the Institute of Geological Sciences was renamed the British Geological Survey. It continues to carry out the geological survey of Great Britain and Northern Ireland (the latter as an agency service for the government of Northern Ireland), and of the surrounding continental shelf, as well as its basic research projects. It also undertakes programmes of British technical aid in geology in developing countries as arranged by the Overseas Development Administration.

The British Geological Survey is a component body of the Natural Environment Research Council.